MATHEMATICS

Textbook for Class VIII

0852

NCERT

राष्ट्रीय शैक्षिक अनुसंधान और प्रशिक्षण परिषद्
NATIONAL COUNCIL OF EDUCATIONAL RESEARCH AND TRAINING

ISBN 978-81-7450-814-0

First Edition
January 2008 Magha 1929
Reprinted
January 2009 Pausa 1930
January 2010 Magha 1931
November 2010 Kartika 1932
January 2012 Magha 1933
November 2012 Kartika 1934
November 2013 Kartika 1935
November 2014 Kartika 1936
December 2015 Agrahayna 1937
December 2016 Pausa 1938
December 2017 Pausa 1939
January 2019 Pausa 1940
August 2019 Bhadrapada 1941

PD 1000T RPS

© National Council of Educational
Research and Training, 2008

₹ 65.00

OFFICES OF THE PUBLICATION DIVISION, NCERT

NCERT Campus
Sri Aurobindo Marg
New Delhi 110 016   Phone : 011-26562708

108, 100 Feet Road
Hosdakere Halli Extension
Banashankari III Stage
Bengaluru 560 085   Phone : 080-26725740

Navjivan Trust Building
P.O. Navjivan
Ahmedabad 380 014   Phone : 079-27541446

CWC Campus
Opp. Dhankal Bus Stop
Panihati
Kolkata 700 114   Phone : 033-25530454

CWC Complex
Maligaon
Guwahati 781 021   Phone : 0361-2674869

Printed on 80 GSM paper with NCERT watermark

Published at the Publication Division by the Secretary, National Council of Educational Research and Training, Sri Aurobindo Marg, New Delhi 110 016 and printed at Amber Press Pvt. Ltd., 143A-143-B, Pahiya Azampur, Kakori, Lucknow (U.P.)

Publication Team

Head, Publication Division   : M. Siraj Anwar

Chief Editor   : Shweta Uppal

Chief Production Officer   : Arun Chitkara

Chief Business Manager   : Bibash Kumar Das

Editor   : Bijnan Sutar

Assistant Production Editor   : Deepak jaiswal

Cover   **Layout Design**
Shweta Rao   Digital Expressions

Illustrations
Prashant Soni

Foreword

The National Curriculum Framework, 2005, recommends that children's life at school must be linked to their life outside the school. This principle marks a departure from the legacy of bookish learning which continues to shape our system and causes a gap between the school, home and community. The syllabi and textbooks developed on the basis of NCF signify an attempt to implement this basic idea. They also attempt to discourage rote learning and the maintenance of sharp boundaries between different subject areas. We hope these measures will take us significantly further in the direction of a child-centred system of education outlined in the National Policy on Education (1986).

The success of this effort depends on the steps that school principals and teachers will take to encourage children to reflect on their own learning and to pursue imaginative activities and questions. We must recognise that, given space, time and freedom, children generate new knowledge by engaging with the information passed on to them by adults. Treating the prescribed textbook as the sole basis of examination is one of the key reasons why other resources and sites of learning are ignored. Inculcating creativity and initiative is possible if we perceive and treat children as participants in learning, not as receivers of a fixed body of knowledge.

These aims imply considerable change in school routines and mode of functioning. Flexibility in the daily time-table is as necessary as rigour in implementing the annual calendar so that the required number of teaching days are actually devoted to teaching. The methods used for teaching and evaluation will also determine how effective this textbook proves for making children's life at school a happy experience, rather than a source of stress or boredom. Syllabus designers have tried to address the problem of curricular burden by restructuring and reorienting knowledge at different stages with greater consideration for child psychology and the time available for teaching. The textbook attempts to enhance this endeavour by giving higher priority and space to opportunities for contemplation and wondering, discussion in small groups, and activities requiring hands-on experience.

NCERT appreciates the hard work done by the textbook development committee responsible for this book. We wish to thank the Chairperson of the advisory group in science and mathematics, Professor J.V. Narlikar and the Chief Advisor for this book, Dr H.K. Dewan for guiding the work of this committee. Several teachers contributed to the development of this textbook; we are grateful to their principals for making this possible. We are indebted to the institutions and organisations which have generously permitted us to draw upon their resources, material and personnel. As an organisation committed to systemic reform and continuous improvement in the quality of its products, NCERT welcomes comments and suggestions which will enable us to undertake further revision and refinement.

New Delhi
30 November 2007

Director
National Council of Educational
Research and Training

Preface

This is the final book of the upper primary series. It has been an interesting journey to define mathematics learning in a different way. The attempt has been to retain the nature of mathematics, engage with the question why learn mathematics while making an attempt to create materials that would address the interest of the learners at this stage and provide sufficient and approachable challenge to them. There have been many views on the purpose of school mathematics. These range from the fully utilitarian to the entirely aesthetic perceptions. Both these end up not engaging with the concepts and enriching the apparatus available to the learner for participating in life. The NCF emphasises the need for developing the ability to mathematise ideas and perhaps experiences as well. An ability to explore the ideas and framework given by mathematics in the struggle to find a richer life and a more meaningful relationship with the world around.

This is not even easy to comprehend, far more difficult to operationalise. But NCF adds to this an even more difficult goal. The task is to involve everyone of that age group in the classroom or outside in doing mathematics. This is the aim we have been attempting to make in the series.

We have, therefore, provided space for children to engage in reflection, creating their own rules and definitions based on problems/tasks solved and following their ideas logically. The emphasis is not on remembering algorithms, doing complicated arithmetical problems or remembering proofs, but understanding how mathematics works and being able to identify the way of moving towards solving problems.

The important concern for us has also been to ensure that all students at this stage learn mathematics and begin to feel confident in relating mathematics. We have attempted to help children read the book and to stop and reflect at each step where a new idea has been presented. In order to make the book less formidable we have included illustrations and diagrams. These combined with the text help the child comprehend the idea. Throughout the series and also therefore in this book we have tried to avoid the use of technical words and complex formulations. We have left many things for the student to describe and write in her own words.

We have made an attempt to use child friendly language. To attract attention to some points blurbs have been used. The attempt has been to reduce the weight of long explanations by using these and the diagrams. The illustrations and fillers also attempt to break the monotony and provide contexts.

Class VIII is the bridge to Class IX where children will deal with more formal mathematics. The attempt here has been to introduce some ideas in a way that is moving towards becoming formal. The tasks included expect generalisation from the gradual use of such language by the child.

The team that developed this textbook consisted teachers with experience and appreciation of children learning mathematics. This team also included people with experience of research in mathematics teaching-learning and an experience of producing materials for children. The feedback on the textbooks for Classes VI and VII was kept in mind while developing this textbook. This process of development also included discussions with teachers during review workshop on the manuscript.

In the end, I would like to express the grateful thanks of our team to Professor Krishna Kumar, *Director*, NCERT, Professor G. Ravindra, *Joint Director*, NCERT and Professor Hukum Singh, *Head*, DESM, for giving us an opportunity to work on this task with freedom and with full support. I am also grateful to Professor J.V. Narlikar, Chairperson of the Advisory Group in Science and Mathematics for his suggestions. I am also grateful for the support of the team members from NCERT, Professor S.K. Singh Gautam, Dr V.P. Singh and in particular Dr Ashutosh K. Wazalwar who coordinated this work and made arrangements possible. In the end I must thank the Publication Department of NCERT for its support and advice and those from Vidya Bhawan who helped produce the book.

It need not be said but I cannot help mentioning that all the authors worked as a team and we accepted ideas and advice from each other. We stretched ourselves to the fullest and hope that we have done some justice to the challenge posed before us.

The process of developing materials is, however, a continuous one and we would hope to make this book better. Suggestions and comments on the book are most welcome.

H.K. DEWAN
Chief Advisor
Textbook Development Committee

A Note for the Teacher

This is the third and the last book of this series. It is a continuation of the processes initiated to help the learners in abstraction of ideas and principles of mathematics. Our students to be able to deal with mathematical ideas and use them need to have the logical foundations to abstract and use postulates and construct new formulations. The main points reflected in the NCF-2005 suggest relating mathematics to development of wider abilities in children, moving away from complex calculations and algorithm following to understanding and constructing a framework of understanding. As you know, mathematical ideas do not develop by telling them. They also do not reach children by merely giving explanations. Children need their own framework of concepts and a classroom where they are discussing ideas, looking for solutions to problems, setting new problems and finding their own ways of solving problems and their own definitions.

As we have said before, it is important to help children to learn to read the textbook and other books related to mathematics with understanding. The reading of materials is clearly required to help the child learn further mathematics. In Class VIII please take stock of where the students have reached and give them more opportunities to read texts that use language with symbols and have brevity and terseness with no redundancy. For this if you can, please get them to read other texts as well. You could also have them relate the physics they learn and the equations they come across in chemistry to the ideas they have learnt in mathematics. These cross-disciplinary references would help them develop a framework and purpose for mathematics. They need to be able to reconstruct logical arguments and appreciate the need for keeping certain factors and constraints while they relate them to other areas as well. Class VIII children need to have opportunity for all this.

As we have already emphasised, mathematics at the Upper Primary Stage has to be close to the experience and environment of the child and be abstract at the same time. From the comfort of context and/or models linked to their experience they need to move towards working with ideas. Learning to abstract helps formulate and understand arguments. The capacity to see interrelations among concepts helps us deal with ideas in other subjects as well. It also helps us understand and make better patterns, maps, appreciate area and volume and see similarities between shapes and sizes. While this is regarding the relationship of other fields of knowledge to mathematics, its meaning in life and our environment needs to be re-emphasised.

Children should be able to identify the principles to be used in contextual situations, for solving problems sift through and choose the relevant information as the first important step. Once students do that they need to be able to find the way to use the knowledge they have and reach where the problem requires them to go. They need to identify and define a problem, select or design possible solutions and revise or redesign the steps, if required. As they go further there would be more to of this to be done. In Class VIII we have to get them to be conscious of the steps they follow. Helping children to develop the ability to construct appropriate models by breaking up the problems and evolving their own strategies and analysis of problems is extremely important. This is in the place of giving them prescriptive algorithms.

Cooperative learning, learning through conversations, desire and capacity to learn from each other and the recognition that conversation is not noise and consultation not cheating is an important part of change in attitude for you as a teacher and for the students as well. They should be asked to make presentations as a group with the inclusion of examples from the contexts of their own experiences. They should be encouraged to read the book in groups and formulate and express what they understand from it. The assessment pattern has to recognise and appreciate this and the classroom groups should be such that all children enjoy being with each other and are contributing to the learning of the group. As you would have seen different groups use different strategies. Some of these are not as efficient as others as they reflect the modeling done and reflect the thinking used. All these are appropriate and need to be analysed with children. The exposure to a variety of strategies deepens the mathematical understanding. Each group moves from where it is and needs to be given an opportunity for that.

For conciseness we present the key ideas of mathematics learning that we would like you to remember in your classroom.

1. Enquiry to understand is one of the natural ways by which students acquire and construct knowledge. The process can use generation of observations to acquire knowledge. Students need to deal with different forms of questioning and challenging investigations- explorative, open-ended, contextual and even error detection from geometry, arithmetic and generalising it to algebraic relations etc.

2. Children need to learn to provide and follow logical arguments, find loopholes in the arguments presented and understand the requirement of a proof. By now children have entered the formal stage. They need to be encouraged to exercise creativity and imagination and to communicate their mathematical reasoning both verbally and in writing.

3. The mathematics classroom should relate language to learning of mathematics. Children should talk about their ideas using their experiences and language. They should be encouraged to use their own words and language but also gradually shift to formal language and use of symbols.

4. The number system has been taken to the level of generalisation of rational numbers and their properties and developing a framework that includes all previous systems as sub-sets of the generalised rational numbers. Generalisations are to be presented in mathematical language and children have to see that algebra and its language helps us express a lot of text in small symbolic forms.

5. As before children should be required to set and solve a lot of problems. We hope that as the nature of the problems set up by them becomes varied and more complex, they would become confident of the ideas they are dealing with.

6. Class VIII book has attempted to bring together the different aspects of mathematics and emphasise the commonality. Unitary method, Ratio and proportion, Interest and dividends are all part of one common logical framework. The idea of variable and equations is needed wherever we need to find an unknown quantity in any branch of mathematics.

We hope that the book will help children learn to enjoy mathematics and be confident in the concepts introduced. We want to recommend the creation of opportunity for thinking individually and collectively.

We look forward to your comments and suggestions regarding the book and hope that you will send interesting exercises, activities and tasks that you develop during the course of teaching, to be included in the future editions. This can only happen if you would find time to listen carefully to children and identify gaps and on the other hand also find the places where they can be given space to articulate their ideas and verbalise their thoughts.

Textbook Development Committee

ACKNOWLEDGEMENTS

The Council gratefully acknowledges the valuable contributions of the following participants of the Textbook Review Workshop: Shri Pradeep Bhardwaj, *TGT* (Mathematics) Bal Sthali Public Secondary School, Kirari, Nangloi, New Delhi; Shri Sankar Misra, *Teacher* in Mathematics, Demonstration Multipurpose School, Regional Institute of Education, Bhubaneswar (Orissa); Shri Manohar M. Dhok, *Supervisor,* M.P. Deo Smruti Lokanchi Shala, Nagpur (Maharashtra); Shri Manjit Singh Jangra, *Maths teacher,* Government Senior Secondary School, Sector-4/7, Gurgoan (Haryana); Dr. Rajendra Kumar Pooniwala, U.D.T., Government Subhash Excellence School, Burhanpur (M.P.); Shri K. Balaji, TGT (Mathematics), Kendriya Vidyalaya No.1, Tirupati (A.P.); Ms. Mala Mani, Amity International School, Sector-44, Noida; Ms. Omlata Singh, *TGT* (Mathematics), Presentation Convent Senior Secondary School, Delhi; Ms. Manju Dutta, Army Public School, Dhaula Kuan, New Delhi; Ms. Nirupama Sahni, *TGT* (Mathematics), Shri Mahaveer Digambar Jain Senior Secondary School, Jaipur (Rajasthan); Shri Nagesh Shankar Mone, *Head Master,* Kantilal Purshottam Das Shah Prashala, Vishrambag, Sangli (Maharashtra); Shri Anil Bhaskar Joshi, *Senior teacher* (Mathematics), Manutai Kanya Shala, Tilak Road, Akola (Maharashtra); Dr. Sushma Jairath, *Reader,* DWS, NCERT, New Delhi; Shri Ishwar Chandra, *Lecturer (S.G.)* (Retd.) NCERT, New Delhi.

The Council is grateful for the suggestions/comments given by the following participants during the workshop of the mathematics Textbook Development Committee – Shri Sanjay Bolia and Shri Deepak Mantri from Vidya Bhawan Basic School, Udaipur; Shri Inder Mohan Singh Chhabra, Vidya Bhawan Educational Resource Centre, Udaipur.

The Council acknowledges the comments/suggestions given by Dr. R.P. Maurya, *Reader,* DESM, NCERT, New Delhi; Dr. Sanjay Mudgal, *Lecturer,* DESM, NCERT, New Delhi; Dr. T.P. Sharma, *Lecturer,* DESM, NCERT, New Delhi for the improvement of the book.

The Council acknowledges the support and facilities provided by Vidya Bhawan Society and its staff, Udaipur, for conducting workshops of the development committee at Udaipur and to the Director, Centre for Science Education and Communication (CSEC), Delhi University for providing library help.

The Council acknowledges the academic and administrative support of Professor Hukum Singh, Head, DESM, NCERT.

The Council also acknowledges the efforts of Sajjad Haider Ansari, Rakesh Kumar, Neelam Walecha, *DTP Operators*; Kanwar Singh, *Copy Editor;* Abhimanu Mohanty, *Proof Reader*, Deepak Kapoor, *Computer Station Incharge*, DESM, NCERT for technical assistance, APC Office and the Administrative Staff, DESM, NCERT and the Publication Department of the NCERT.

Contents

Rational Numbers

0852CH01

1.1 Introduction

In Mathematics, we frequently come across simple equations to be solved. For example, the equation

$$x + 2 = 13 \tag{1}$$

is solved when $x = 11$, because this value of x satisfies the given equation. The solution 11 is a **natural number**. On the other hand, for the equation

$$x + 5 = 5 \tag{2}$$

the solution gives the **whole number** 0 (zero). If we consider only natural numbers, equation (2) cannot be solved. To solve equations like (2), we added the number zero to the collection of natural numbers and obtained the whole numbers. Even whole numbers will not be sufficient to solve equations of type

$$x + 18 = 5 \tag{3}$$

Do you see 'why'? We require the number –13 which is not a whole number. This led us to think of **integers, (positive and negative)**. Note that the positive integers correspond to natural numbers. One may think that we have enough numbers to solve all simple equations with the available list of integers. Now consider the equations

$$2x = 3 \tag{4}$$

$$5x + 7 = 0 \tag{5}$$

for which we cannot find a solution from the integers. (Check this)

We need the numbers $\dfrac{3}{2}$ to solve equation (4) and $\dfrac{-7}{5}$ to solve

equation (5). This leads us to the collection of **rational numbers**.

We have already seen basic operations on rational numbers. We now try to explore some properties of operations on the different types of numbers seen so far.

1.2 Properties of Rational Numbers

1.2.1 Closure

(i) Whole numbers

Let us revisit the closure property for all the operations on whole numbers in brief.

Operation	Numbers	Remarks
Addition	$0 + 5 = 5$, a whole number $4 + 7 = ...$. Is it a whole number? In general, $a + b$ is a whole number for any two whole numbers a and b.	Whole numbers are closed under addition.
Subtraction	$5 - 7 = -2$, which is not a whole number.	Whole numbers are **not** closed under subtraction.
Multiplication	$0 \times 3 = 0$, a whole number $3 \times 7 = ...$. Is it a whole number? In general, if a and b are any two whole numbers, their product ab is a whole number.	Whole numbers are closed under multiplication.
Division	$5 \div 8 = \dfrac{5}{8}$, which is not a whole number.	Whole numbers are **not** closed under division.

Check for closure property under all the four operations for natural numbers.

(ii) Integers

Let us now recall the operations under which integers are closed.

Operation	Numbers	Remarks
Addition	$-6 + 5 = -1$, an integer Is $-7 + (-5)$ an integer? Is $8 + 5$ an integer? In general, $a + b$ is an integer for any two integers a and b.	Integers are closed under addition.
Subtraction	$7 - 5 = 2$, an integer Is $5 - 7$ an integer? $-6 - 8 = -14$, an integer	Integers are closed under subtraction.

	$-6-(-8)=2$, an integer Is $8-(-6)$ an integer? In general, for any two integers a and b, $a-b$ is again an integer. Check if $b-a$ is also an integer.	
Multiplication	$5 \times 8 = 40$, an integer Is -5×8 an integer? $-5 \times (-8) = 40$, an integer In general, for any two integers a and b, $a \times b$ is also an integer.	Integers are closed under multiplication.
Division	$5 \div 8 = \dfrac{5}{8}$, which is not an integer.	Integers are **not** closed under division.

You have seen that whole numbers are closed under addition and multiplication but not under subtraction and division. However, integers are closed under addition, subtraction and multiplication but not under division.

(iii) Rational numbers

Recall that a number which can be written in the form $\dfrac{p}{q}$, where p and q are integers and $q \neq 0$ is called a **rational number**. For example, $-\dfrac{2}{3}, \dfrac{6}{7}, \dfrac{9}{-5}$ are all rational numbers. Since the numbers $0, -2, 4$ can be written in the form $\dfrac{p}{q}$, they are also rational numbers. (Check it!)

(a) You know how to add two rational numbers. Let us add a few pairs.

$$\frac{3}{8} + \frac{(-5)}{7} = \frac{21 + (-40)}{56} = \frac{-19}{56} \qquad \text{(a rational number)}$$

$$\frac{-3}{8} + \frac{(-4)}{5} = \frac{-15 + (-32)}{40} = \dots \qquad \text{Is it a rational number?}$$

$$\frac{4}{7} + \frac{6}{11} = \dots \qquad \text{Is it a rational number?}$$

We find that sum of two rational numbers is again a rational number. Check it for a few more pairs of rational numbers.

We say that *rational numbers are closed under addition. That is, for any two rational numbers a and b, a + b is also a rational number.*

(b) Will the difference of two rational numbers be again a rational number? We have,

$$\frac{-5}{7} - \frac{2}{3} = \frac{-5 \times 3 - 2 \times 7}{21} = \frac{-29}{21} \qquad \text{(a rational number)}$$

$$\frac{5}{8} - \frac{4}{5} = \frac{25-32}{40} = \dots$$ Is it a rational number?

$$\frac{3}{7} - \left(\frac{-8}{5}\right) = \dots$$ Is it a rational number?

Try this for some more pairs of rational numbers. We find that *rational numbers are closed under subtraction. That is, for any two rational numbers a and b, a – b is also a rational number.*

(c) Let us now see the product of two rational numbers.

$$\frac{-2}{3} \times \frac{4}{5} = \frac{-8}{15}; \frac{3}{7} \times \frac{2}{5} = \frac{6}{35}$$ (both the products are rational numbers)

$$-\frac{4}{5} \times \frac{-6}{11} = \dots$$ Is it a rational number?

Take some more pairs of rational numbers and check that their product is again a rational number.

We say that *rational numbers are closed under multiplication. That is, for any two rational numbers a and b, a × b is also a rational number.*

(d) We note that $\frac{-5}{3} \div \frac{2}{5} = \frac{-25}{6}$ (a rational number)

$\frac{2}{7} \div \frac{5}{3} = \dots$. Is it a rational number? $\frac{-3}{8} \div \frac{-2}{9} = \dots$. Is it a rational number?

Can you say that rational numbers are closed under division?

We find that for any rational number a, $a \div 0$ is **not defined**.

So rational numbers are **not closed** under division.

However, if we exclude zero then the collection of, all other rational numbers is closed under division.

TRY THESE

Fill in the blanks in the following table.

Numbers	Closed under			
	addition	**subtraction**	**multiplication**	**division**
Rational numbers	Yes	Yes	...	No
Integers	...	Yes	...	No
Whole numbers	...	...	Yes	...
Natural numbers	...	No	...	...

1.2.2 Commutativity

(i) Whole numbers

Recall the commutativity of different operations for whole numbers by filling the following table.

Operation	Numbers	Remarks
Addition	$0 + 7 = 7 + 0 = 7$ $2 + 3 = ... + ... = ...$ For any two whole numbers a and b, $a + b = b + a$	Addition is commutative.
Subtraction	....	Subtraction is not commutative.
Multiplication	....	Multiplication is commutative.
Division	....	Division is not commutative.

Check whether the commutativity of the operations hold for natural numbers also.

(ii) Integers

Fill in the following table and check the commutativity of different operations for integers:

Operation	Numbers	Remarks
Addition	....	Addition is commutative.
Subtraction	Is $5 - (-3) = -3 - 5$?	Subtraction is not commutative.
Multiplication	....	Multiplication is commutative.
Division	....	Division is not commutative.

(iii) Rational numbers

(a) Addition

You know how to add two rational numbers. Let us add a few pairs here.

$$\frac{-2}{3} + \frac{5}{7} = \frac{1}{21} \text{ and } \frac{5}{7} + \left(\frac{-2}{3}\right) = \frac{1}{21}$$

So,
$$\frac{-2}{3} + \frac{5}{7} = \frac{5}{7} + \left(\frac{-2}{3}\right)$$

Also,
$$\frac{-6}{5} + \left(\frac{-8}{3}\right) = ... \text{ and } \frac{-8}{3} + \left(\frac{-6}{5}\right) = ...$$

Is
$$\frac{-6}{5} + \left(\frac{-8}{3}\right) = \left(\frac{-8}{3}\right) + \left(\frac{-6}{5}\right)?$$

Is $\qquad \dfrac{-3}{8}+\dfrac{1}{7}=\dfrac{1}{7}+\left(\dfrac{-3}{8}\right)$?

You find that two *rational numbers can be added in any order. We say that addition is commutative for rational numbers. That is, for any two rational numbers a and b, a + b = b + a.*

(b) Subtraction

Is $\qquad \dfrac{2}{3}-\dfrac{5}{4}=\dfrac{5}{4}-\dfrac{2}{3}$?

Is $\qquad \dfrac{1}{2}-\dfrac{3}{5}=\dfrac{3}{5}-\dfrac{1}{2}$?

You will find that subtraction is not commutative for rational numbers.

Note that subtraction is not commutative for integers and integers are also rational numbers. So, subtraction will not be commutative for rational numbers too.

(c) Multiplication

We have, $\qquad \dfrac{-7}{3}\times\dfrac{6}{5}=\dfrac{-42}{15}=\dfrac{6}{5}\times\left(\dfrac{-7}{3}\right)$

Is $\qquad \dfrac{-8}{9}\times\left(\dfrac{-4}{7}\right)=\dfrac{-4}{7}\times\left(\dfrac{-8}{9}\right)$?

Check for some more such products.

You will find that *multiplication is commutative for rational numbers.*

In general, a × b = b × a for any two rational numbers a and b.

(d) Division

Is $\qquad \dfrac{-5}{4}\div\dfrac{3}{7}=\dfrac{3}{7}\div\left(\dfrac{-5}{4}\right)$?

You will find that expressions on both sides are not equal.

So division is **not commutative** for rational numbers.

TRY THESE

Complete the following table:

Numbers	Commutative for			
	addition	subtraction	multiplication	division
Rational numbers	Yes	...	...	...
Integers	...	No	...	...
Whole numbers	...	...	Yes	...
Natural numbers	...	...	...	No

1.2.3 Associativity

(i) Whole numbers

Recall the associativity of the four operations for whole numbers through this table:

Operation	Numbers	Remarks
Addition	....	Addition is associative
Subtraction	....	Subtraction is **not** associative
Multiplication	Is $7 \times (2 \times 5) = (7 \times 2) \times 5$? Is $4 \times (6 \times 0) = (4 \times 6) \times 0$? For any three whole numbers a, b and c $a \times (b \times c) = (a \times b) \times c$	Multiplication is associative
Division	....	Division is **not** associative

Fill in this table and verify the remarks given in the last column.
Check for yourself the associativity of different operations for natural numbers.

(ii) Integers

Associativity of the four operations for integers can be seen from this table

Operation	Numbers	Remarks
Addition	Is $(-2) + [3 + (-4)]$ $= [(-2) + 3)] + (-4)$? Is $(-6) + [(-4) + (-5)]$ $= [(-6) + (-4)] + (-5)$? For any three integers a, b and c $a + (b + c) = (a + b) + c$	Addition is associative
Subtraction	Is $5 - (7 - 3) = (5 - 7) - 3$?	Subtraction is **not** associative
Multiplication	Is $5 \times [(-7) \times (-8)$ $= [5 \times (-7)] \times (-8)$? Is $(-4) \times [(-8) \times (-5)]$ $= [(-4) \times (-8)] \times (-5)$? For any three integers a, b and c $a \times (b \times c) = (a \times b) \times c$	Multiplication is associative
Division	Is $[(-10) \div 2] \div (-5)$ $= (-10) \div [2 \div (-5)]$?	Division is **not** associative

(iii) Rational numbers

(a) Addition

We have $\dfrac{-2}{3} + \left[\dfrac{3}{5} + \left(\dfrac{-5}{6} \right) \right] = \dfrac{-2}{3} + \left(\dfrac{-7}{30} \right) = \dfrac{-27}{30} = \dfrac{-9}{10}$

$\left[\dfrac{-2}{3} + \dfrac{3}{5} \right] + \left(\dfrac{-5}{6} \right) = \dfrac{-1}{15} + \left(\dfrac{-5}{6} \right) = \dfrac{-27}{30} = \dfrac{-9}{10}$

So, $\dfrac{-2}{3} + \left[\dfrac{3}{5} + \left(\dfrac{-5}{6} \right) \right] = \left[\dfrac{-2}{3} + \dfrac{3}{5} \right] + \left(\dfrac{-5}{6} \right)$

Find $\dfrac{-1}{2} + \left[\dfrac{3}{7} + \left(\dfrac{-4}{3} \right) \right]$ and $\left[\dfrac{-1}{2} + \dfrac{3}{7} \right] + \left(\dfrac{-4}{3} \right)$. Are the two sums equal?

Take some more rational numbers, add them as above and see if the two sums are equal. We find that *addition is associative for rational numbers. That is, for any three rational numbers a, b and c, a + (b + c) = (a + b) + c.*

(b) Subtraction

You already know that subtraction is not associative for integers, then what about rational numbers.

Is $\dfrac{-2}{3} - \left[\dfrac{-4}{5} - \dfrac{1}{2} \right] = \left[\dfrac{2}{3} - \left(\dfrac{-4}{5} \right) \right] - \dfrac{1}{2}$?

Check for yourself.

Subtraction is **not associative** for rational numbers.

(c) Multiplication

Let us check the associativity for multiplication.

$$\dfrac{-7}{3} \times \left(\dfrac{5}{4} \times \dfrac{2}{9} \right) = \dfrac{-7}{3} \times \dfrac{10}{36} = \dfrac{-70}{108} = \dfrac{-35}{54}$$

$$\left(\dfrac{-7}{3} \times \dfrac{5}{4} \right) \times \dfrac{2}{9} = \dots$$

We find that $\dfrac{-7}{3} \times \left(\dfrac{5}{4} \times \dfrac{2}{9} \right) = \left(\dfrac{-7}{3} \times \dfrac{5}{4} \right) \times \dfrac{2}{9}$

Is $\dfrac{2}{3} \times \left(\dfrac{-6}{7} \times \dfrac{4}{5} \right) = \left(\dfrac{2}{3} \times \dfrac{-6}{7} \right) \times \dfrac{4}{5}$?

Take some more rational numbers and check for yourself.

We observe that *multiplication is associative for rational numbers. That is for any three rational numbers a, b and c, a × (b × c) = (a × b) × c.*

(d) Division

Recall that division is not associative for integers, then what about rational numbers?

Let us see if $\dfrac{1}{2} \div \left[\dfrac{-1}{3} \div \dfrac{2}{5} \right] = \left[\dfrac{1}{2} \div \left(\dfrac{-1}{3} \right) \right] \div \dfrac{2}{5}$

We have, LHS $= \dfrac{1}{2} \div \left(\dfrac{-1}{3} \div \dfrac{2}{5} \right) = \dfrac{1}{2} \div \left(\dfrac{-1}{3} \times \dfrac{5}{2} \right)$ (reciprocal of $\dfrac{2}{5}$ is $\dfrac{5}{2}$)

$= \dfrac{1}{2} \div \left(-\dfrac{5}{6} \right) = \ldots$

RHS $= \left[\dfrac{1}{2} \div \left(\dfrac{-1}{3} \right) \right] \div \dfrac{2}{5}$

$= \left(\dfrac{1}{2} \times \dfrac{-3}{1} \right) \div \dfrac{2}{5} = \dfrac{-3}{2} \div \dfrac{2}{5} = \ldots$

Is LHS = RHS? Check for yourself. You will find that division is **not associative** for rational numbers.

TRY THESE

Complete the following table:

Numbers	Associative for			
	addition	subtraction	multiplication	division
Rational numbers	...	...	...	No
Integers	...	...	Yes	...
Whole numbers	Yes	...	...	...
Natural numbers	...	No	...	...

Example 1: Find $\dfrac{3}{7} + \left(\dfrac{-6}{11} \right) + \left(\dfrac{-8}{21} \right) + \left(\dfrac{5}{22} \right)$

Solution: $\dfrac{3}{7} + \left(\dfrac{-6}{11} \right) + \left(\dfrac{-8}{21} \right) + \left(\dfrac{5}{22} \right)$

$= \dfrac{198}{462} + \left(\dfrac{-252}{462} \right) + \left(\dfrac{-176}{462} \right) + \left(\dfrac{105}{462} \right)$ (Note that 462 is the LCM of 7, 11, 21 and 22)

$= \dfrac{198 - 252 - 176 + 105}{462} = \dfrac{-125}{462}$

We can also solve it as.

$$\frac{3}{7} + \left(\frac{-6}{11}\right) + \left(\frac{-8}{21}\right) + \frac{5}{22}$$

$$= \left[\frac{3}{7} + \left(\frac{-8}{21}\right)\right] + \left[\frac{-6}{11} + \frac{5}{22}\right] \qquad \text{(by using commutativity and associativity)}$$

$$= \left[\frac{9 + (-8)}{21}\right] + \left[\frac{-12 + 5}{22}\right] \qquad \text{(LCM of 7 and 21 is 21; LCM of 11 and 22 is 22)}$$

$$= \frac{1}{21} + \left(\frac{-7}{22}\right) = \frac{22 - 147}{462} = \frac{-125}{462}$$

Do you think the properties of commutativity and associativity made the calculations easier?

Example 2: Find $\dfrac{-4}{5} \times \dfrac{3}{7} \times \dfrac{15}{16} \times \left(\dfrac{-14}{9}\right)$

Solution: We have

$$\frac{-4}{5} \times \frac{3}{7} \times \frac{15}{16} \times \left(\frac{-14}{9}\right)$$

$$= \left(-\frac{4 \times 3}{5 \times 7}\right) \times \left(\frac{15 \times (-14)}{16 \times 9}\right)$$

$$= \frac{-12}{35} \times \left(\frac{-35}{24}\right) = \frac{-12 \times (-35)}{35 \times 24} = \frac{1}{2}$$

We can also do it as.

$$\frac{-4}{5} \times \frac{3}{7} \times \frac{15}{16} \times \left(\frac{-14}{9}\right)$$

$$= \left(\frac{-4}{5} \times \frac{15}{16}\right) \times \left[\frac{3}{7} \times \left(\frac{-14}{9}\right)\right] \quad \text{(Using commutativity and associativity)}$$

$$= \frac{-3}{4} \times \left(\frac{-2}{3}\right) = \frac{1}{2}$$

1.2.4 The role of zero (0)

Look at the following.

$$2 + 0 = 0 + 2 = 2 \qquad \text{(Addition of 0 to a whole number)}$$

$$-5 + 0 = \dots + \dots = -5 \qquad \text{(Addition of 0 to an integer)}$$

$$\frac{-2}{7} + \dots = 0 + \left(\frac{-2}{7}\right) = \frac{-2}{7} \qquad \text{(Addition of 0 to a rational number)}$$

You have done such additions earlier also. Do a few more such additions.

What do you observe? You will find that when you add 0 to a whole number, the sum is again that whole number. This happens for integers and rational numbers also.

In general,

$$a + 0 = 0 + a = a, \qquad \text{where } a \text{ is a whole number}$$
$$b + 0 = 0 + b = b, \qquad \text{where } b \text{ is an integer}$$
$$c + 0 = 0 + c = c, \qquad \text{where } c \text{ is a rational number}$$

Zero is called the identity for the addition of rational numbers. It is the additive identity for integers and whole numbers as well.

1.2.5 The role of 1

We have,

$$5 \times 1 = 5 = 1 \times 5 \qquad \text{(Multiplication of 1 with a whole number)}$$

$$\frac{-2}{7} \times 1 = \ldots \times \ldots = \frac{-2}{7}$$

$$\frac{3}{8} \times \ldots = 1 \times \frac{3}{8} = \frac{3}{8}$$

What do you find?

You will find that when you multiply any rational number with 1, you get back the same rational number as the product. Check this for a few more rational numbers. You will find that, $a \times 1 = 1 \times a = a$ for any rational number a.

We say *that 1 is the multiplicative identity for rational numbers.*

Is 1 the multiplicative identity for integers? For whole numbers?

THINK, DISCUSS AND WRITE

If a property holds for rational numbers, will it also hold for integers? For whole numbers? Which will? Which will not?

1.2.6 Negative of a number

While studying integers you have come across negatives of integers. What is the negative of 1? It is -1 because $1 + (-1) = (-1) + 1 = 0$

So, what will be the negative of (-1)? It will be 1.

Also, $2 + (-2) = (-2) + 2 = 0$, so we say 2 is the **negative or additive inverse** of -2 and vice-versa. In general, for an integer a, we have, $a + (-a) = (-a) + a = 0$; so, a is the negative of $-a$ and $-a$ is the negative of a.

For the rational number $\dfrac{2}{3}$, we have,

$$\frac{2}{3} + \left(-\frac{2}{3}\right) = \frac{2 + (-2)}{3} = 0$$

Also, $\left(-\dfrac{2}{3}\right) + \dfrac{2}{3} = 0$ (How?)

Similarly, $\dfrac{-8}{9} + \dots = \dots + \left(\dfrac{-8}{9}\right) = 0$

$$\dots + \left(\dfrac{-11}{7}\right) = \left(\dfrac{-11}{7}\right) + \dots = 0$$

In general, for a rational number $\dfrac{a}{b}$, we have, $\dfrac{a}{b} + \left(-\dfrac{a}{b}\right) = \left(-\dfrac{a}{b}\right) + \dfrac{a}{b} = 0$. We say

that $-\dfrac{a}{b}$ *is the additive inverse of* $\dfrac{a}{b}$ *and* $\dfrac{a}{b}$ *is the additive inverse of* $\left(-\dfrac{a}{b}\right)$.

1.2.7 Reciprocal

By which rational number would you multiply $\dfrac{8}{21}$, to get the product 1? Obviously by

$\dfrac{21}{8}$, since $\dfrac{8}{21} \times \dfrac{21}{8} = 1$.

Similarly, $\dfrac{-5}{7}$ must be multiplied by $\dfrac{7}{-5}$ so as to get the product 1.

We say that $\dfrac{21}{8}$ is the reciprocal of $\dfrac{8}{21}$ and $\dfrac{7}{-5}$ is the reciprocal of $\dfrac{-5}{7}$.

Can you say what is the reciprocal of 0 (zero)?

Is there a rational number which when multiplied by 0 gives 1? Thus, zero has no reciprocal.

We say that a rational number $\dfrac{c}{d}$ is called the **reciprocal** or **multiplicative inverse** of

another non-zero rational number $\dfrac{a}{b}$ if $\dfrac{a}{b} \times \dfrac{c}{d} = 1$.

1.2.8 Distributivity of multiplication over addition for rational numbers

To understand this, consider the rational numbers $\dfrac{-3}{4}, \dfrac{2}{3}$ and $\dfrac{-5}{6}$.

$$\dfrac{-3}{4} \times \left\{\dfrac{2}{3} + \left(\dfrac{-5}{6}\right)\right\} = \dfrac{-3}{4} \times \left\{\dfrac{(4) + (-5)}{6}\right\}$$

$$= \dfrac{-3}{4} \times \left(\dfrac{-1}{6}\right) = \dfrac{3}{24} = \dfrac{1}{8}$$

Also $\dfrac{-3}{4} \times \dfrac{2}{3} = \dfrac{-3 \times 2}{4 \times 3} = \dfrac{-6}{12} = \dfrac{-1}{2}$

And $\dfrac{-3}{4} \times \dfrac{-5}{6} = \dfrac{5}{8}$

Therefore $\left(\dfrac{-3}{4} \times \dfrac{2}{3}\right) + \left(\dfrac{-3}{4} \times \dfrac{-5}{6}\right) = \dfrac{-1}{2} + \dfrac{5}{8} = \dfrac{1}{8}$

Thus, $\dfrac{-3}{4} \times \left\{\dfrac{2}{3} + \dfrac{-5}{6}\right\} = \left(\dfrac{-3}{4} \times \dfrac{2}{3}\right) + \left(\dfrac{-3}{4} \times \dfrac{-5}{6}\right)$

> **Distributivity of Multiplication over Addition and Subtraction.**
> For all rational numbers a, b and c,
> $a(b + c) = ab + ac$
> $a(b - c) = ab - ac$

TRY THESE

Find using distributivity. (i) $\left\{\dfrac{7}{5} \times \left(\dfrac{-3}{12}\right)\right\} + \left\{\dfrac{7}{5} \times \dfrac{5}{12}\right\}$ (ii) $\left\{\dfrac{9}{16} \times \dfrac{4}{12}\right\} + \left\{\dfrac{9}{16} \times \dfrac{-3}{9}\right\}$

Example 3: Write the additive inverse of the following:

(i) $\dfrac{-7}{19}$

(ii) $\dfrac{21}{112}$

> When you use distributivity, you split a product as a sum or difference of two products.

Solution:

(i) $\dfrac{7}{19}$ is the additive inverse of $\dfrac{-7}{19}$ because $\dfrac{-7}{19} + \dfrac{7}{19} = \dfrac{-7+7}{19} = \dfrac{0}{19} = 0$

(ii) The additive inverse of $\dfrac{21}{112}$ is $\dfrac{-21}{112}$ (Check!)

Example 4: Verify that $-(-x)$ is the same as x for

(i) $x = \dfrac{13}{17}$

(ii) $x = \dfrac{-21}{31}$

Solution: (i) We have, $x = \dfrac{13}{17}$

The additive inverse of $x = \dfrac{13}{17}$ is $-x = \dfrac{-13}{17}$ since $\dfrac{13}{17} + \left(\dfrac{-13}{17}\right) = 0$.

The same equality $\dfrac{13}{17} + \left(\dfrac{-13}{17}\right) = 0$, shows that the additive inverse of $\dfrac{-13}{17}$ is $\dfrac{13}{17}$

or $-\left(\dfrac{-13}{17}\right) = \dfrac{13}{17}$, i.e., $-(-x) = x$.

(ii) Additive inverse of $x = \dfrac{-21}{31}$ is $-x = \dfrac{21}{31}$ since $\dfrac{-21}{31} + \dfrac{21}{31} = 0$.

The same equality $\dfrac{-21}{31} + \dfrac{21}{31} = 0$, shows that the additive inverse of $\dfrac{21}{31}$ is $\dfrac{-21}{31}$, i.e., $-(-x) = x$.

Example 5: Find $\dfrac{2}{5} \times \dfrac{-3}{7} - \dfrac{1}{14} - \dfrac{3}{7} \times \dfrac{3}{5}$

Solution: $\dfrac{2}{5} \times \dfrac{-3}{7} - \dfrac{1}{14} - \dfrac{3}{7} \times \dfrac{3}{5} = \dfrac{2}{5} \times \dfrac{-3}{7} - \dfrac{3}{7} \times \dfrac{3}{5} - \dfrac{1}{14}$ (by commutativity)

$$= \dfrac{2}{5} \times \dfrac{-3}{7} + \left(\dfrac{-3}{7}\right) \times \dfrac{3}{5} - \dfrac{1}{14}$$

$$= \dfrac{-3}{7}\left(\dfrac{2}{5} + \dfrac{3}{5}\right) - \dfrac{1}{14} \qquad \text{(by distributivity)}$$

$$= \dfrac{-3}{7} \times 1 - \dfrac{1}{14} = \dfrac{-6-1}{14} = \dfrac{-1}{2}$$

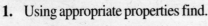

EXERCISE 1.1

1. Using appropriate properties find.

   (i) $-\dfrac{2}{3} \times \dfrac{3}{5} + \dfrac{5}{2} - \dfrac{3}{5} \times \dfrac{1}{6}$

   (ii) $\dfrac{2}{5} \times \left(-\dfrac{3}{7}\right) - \dfrac{1}{6} \times \dfrac{3}{2} + \dfrac{1}{14} \times \dfrac{2}{5}$

2. Write the additive inverse of each of the following.

   (i) $\dfrac{2}{8}$ (ii) $\dfrac{-5}{9}$ (iii) $\dfrac{-6}{-5}$ (iv) $\dfrac{2}{-9}$ (v) $\dfrac{19}{-6}$

3. Verify that $-(-x) = x$ for.

   (i) $x = \dfrac{11}{15}$ (ii) $x = -\dfrac{13}{17}$

4. Find the multiplicative inverse of the following.

   (i) -13 (ii) $\dfrac{-13}{19}$ (iii) $\dfrac{1}{5}$ (iv) $\dfrac{-5}{8} \times \dfrac{-3}{7}$

   (v) $-1 \times \dfrac{-2}{5}$ (vi) -1

5. Name the property under multiplication used in each of the following.

   (i) $\dfrac{-4}{5} \times 1 = 1 \times \dfrac{-4}{5} = -\dfrac{4}{5}$ (ii) $-\dfrac{13}{17} \times \dfrac{-2}{7} = \dfrac{-2}{7} \times \dfrac{-13}{17}$

   (iii) $\dfrac{-19}{29} \times \dfrac{29}{-19} = 1$

6. Multiply $\dfrac{6}{13}$ by the reciprocal of $\dfrac{-7}{16}$.

7. Tell what property allows you to compute $\dfrac{1}{3} \times \left(6 \times \dfrac{4}{3}\right)$ as $\left(\dfrac{1}{3} \times 6\right) \times \dfrac{4}{3}$.

8. Is $\dfrac{8}{9}$ the multiplicative inverse of $-1\dfrac{1}{8}$? Why or why not?

9. Is 0.3 the multiplicative inverse of $3\dfrac{1}{3}$? Why or why not?

10. Write.

    (i) The rational number that does not have a reciprocal.

    (ii) The rational numbers that are equal to their reciprocals.

    (iii) The rational number that is equal to its negative.

11. Fill in the blanks.

    (i) Zero has _____ reciprocal.

    (ii) The numbers _____ and _____ are their own reciprocals

    (iii) The reciprocal of -5 is _____.

    (iv) Reciprocal of $\dfrac{1}{x}$, where $x \neq 0$ is _____.

    (v) The product of two rational numbers is always a _____.

    (vi) The reciprocal of a positive rational number is _____.

1.3 Representation of Rational Numbers on the Number Line

You have learnt to represent natural numbers, whole numbers, integers and rational numbers on a number line. Let us revise them.

Natural numbers

  (i)

The line extends indefinitely only to the right side of 1.

Whole numbers

  (ii)

The line extends indefinitely to the right, but from 0. There are no numbers to the left of 0.

Integers

  (iii)

The line extends indefinitely on both sides. Do you see any numbers between -1, 0; 0, 1 etc.?

Rational numbers

  (iv)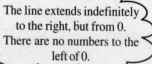

  (v)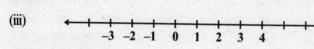

The line extends indefinitely on both sides. But you can now see numbers between -1, 0; 0, 1 etc.

The point on the number line (iv) which is half way between 0 and 1 has been labelled $\dfrac{1}{2}$. Also, the first of the equally spaced points that divides the distance between 0 and 1 into three equal parts can be labelled $\dfrac{1}{3}$, as on number line (v). How would you label the second of these division points on number line (v)?

The point to be labelled is twice as far from and to the right of 0 as the point labelled $\frac{1}{3}$. So it is two times $\frac{1}{3}$, i.e., $\frac{2}{3}$. You can continue to label equally-spaced points on the number line in the same way. In this continuation, the next marking is 1. You can see that 1 is the same as $\frac{3}{3}$.

Then comes $\frac{4}{3}, \frac{5}{3}, \frac{6}{3}$ (or 2), $\frac{7}{3}$ and so on as shown on the number line (vi)

(vi)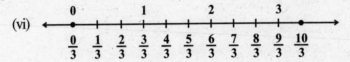

Similarly, to represent $\frac{1}{8}$, the number line may be divided into eight equal parts as shown:

We use the number $\frac{1}{8}$ to name the first point of this division. The second point of division will be labelled $\frac{2}{8}$, the third point $\frac{3}{8}$, and so on as shown on number line (vii)

(vii)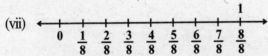

Any rational number can be represented on the number line in this way. In a rational number, the numeral below the bar, i.e., the denominator, tells the number of equal parts into which the first unit has been divided. The numeral above the bar i.e., the numerator, tells 'how many' of these parts are considered. So, a rational number such as $\frac{4}{9}$ means four of nine equal parts on the right of 0 (number line viii) and for $\frac{-7}{4}$, we make 7 markings of distance $\frac{1}{4}$ each on the *left* of zero and starting from 0. The seventh marking is $\frac{-7}{4}$ [number line (ix)].

(viii)

(ix)

TRY THESE

Write the rational number for each point labelled with a letter.

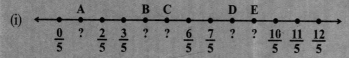

1.4 Rational Numbers between Two Rational Numbers

Can you tell the natural numbers between 1 and 5? They are 2, 3 and 4.

How many natural numbers are there between 7 and 9? There is one and it is 8.

How many natural numbers are there between 10 and 11? Obviously none.

List the integers that lie between –5 and 4. They are – 4, – 3, –2, –1, 0, 1, 2, 3.

How many integers are there between –1 and 1?

How many integers are there between –9 and –10?

You will find a definite number of natural numbers (integers) between two natural numbers (integers).

How many rational numbers are there between $\dfrac{3}{10}$ and $\dfrac{7}{10}$?

You may have thought that they are only $\dfrac{4}{10}, \dfrac{5}{10}$ and $\dfrac{6}{10}$.

But you can also write $\dfrac{3}{10}$ as $\dfrac{30}{100}$ and $\dfrac{7}{10}$ as $\dfrac{70}{100}$. Now the numbers, $\dfrac{31}{100}, \dfrac{32}{100}, \dfrac{33}{100}$,... $\dfrac{68}{100}, \dfrac{69}{100}$, are all between $\dfrac{3}{10}$ and $\dfrac{7}{10}$. The number of these rational numbers is 39.

Also $\dfrac{3}{10}$ can be expressed as $\dfrac{3000}{10000}$ and $\dfrac{7}{10}$ as $\dfrac{7000}{10000}$. Now, we see that the rational numbers $\dfrac{3001}{10000}, \dfrac{3002}{10000}, ..., \dfrac{6998}{10000}, \dfrac{6999}{10000}$ are between $\dfrac{3}{10}$ and $\dfrac{7}{10}$. These are 3999 numbers in all.

In this way, we can go on inserting more and more rational numbers between $\dfrac{3}{10}$ and $\dfrac{7}{10}$. So unlike natural numbers and integers, the number of rational numbers between two rational numbers is not definite. Here is one more example.

How many rational numbers are there between $\dfrac{-1}{10}$ and $\dfrac{3}{10}$?

Obviously $\dfrac{0}{10}, \dfrac{1}{10}, \dfrac{2}{10}$ are rational numbers between the given numbers.

If we write $\dfrac{-1}{10}$ as $\dfrac{-10000}{100000}$ and $\dfrac{3}{10}$ as $\dfrac{30000}{100000}$, we get the rational numbers

$\dfrac{-9999}{100000}, \dfrac{-9998}{100000}, ..., \dfrac{-29998}{100000}, \dfrac{29999}{100000}$, between $\dfrac{-1}{10}$ and $\dfrac{3}{10}$.

You will find that *you get countless rational numbers between any two given rational numbers*.

Example 6: Write any 3 rational numbers between –2 and 0.

Solution: –2 can be written as $\dfrac{-20}{10}$ and 0 as $\dfrac{0}{10}$.

Thus we have $\dfrac{-19}{10}, \dfrac{-18}{10}, \dfrac{-17}{10}, \dfrac{-16}{10}, \dfrac{-15}{10}, ..., \dfrac{-1}{10}$ between –2 and 0.

You can take any three of these.

Example 7: Find any ten rational numbers between $\dfrac{-5}{6}$ and $\dfrac{5}{8}$.

Solution: We first convert $\dfrac{-5}{6}$ and $\dfrac{5}{8}$ to rational numbers with the same denominators.

$$\dfrac{-5 \times 4}{6 \times 4} = \dfrac{-20}{24} \quad \text{and} \quad \dfrac{5 \times 3}{8 \times 3} = \dfrac{15}{24}$$

Thus we have $\dfrac{-19}{24}, \dfrac{-18}{24}, \dfrac{-17}{24}, ..., \dfrac{14}{24}$ as the rational numbers between $\dfrac{-20}{24}$ and $\dfrac{15}{24}$.

You can take any ten of these.

Another Method

Let us find rational numbers between 1 and 2. One of them is 1.5 or $1\dfrac{1}{2}$ or $\dfrac{3}{2}$. This is the **mean** of 1 and 2. You have studied mean in Class VII.

We find that *between any two given numbers, we need not necessarily get an integer but there will always lie a rational number*.

We can use the idea of mean also to find rational numbers between any two given rational numbers.

Example 8: Find a rational number between $\dfrac{1}{4}$ and $\dfrac{1}{2}$.

Solution: We find the mean of the given rational numbers.

$$\left(\dfrac{1}{4} + \dfrac{1}{2}\right) \div 2 = \left(\dfrac{1+2}{4}\right) \div 2 = \dfrac{3}{4} \times \dfrac{1}{2} = \dfrac{3}{8}$$

$\dfrac{3}{8}$ lies between $\dfrac{1}{4}$ and $\dfrac{1}{2}$.

This can be seen on the number line also.

$$\left(\dfrac{1}{4} + \dfrac{1}{2}\right) \div 2 = \dfrac{3}{8}$$

We find the mid point of AB which is C, represented by $\left(\dfrac{1}{4} + \dfrac{1}{2}\right) \div 2 = \dfrac{3}{8}$.

We find that $\dfrac{1}{4} < \dfrac{3}{8} < \dfrac{1}{2}$.

If a and b are two rational numbers, then $\dfrac{a+b}{2}$ is a rational number between a and b such that $a < \dfrac{a+b}{2} < b$.

This again shows that there are countless number of rational numbers between any two given rational numbers.

Example 9: Find three rational numbers between $\dfrac{1}{4}$ and $\dfrac{1}{2}$.

Solution: We find the mean of the given rational numbers.

As given in the above example, the mean is $\dfrac{3}{8}$ and $\dfrac{1}{4} < \dfrac{3}{8} < \dfrac{1}{2}$.

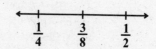

We now find another rational number between $\dfrac{1}{4}$ and $\dfrac{3}{8}$. For this, we again find the mean

of $\dfrac{1}{4}$ and $\dfrac{3}{8}$. That is, $\left(\dfrac{1}{4} + \dfrac{3}{8}\right) \div 2 = \dfrac{5}{8} \times \dfrac{1}{2} = \dfrac{5}{16}$

$$\dfrac{1}{4} < \dfrac{5}{16} < \dfrac{3}{8} < \dfrac{1}{2}$$

Now find the mean of $\dfrac{3}{8}$ and $\dfrac{1}{2}$. We have, $\left(\dfrac{3}{8} + \dfrac{1}{2}\right) \div 2 = \dfrac{7}{8} \times \dfrac{1}{2} = \dfrac{7}{16}$

Thus we get $\dfrac{1}{4} < \dfrac{5}{16} < \dfrac{3}{8} < \dfrac{7}{16} < \dfrac{1}{2}$.

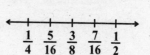

Thus, $\dfrac{5}{16}, \dfrac{3}{8}, \dfrac{7}{16}$ are the three rational numbers between $\dfrac{1}{4}$ and $\dfrac{1}{2}$.

This can clearly be shown on the number line as follows:

In the same way we can obtain as many rational numbers as we want between two given rational numbers . You have noticed that there are countless rational numbers between any two given rational numbers.

EXERCISE 1.2

1. Represent these numbers on the number line. (i) $\dfrac{7}{4}$ (ii) $\dfrac{-5}{6}$

2. Represent $\dfrac{-2}{11}, \dfrac{-5}{11}, \dfrac{-9}{11}$ on the number line.

3. Write five rational numbers which are smaller than 2.

4. Find ten rational numbers between $\dfrac{-2}{5}$ and $\dfrac{1}{2}$.

5. Find five rational numbers between.

   (i) $\dfrac{2}{3}$ and $\dfrac{4}{5}$ (ii) $\dfrac{-3}{2}$ and $\dfrac{5}{3}$ (iii) $\dfrac{1}{4}$ and $\dfrac{1}{2}$

6. Write five rational numbers greater than –2.

7. Find ten rational numbers between $\dfrac{3}{5}$ and $\dfrac{3}{4}$.

WHAT HAVE WE DISCUSSED?

1. Rational numbers are **closed** under the operations of addition, subtraction and multiplication.

2. The operations addition and multiplication are
   (i) **commutative** for rational numbers.
   (ii) **associative** for rational numbers.

3. The rational number 0 is the **additive identity** for rational numbers.

4. The rational number 1 is the **multiplicative identity** for rational numbers.

5. The **additive inverse** of the rational number $\dfrac{a}{b}$ is $-\dfrac{a}{b}$ and vice-versa.

6. The **reciprocal** or **multiplicative inverse** of the rational number $\dfrac{a}{b}$ is $\dfrac{c}{d}$ if $\dfrac{a}{b} \times \dfrac{c}{d} = 1$.

7. **Distributivity** of rational numbers: For all rational numbers a, b and c,
   $a(b + c) = ab + ac$ and $a(b - c) = ab - ac$

8. Rational numbers can be represented on a number line.

9. Between any two given rational numbers there are countless rational numbers. The idea of **mean** helps us to find rational numbers between two rational numbers.

Linear Equations in One Variable

0852CH02

2.1 Introduction

In the earlier classes, you have come across several **algebraic expressions** and **equations**. Some examples of expressions we have so far worked with are:

$$5x, 2x - 3, 3x + y, 2xy + 5, xyz + x + y + z, x^2 + 1, y + y^2$$

Some examples of equations are: $5x = 25$, $2x - 3 = 9$, $2y + \dfrac{5}{2} = \dfrac{37}{2}$, $6z + 10 = -2$

You would remember that equations use the *equality* (=) sign; it is missing in expressions.

Of these given expressions, many have more than one variable. For example, $2xy + 5$ has two variables. We however, restrict to expressions with only one variable when we form equations. Moreover, the expressions we use to form equations are linear. This means that the highest power of the variable appearing in the expression is 1.

These are linear expressions:

$$2x, 2x + 1, 3y - 7, 12 - 5z, \dfrac{5}{4}(x - 4) + 10$$

These are **not** linear expressions:

$$x^2 + 1, y + y^2, 1 + z + z^2 + z^3 \qquad \text{(since highest power of variable > 1)}$$

Here we will deal with equations with linear expressions in one variable only. Such equations are known as **linear equations in one variable**. The simple equations which you studied in the earlier classes were all of this type.

Let us briefly revise what we know:

(a) *An algebraic equation is an equality involving variables*. It has an *equality sign*. The expression on the left of the equality sign is the *Left Hand Side* (LHS). The expression on the right of the equality sign is the *Right Hand Side* (RHS).

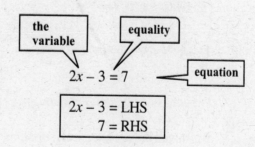

(b) In an equation the *values of the expressions on the LHS and RHS are equal*. This happens to be *true* only for certain values of the variable. These values are the **solutions** of the equation.

$x = 5$ is the solution of the equation $2x - 3 = 7$. For $x = 5$,

LHS $= 2 \times 5 - 3 = 7 =$ RHS

On the other hand $x = 10$ is not a solution of the equation. For $x = 10$, LHS $= 2 \times 10 - 3 = 17$. This is not equal to the RHS

(c) *How to find the solution of an equation?*

We assume that the two sides of the equation are balanced. We perform the same mathematical operations on both sides of the equation, so that the balance is not disturbed. A few such steps give the solution.

2.2 Solving Equations which have Linear Expressions on one Side and Numbers on the other Side

Let us recall the technique of solving equations with some examples. Observe the solutions; they can be any rational number.

Example 1: Find the solution of $2x - 3 = 7$

Solution:

Step 1 Add 3 to both sides.

$$2x - 3 + 3 = 7 + 3 \qquad \text{(The balance is not disturbed)}$$

or $$2x = 10$$

Step 2 Next divide both sides by 2.

$$\frac{2x}{2} = \frac{10}{2}$$

or $$x = 5 \qquad \text{(required solution)}$$

Example 2: Solve $2y + 9 = 4$

Solution: Transposing 9 to RHS

$$2y = 4 - 9$$

or $$2y = -5$$

Dividing both sides by 2, $$y = \frac{-5}{2} \qquad \text{(solution)}$$

To check the answer: LHS $= 2\left(\dfrac{-5}{2}\right) + 9 = -5 + 9 = 4 =$ RHS $\qquad$ (as required)

Do you notice that the solution $\left(\dfrac{-5}{2}\right)$ is a rational number? In Class VII, the equations we solved did not have such solutions.

Example 3: Solve $\dfrac{x}{3} + \dfrac{5}{2} = -\dfrac{3}{2}$

Solution: Transposing $\dfrac{5}{2}$ to the RHS, we get $\dfrac{x}{3} = \dfrac{-3}{2} - \dfrac{5}{2} = -\dfrac{8}{2}$

or $$\dfrac{x}{3} = -4$$

Multiply both sides by 3, $\qquad x = -4 \times 3$

or $\qquad\qquad\qquad\qquad\qquad x = -12$ (solution)

Check: LHS $= -\dfrac{12}{3} + \dfrac{5}{2} = -4 + \dfrac{5}{2} = \dfrac{-8+5}{2} = \dfrac{-3}{2} =$ RHS (as required)

Do you now see that the coefficient of a variable in an equation need not be an integer?

Example 4: Solve $\dfrac{15}{4} - 7x = 9$

Solution: We have $\qquad\qquad \dfrac{15}{4} - 7x = 9$

or $\qquad\qquad\qquad\qquad -7x = 9 - \dfrac{15}{4}$ (transposing $\dfrac{15}{4}$ to R H S)

or $\qquad\qquad\qquad\qquad -7x = \dfrac{21}{4}$

or $\qquad\qquad\qquad\qquad x = \dfrac{21}{4 \times (-7)}$ (dividing both sides by -7)

or $\qquad\qquad\qquad\qquad x = -\dfrac{3 \times 7}{4 \times 7}$

or $\qquad\qquad\qquad\qquad x = -\dfrac{3}{4}$ (solution)

Check: LHS $= \dfrac{15}{4} - 7\left(\dfrac{-3}{4}\right) = \dfrac{15}{4} + \dfrac{21}{4} = \dfrac{36}{4} = 9 =$ RHS (as required)

EXERCISE 2.1

Solve the following equations.

1. $x - 2 = 7$
2. $y + 3 = 10$
3. $6 = z + 2$
4. $\dfrac{3}{7} + x = \dfrac{17}{7}$
5. $6x = 12$
6. $\dfrac{t}{5} = 10$
7. $\dfrac{2x}{3} = 18$
8. $1.6 = \dfrac{y}{1.5}$
9. $7x - 9 = 16$

10. $14y - 8 = 13$ **11.** $17 + 6p = 9$ **12.** $\dfrac{x}{3} + 1 = \dfrac{7}{15}$

2.3 Some Applications

We begin with a simple example.

Sum of two numbers is 74. One of the numbers is 10 more than the other. What are the numbers?

We have a puzzle here. We do not know either of the two numbers, and we have to find them. We are given two conditions.

(i) One of the numbers is 10 more than the other.

(ii) Their sum is 74.

We already know from Class VII how to proceed. If the smaller number is taken to be x, the larger number is 10 more than x, i.e., $x + 10$. The other condition says that the sum of these two numbers x and $x + 10$ is 74.

This means that $x + (x + 10) = 74$.

or $\qquad\qquad\qquad\qquad\qquad\qquad 2x + 10 = 74$

Transposing 10 to RHS, $\qquad\qquad\qquad 2x = 74 - 10$

or $\qquad\qquad\qquad\qquad\qquad\qquad 2x = 64$

Dividing both sides by 2, $\qquad\qquad x = 32$. This is one number.

The other number is $\qquad\qquad\quad x + 10 = 32 + 10 = 42$

The desired numbers are 32 and 42. (Their sum is indeed 74 as given and also one number is 10 more than the other.)

We shall now consider several examples to show how useful this method is.

Example 5: What should be added to twice the rational number $\dfrac{-7}{3}$ to get $\dfrac{3}{7}$?

Solution: Twice the rational number $\dfrac{-7}{3}$ is $2 \times \left(\dfrac{-7}{3}\right) = \dfrac{-14}{3}$. Suppose x added to this number gives $\dfrac{3}{7}$; i.e.,

$$x + \left(\dfrac{-14}{3}\right) = \dfrac{3}{7}$$

or $\qquad\qquad\qquad\qquad x - \dfrac{14}{3} = \dfrac{3}{7}$

or $\qquad\qquad\qquad\qquad x = \dfrac{3}{7} + \dfrac{14}{3} \qquad\qquad$ (transposing $\dfrac{14}{3}$ to RHS)

$$= \dfrac{(3 \times 3) + (14 \times 7)}{21} = \dfrac{9 + 98}{21} = \dfrac{107}{21}.$$

Thus $\dfrac{107}{21}$ should be added to $2 \times \left(\dfrac{-7}{3}\right)$ to give $\dfrac{3}{7}$.

Example 6: The perimeter of a rectangle is 13 cm and its width is $2\dfrac{3}{4}$ cm. Find its length.

Solution: Assume the length of the rectangle to be x cm.

The perimeter of the rectangle $= 2 \times (\text{length} + \text{width})$

$$= 2 \times (x + 2\tfrac{3}{4})$$

$$= 2\left(x + \dfrac{11}{4}\right)$$

The perimeter is given to be 13 cm. Therefore,

$$2\left(x + \dfrac{11}{4}\right) = 13$$

or $$x + \dfrac{11}{4} = \dfrac{13}{2} \qquad \text{(dividing both sides by 2)}$$

or $$x = \dfrac{13}{2} - \dfrac{11}{4}$$

$$= \dfrac{26}{4} - \dfrac{11}{4} = \dfrac{15}{4} = 3\dfrac{3}{4}$$

The length of the rectangle is $3\dfrac{3}{4}$ cm.

Example 7: The present age of Sahil's mother is three times the present age of Sahil. After 5 years their ages will add to 66 years. Find their present ages.

Solution: Let Sahil's present age be x years.

We could also choose Sahil's age 5 years later to be x and proceed. Why don't you try it that way?		Sahil	Mother	Sum
	Present age	x	$3x$	
	Age 5 years later	$x + 5$	$3x + 5$	$4x + 10$

It is given that this sum is 66 years.

Therefore, $\qquad\qquad 4x + 10 = 66$

This equation determines Sahil's present age which is x years. To solve the equation,

we transpose 10 to RHS,

$$4x = 66 - 10$$

or
$$4x = 56$$

or
$$x = \frac{56}{4} = 14 \qquad \text{(solution)}$$

Thus, Sahil's present age is 14 years and his mother's age is 42 years. (You may easily check that 5 years from now the sum of their ages will be 66 years.)

Example 8: Bansi has 3 times as many two-rupee coins as he has five-rupee coins. If he has in all a sum of ₹77, how many coins of each denomination does he have?

Solution: Let the number of five-rupee coins that Bansi has be x. Then the number of two-rupee coins he has is 3 times x or $3x$.

The amount Bansi has:

(i) from 5 rupee coins, ₹$5 \times x = $₹$5x$

(ii) from 2 rupee coins, ₹$2 \times 3x = $₹$6x$

Hence the total money he has = ₹$11x$

But this is given to be ₹77; therefore,

$$11x = 77$$

or
$$x = \frac{77}{11} = 7$$

Thus,   number of five-rupee coins = $x = 7$

and   number of two-rupee coins = $3x = 21$ \qquad (solution)

(You can check that the total money with Bansi is ₹77.)

Example 9: The sum of three consecutive multiples of 11 is 363. Find these multiples.

Solution: If x is a multiple of 11, the next multiple is $x + 11$. The next to this is $x + 11 + 11$ or $x + 22$. So we can take three consecutive multiples of 11 as $x, x + 11$ and $x + 22$.

It is given that the sum of these consecutive multiples of 11 is 363. This will give the following equation:

$$x + (x + 11) + (x + 22) = 363$$

or
$$x + x + 11 + x + 22 = 363$$

or
$$3x + 33 = 363$$

or
$$3x = 363 - 33$$

or
$$3x = 330$$

Alternatively, we may think of the multiple of 11 immediately before x. This is $(x - 11)$. Therefore, we may take three consecutive multiples of 11 as $x - 11, x, x + 11$.

In this case we arrive at the equation
$$(x - 11) + x + (x + 11) = 363$$
or
$$3x = 363$$

or $\qquad x = \dfrac{330}{3}$

$\qquad\qquad = 110$

> or $\qquad x = \dfrac{363}{3} = 121.$ Therefore,
>
> $x = 121, x - 11 = 110, x + 11 = 132$
>
> Hence, the three consecutive multiples are 110, 121, 132.

Hence, the three consecutive multiples are 110, 121, 132 (answer).

We can see that we can adopt different ways to find a solution for the problem.

Example 10: The difference between two whole numbers is 66. The ratio of the two numbers is 2 : 5. What are the two numbers?

Solution: Since the ratio of the two numbers is 2 : 5, we may take one number to be $2x$ and the other to be $5x$. (Note that $2x : 5x$ is same as 2 : 5.)

The difference between the two numbers is $(5x - 2x)$. It is given that the difference is 66. Therefore,

$$5x - 2x = 66$$

or $\qquad\qquad 3x = 66$

or $\qquad\qquad x = 22$

Since the numbers are $2x$ and $5x$, they are 2×22 or 44 and 5×22 or 110, respectively.

The difference between the two numbers is $110 - 44 = 66$ as desired.

Example 11: Deveshi has a total of ₹ 590 as currency notes in the denominations of ₹ 50, ₹ 20 and ₹ 10. The ratio of the number of ₹ 50 notes and ₹ 20 notes is 3:5. If she has a total of 25 notes, how many notes of each denomination she has?

Solution: Let the number of ₹ 50 notes and ₹ 20 notes be $3x$ and $5x$, respectively.

But she has 25 notes in total.

Therefore, the number of ₹ 10 notes = $25 - (3x + 5x) = 25 - 8x$

The amount she has

from ₹ 50 notes : $3x \times 50 = ₹ 150x$

from ₹ 20 notes : $5x \times 20 = ₹ 100x$

from ₹ 10 notes : $(25 - 8x) \times 10 = ₹ (250 - 80x)$

Hence the total money she has $= 150x + 100x + (250 - 80x) = ₹ (170x + 250)$

But she has ₹ 590. Therefore, $\qquad 170x + 250 = 590$

or $\qquad\qquad 170x = 590 - 250 = 340$

or $\qquad\qquad x = \dfrac{340}{170} = 2$

The number of ₹ 50 notes she has $= 3x$

$\qquad\qquad = 3 \times 2 = 6$

The number of ₹ 20 notes she has $= 5x = 5 \times 2 = 10$

The number of ₹ 10 notes she has $= 25 - 8x$

$\qquad\qquad = 25 - (8 \times 2) = 25 - 16 = 9$

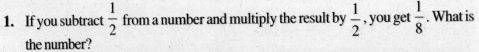

EXERCISE 2.2

1. If you subtract $\frac{1}{2}$ from a number and multiply the result by $\frac{1}{2}$, you get $\frac{1}{8}$. What is the number?

2. The perimeter of a rectangular swimming pool is 154 m. Its length is 2 m more than twice its breadth. What are the length and the breadth of the pool?

3. The base of an isosceles triangle is $\frac{4}{3}$ cm. The perimeter of the triangle is $4\frac{2}{15}$ cm. What is the length of either of the remaining equal sides?

4. Sum of two numbers is 95. If one exceeds the other by 15, find the numbers.

5. Two numbers are in the ratio 5:3. If they differ by 18, what are the numbers?

6. Three consecutive integers add up to 51. What are these integers?

7. The sum of three consecutive multiples of 8 is 888. Find the multiples.

8. Three consecutive integers are such that when they are taken in increasing order and multiplied by 2, 3 and 4 respectively, they add up to 74. Find these numbers.

9. The ages of Rahul and Haroon are in the ratio 5:7. Four years later the sum of their ages will be 56 years. What are their present ages?

10. The number of boys and girls in a class are in the ratio 7:5. The number of boys is 8 more than the number of girls. What is the total class strength?

11. Baichung's father is 26 years younger than Baichung's grandfather and 29 years older than Baichung. The sum of the ages of all the three is 135 years. What is the age of each one of them?

12. Fifteen years from now Ravi's age will be four times his present age. What is Ravi's present age?

13. A rational number is such that when you multiply it by $\frac{5}{2}$ and add $\frac{2}{3}$ to the product, you get $-\frac{7}{12}$. What is the number?

14. Lakshmi is a cashier in a bank. She has currency notes of denominations ₹ 100, ₹ 50 and ₹ 10, respectively. The ratio of the number of these notes is 2:3:5. The total cash with Lakshmi is ₹ 4,00,000. How many notes of each denomination does she have?

15. I have a total of ₹ 300 in coins of denomination ₹ 1, ₹ 2 and ₹ 5. The number of ₹ 2 coins is 3 times the number of ₹ 5 coins. The total number of coins is 160. How many coins of each denomination are with me?

16. The organisers of an essay competition decide that a winner in the competition gets a prize of ₹ 100 and a participant who does not win gets a prize of ₹ 25. The total prize money distributed is ₹ 3,000. Find the number of winners, if the total number of participants is 63.

2.4 Solving Equations having the Variable on both Sides

An equation is the equality of the values of two expressions. In the equation $2x - 3 = 7$, the two expressions are $2x - 3$ and 7. In most examples that we have come across so far, the RHS is just a number. But this need not always be so; both sides could have expressions with variables. For example, the equation $2x - 3 = x + 2$ has expressions with a variable on both sides; the expression on the LHS is $(2x - 3)$ and the expression on the RHS is $(x + 2)$.

- We now discuss how to solve such equations which have expressions with the variable on both sides.

Example 12: Solve $2x - 3 = x + 2$

Solution: We have

$$2x = x + 2 + 3$$

or $\qquad\qquad 2x = x + 5$

or $\qquad\qquad 2x - x = x + 5 - x \qquad$ (subtracting x from both sides)

or $\qquad\qquad\qquad x = 5 \qquad\qquad\qquad$ (solution)

Here we subtracted from both sides of the equation, not a number (constant), but a term involving the variable. We can do this as variables are also numbers. Also, note that subtracting x from both sides amounts to transposing x to LHS.

Example 13: Solve $5x + \dfrac{7}{2} = \dfrac{3}{2}x - 14$

Solution: Multiply both sides of the equation by 2. We get

$$2 \times \left(5x + \frac{7}{2}\right) = 2 \times \left(\frac{3}{2}x - 14\right)$$

$$(2 \times 5x) + \left(2 \times \frac{7}{2}\right) = \left(2 \times \frac{3}{2}x\right) - (2 \times 14)$$

or $\qquad\qquad 10x + 7 = 3x - 28$

or $\qquad\qquad 10x - 3x + 7 = -28 \qquad$ (transposing $3x$ to LHS)

or $\qquad\qquad 7x + 7 = -28$

or $\qquad\qquad 7x = -28 - 7$

or $\qquad\qquad 7x = -35$

or $\qquad x = \dfrac{-35}{7} \qquad\qquad$ or $\qquad\qquad x = -5 \qquad\qquad$ (solution)

EXERCISE 2.3

Solve the following equations and check your results.

1. $3x = 2x + 18$

2. $5t - 3 = 3t - 5$

3. $5x + 9 = 5 + 3x$

4. $4z + 3 = 6 + 2z$

5. $2x - 1 = 14 - x$

6. $8x + 4 = 3(x - 1) + 7$

7. $x = \dfrac{4}{5}(x + 10)$

8. $\dfrac{2x}{3} + 1 = \dfrac{7x}{15} + 3$

9. $2y + \dfrac{5}{3} = \dfrac{26}{3} - y$

10. $3m = 5m - \dfrac{8}{5}$

2.5 Some More Applications

Example 14: The digits of a two-digit number differ by 3. If the digits are interchanged, and the resulting number is added to the original number, we get 143. What can be the original number?

Solution: Take, for example, a two-digit number, say, 56. It can be written as $56 = (10 \times 5) + 6$.

If the digits in 56 are interchanged, we get 65, which can be written as $(10 \times 6) + 5$.

Let us take the two digit number such that the digit in the units place is b. The digit in the tens place differs from b by 3. Let us take it as $b + 3$. So the two-digit number is $10(b + 3) + b = 10b + 30 + b = 11b + 30$.

With interchange of digits, the resulting two-digit number will be

$$10b + (b + 3) = 11b + 3$$

> Could we take the tens place digit to be $(b - 3)$? Try it and see what solution you get.

If we add these two two-digit numbers, their sum is

$$(11b + 30) + (11b + 3) = 11b + 11b + 30 + 3 = 22b + 33$$

It is given that the sum is 143. Therefore, $22b + 33 = 143$

or $22b = 143 - 33$

or $22b = 110$

or $b = \dfrac{110}{22}$

> Remember, this is the solution when we choose the tens digits to be 3 more than the unit's digits. What happens if we take the tens digit to be $(b - 3)$?

or $b = 5$

The units digit is 5 and therefore the tens digit is $5 + 3$ which is 8. The number is 85.

> The statement of the example is valid for both 58 and 85 and both are correct answers.

Check: On interchange of digits the number we get is 58. The sum of 85 and 58 is 143 as given.

Example 15: Arjun is twice as old as Shriya. Five years ago his age was three times Shriya's age. Find their present ages.

Solution: Let us take Shriya's present age to be x years.

Then Arjun's present age would be $2x$ years.

Shriya's age five years ago was $(x-5)$ years.

Arjun's age five years ago was $(2x-5)$ years.

It is given that Arjun's age five years ago was three times Shriya's age.

Thus, $2x - 5 = 3(x - 5)$

or $2x - 5 = 3x - 15$

or $15 - 5 = 3x - 2x$

or $10 = x$

So, Shriya's present age $= x = 10$ years.

Therefore, Arjun's present age $= 2x = 2 \times 10 = 20$ years.

EXERCISE 2.4

1. Amina thinks of a number and subtracts $\dfrac{5}{2}$ from it. She multiplies the result by 8. The result now obtained is 3 times the same number she thought of. What is the number?

2. A positive number is 5 times another number. If 21 is added to both the numbers, then one of the new numbers becomes twice the other new number. What are the numbers?

3. Sum of the digits of a two-digit number is 9. When we interchange the digits, it is found that the resulting new number is greater than the original number by 27. What is the two-digit number?

4. One of the two digits of a two digit number is three times the other digit. If you interchange the digits of this two-digit number and add the resulting number to the original number, you get 88. What is the original number?

5. Shobo's mother's present age is six times Shobo's present age. Shobo's age five years from now will be one third of his mother's present age. What are their present ages?

6. There is a narrow rectangular plot, reserved for a school, in Mahuli village. The length and breadth of the plot are in the ratio 11:4. At the rate ₹100 per metre it will cost the village panchayat ₹75000 to fence the plot. What are the dimensions of the plot?

7. Hasan buys two kinds of cloth materials for school uniforms, shirt material that costs him ₹ 50 per metre and trouser material that costs him ₹ 90 per metre.

For every 3 meters of the shirt material he buys 2 metres of the trouser material. He sells the materials at 12% and 10% profit respectively. His total sale is ₹ 36,600. How much trouser material did he buy?

8. Half of a herd of deer are grazing in the field and three fourths of the remaining are playing nearby. The rest 9 are drinking water from the pond. Find the number of deer in the herd.

9. A grandfather is ten times older than his granddaughter. He is also 54 years older than her. Find their present ages.

10. Aman's age is three times his son's age. Ten years ago he was five times his son's age. Find their present ages.

2.6 Reducing Equations to Simpler Form

Example 16: Solve $\dfrac{6x+1}{3}+1=\dfrac{x-3}{6}$

Solution: Multiplying both sides of the equation by 6,

> Why 6? Because it is the smallest multiple (or LCM) of the given denominators.

$$\frac{6(6x+1)}{3}+6\times1=\frac{6(x-3)}{6}$$

or $\qquad 2(6x+1)+6=x-3$

or $\qquad 12x+2+6=x-3$ $\qquad$ (opening the brackets)

or $\qquad 12x+8=x-3$

or $\qquad 12x-x+8=-3$

or $\qquad 11x+8=-3$

or $\qquad 11x=-3-8$

or $\qquad 11x=-11$

or $\qquad x=-1$ $\qquad$ (required solution)

Check: LHS $=\dfrac{6(-1)+1}{3}+1=\dfrac{-6+1}{3}+1=\dfrac{-5}{3}+\dfrac{3}{3}=\dfrac{-5+3}{3}=\dfrac{-2}{3}$

RHS $=\dfrac{(-1)-3}{6}=\dfrac{-4}{6}=\dfrac{-2}{3}$

LHS = RHS. $\qquad$ (as required)

Example 17: Solve $5x-2(2x-7)=2(3x-1)+\dfrac{7}{2}$

Solution: Let us open the brackets,

$\qquad$ LHS $=5x-4x+14=x+14$

$$\text{RHS} = 6x - 2 + \frac{7}{2} = 6x - \frac{4}{2} + \frac{7}{2} = 6x + \frac{3}{2}$$

The equation is $x + 14 = 6x + \dfrac{3}{2}$

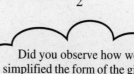

or $\qquad\qquad 14 = 6x - x + \dfrac{3}{2}$

or $\qquad\qquad 14 = 5x + \dfrac{3}{2}$

or $\qquad\qquad 14 - \dfrac{3}{2} = 5x \qquad\qquad$ (transposing $\dfrac{3}{2}$)

or $\qquad\qquad \dfrac{28-3}{2} = 5x$

or $\qquad\qquad \dfrac{25}{2} = 5x$

> Did you observe how we simplified the form of the given equation? Here, we had to multiply both sides of the equation by the LCM of the denominators of the terms in the expressions of the equation.

or $\qquad\qquad x = \dfrac{25}{2} \times \dfrac{1}{5} = \dfrac{5 \times 5}{2 \times 5} = \dfrac{5}{2}$

Therefore, required solution is $x = \dfrac{5}{2}$.

Check: $\text{LHS} = 5 \times \dfrac{5}{2} - 2\left(\dfrac{5}{2} \times 2 - 7\right)$

$$= \dfrac{25}{2} - 2(5-7) = \dfrac{25}{2} - 2(-2) = \dfrac{25}{2} + 4 = \dfrac{25+8}{2} = \dfrac{33}{2}$$

$$\text{RHS} = 2\left(\dfrac{5}{2} \times 3 - 1\right) + \dfrac{7}{2} = 2\left(\dfrac{15}{2} - \dfrac{2}{2}\right) + \dfrac{7}{2} = \dfrac{2 \times 13}{2} + \dfrac{7}{2}$$

$$= \dfrac{26+7}{2} = \dfrac{33}{2} = \text{LHS}. \quad \text{(as required)}$$

> Note, in this example we brought the equation to a simpler form by opening brackets and combining like terms on both sides of the equation.

EXERCISE 2.5

Solve the following linear equations.

1. $\dfrac{x}{2} - \dfrac{1}{5} = \dfrac{x}{3} + \dfrac{1}{4}$

2. $\dfrac{n}{2} - \dfrac{3n}{4} + \dfrac{5n}{6} = 21$

3. $x + 7 - \dfrac{8x}{3} = \dfrac{17}{6} - \dfrac{5x}{2}$

4. $\dfrac{x-5}{3} = \dfrac{x-3}{5}$ **5.** $\dfrac{3t-2}{4} - \dfrac{2t+3}{3} = \dfrac{2}{3} - t$ **6.** $m - \dfrac{m-1}{2} = 1 - \dfrac{m-2}{3}$

Simplify and solve the following linear equations.

7. $3(t-3) = 5(2t+1)$ **8.** $15(y-4) - 2(y-9) + 5(y+6) = 0$

9. $3(5z-7) - 2(9z-11) = 4(8z-13) - 17$

10. $0.25(4f-3) = 0.05(10f-9)$

2.7 Equations Reducible to the Linear Form

Example 18: Solve $\dfrac{x+1}{2x+3} = \dfrac{3}{8}$

Solution: Observe that the equation is not a linear equation, since the expression on its LHS is not linear. But we can put it into the form of a linear equation. We multiply both sides of the equation by $(2x+3)$,

$$\left(\frac{x+1}{2x+3}\right) \times (2x+3) = \frac{3}{8} \times (2x+3)$$

> Note that
> $2x + 3 \neq 0$ (Why?)

Notice that $(2x+3)$ gets cancelled on the LHS We have then,

$$x + 1 = \frac{3(2x+3)}{8}$$

We have now a linear equation which we know how to solve.
Multiplying both sides by 8

$$8(x+1) = 3(2x+3)$$

> This step can be directly obtained by 'cross-multiplication'
> $$\frac{x+1}{2x+3} \diagup\!\!\!\!\diagdown \frac{3}{8}$$

or $8x + 8 = 6x + 9$

or $8x = 6x + 9 - 8$

or $8x = 6x + 1$

or $8x - 6x = 1$

or $2x = 1$

or $x = \dfrac{1}{2}$

The solution is $x = \dfrac{1}{2}$.

Check : Numerator of LHS $= \dfrac{1}{2} + 1 = \dfrac{1+2}{2} = \dfrac{3}{2}$

Denominator of LHS $= 2x + 3 = 2 \times \dfrac{1}{2} + 3 = 1 + 3 = 4$

$$\text{LHS} = \text{numerator} \div \text{denominator} = \frac{3}{2} \div 4 = \frac{3}{2} \times \frac{1}{4} = \frac{3}{8}$$

LHS = RHS.

Example 19: Present ages of Anu and Raj are in the ratio 4:5. Eight years from now the ratio of their ages will be 5:6. Find their present ages.

Solution: Let the present ages of Anu and Raj be $4x$ years and $5x$ years respectively.

After eight years. Anu's age = $(4x + 8)$ years;

After eight years, Raj's age = $(5x + 8)$ years.

Therefore, the ratio of their ages after eight years $= \dfrac{4x + 8}{5x + 8}$

This is given to be $5 : 6$

Therefore, $\qquad\qquad \dfrac{4x + 8}{5x + 8} = \dfrac{5}{6}$

Cross-multiplication gives $\qquad 6(4x + 8) = 5(5x + 8)$

or $\qquad\qquad\qquad 24x + 48 = 25x + 40$

or $\qquad\qquad 24x + 48 - 40 = 25x$

or $\qquad\qquad\qquad 24x + 8 = 25x$

or $\qquad\qquad\qquad\qquad 8 = 25x - 24x$

or $\qquad\qquad\qquad\qquad 8 = x$

Therefore, $\qquad$ Anu's present age $= 4x = 4 \times 8 = 32$ years

$\qquad\qquad\qquad$ Raj's present age $= 5x = 5 \times 8 = 40$ years

EXERCISE 2.6

Solve the following equations.

1. $\dfrac{8x - 3}{3x} = 2$

2. $\dfrac{9x}{7 - 6x} = 15$

3. $\dfrac{z}{z + 15} = \dfrac{4}{9}$

4. $\dfrac{3y + 4}{2 - 6y} = \dfrac{-2}{5}$

5. $\dfrac{7y + 4}{y + 2} = \dfrac{-4}{3}$

6. The ages of Hari and Harry are in the ratio 5:7. Four years from now the ratio of their ages will be 3:4. Find their present ages.

7. The denominator of a rational number is greater than its numerator by 8. If the numerator is increased by 17 and the denominator is decreased by 1, the number obtained is $\dfrac{3}{2}$. Find the rational number.

WHAT HAVE WE DISCUSSED?

1. An algebraic equation is an equality involving variables. It says that the value of the expression on one side of the equality sign is equal to the value of the expression on the other side.

2. The equations we study in Classes VI, VII and VIII are linear equations in one variable. In such equations, the expressions which form the equation contain only one variable. Further, the equations are linear, i.e., the highest power of the variable appearing in the equation is 1.

3. A linear equation may have for its solution any rational number.

4. An equation may have linear expressions on both sides. Equations that we studied in Classes VI and VII had just a number on one side of the equation.

5. Just as numbers, variables can, also, be transposed from one side of the equation to the other.

6. Occasionally, the expressions forming equations have to be simplified before we can solve them by usual methods. Some equations may not even be linear to begin with, but they can be brought to a linear form by multiplying both sides of the equation by a suitable expression.

7. The utility of linear equations is in their diverse applications; different problems on numbers, ages, perimeters, combination of currency notes, and so on can be solved using linear equations.

Understanding Quadrilaterals

0852CH03

3.1 Introduction

You know that the paper is a model for a **plane surface**. When you join a number of points without lifting a pencil from the paper (and without retracing any portion of the drawing other than single points), you get a **plane curve**.

Try to recall different varieties of curves you have seen in the earlier classes.

Match the following: (Caution! A figure may match to more than one type).

Figure		Type	
(1)		(a)	Simple closed curve
(2)		(b)	A closed curve that is not simple
(3)		(c)	Simple curve that is not closed
(4)		(d)	Not a simple curve

Compare your matchings with those of your friends. Do they agree?

3.2 Polygons

A simple closed curve made up of only line segments is called a **polygon**.

Curves that are polygons

Curves that are not polygons

Try to give a few more examples and non-examples for a polygon.

Draw a rough figure of a polygon and identify its sides and vertices.

3.2.1 Classification of polygons

We classify polygons according to the number of sides (or vertices) they have.

Number of sides or vertices	Classification	Sample figure
3	Triangle	
4	Quadrilateral	
5	Pentagon	
6	Hexagon	
7	Heptagon	
8	Octagon	
9	Nonagon	
10	Decagon	
⋮	⋮	⋮
n	n-gon	

3.2.2 Diagonals

A **diagonal** is a line segment connecting two non-consecutive vertices of a polygon (Fig 3.1).

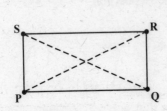
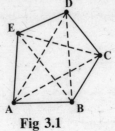
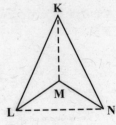

Fig 3.1

Can you name the diagonals in each of the above figures? (Fig 3.1)

Is $\overline{PQ}$ a diagonal? What about $\overline{LN}$?

You already know what we mean by **interior** and **exterior** of a closed curve (Fig 3.2).

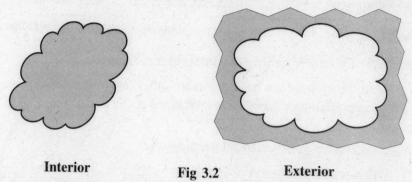

Interior   **Fig 3.2**   Exterior

The interior has a boundary. Does the exterior have a boundary? Discuss with your friends.

3.2.3 Convex and concave polygons

Here are some convex polygons and some concave polygons. (Fig 3.3)

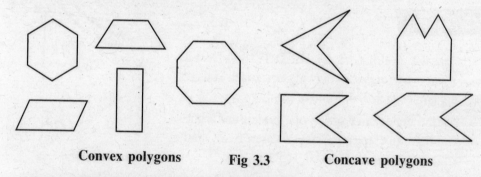

Convex polygons   **Fig 3.3**   **Concave polygons**

Can you find how these types of polygons differ from one another? Polygons that are convex have no portions of their diagonals in their exteriors or any line segment joining any two different points, in the interior of the polygon, lies wholly in the interior of it . Is this true with concave polygons? Study the figures given. Then try to describe in your own words what we mean by a convex polygon and what we mean by a concave polygon. Give two rough sketches of each kind.

In our work in this class, we will be dealing with convex polygons only.

3.2.4 Regular and irregular polygons

A regular polygon is both 'equiangular' and 'equilateral'. For example, a square has sides of equal length and angles of equal measure. Hence it is a regular polygon. A rectangle is equiangular but not equilateral. Is a rectangle a regular polygon? Is an equilateral triangle a regular polygon? Why?

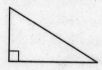
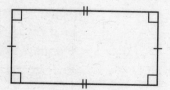

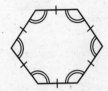 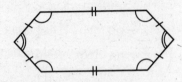

Regular polygons   **Polygons that are not regular**

[**Note:** Use of ⟨ or ⟨ indicates segments of equal length].

In the previous classes, have you come across any quadrilateral that is equilateral but not equiangular? Recall the quadrilateral shapes you saw in earlier classes – Rectangle, Square, Rhombus etc.

Is there a triangle that is equilateral but not equiangular?

3.2.5 Angle sum property

Do you remember the angle-sum property of a triangle? The sum of the measures of the three angles of a triangle is 180°. Recall the methods by which we tried to visualise this fact. We now extend these ideas to a quadrilateral.

DO THIS

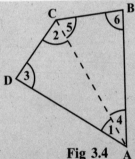

1. Take any quadrilateral, say ABCD (Fig 3.4). Divide it into two triangles, by drawing a diagonal. You get six angles 1, 2, 3, 4, 5 and 6.

   Use the angle-sum property of a triangle and argue how the sum of the measures of ∠A, ∠B, ∠C and ∠D amounts to 180° + 180° = 360°.

   Fig 3.4

2. Take four congruent card-board copies of any quadrilateral ABCD, with angles as shown [Fig 3.5 (i)]. Arrange the copies as shown in the figure, where angles ∠1, ∠2, ∠3, ∠4 meet at a point [Fig 3.5 (ii)].

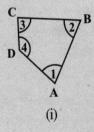 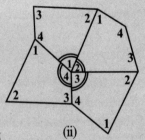

For doing this you may have to turn and match appropriate corners so that they fit.

(i)   (ii)

Fig 3.5

What can you say about the sum of the angles ∠1, ∠2, ∠3 and ∠4?

[**Note:** We denote the angles by ∠1, ∠2, ∠3, etc., and their respective measures by m∠1, m∠2, m∠3, etc.]

The sum of the measures of the four angles of a quadrilateral is_____.

You may arrive at this result in several other ways also.

3. As before consider quadrilateral ABCD (Fig 3.6). Let P be any point in its interior. Join P to vertices A, B, C and D. In the figure, consider ΔPAB. From this we see $x = 180° - m\angle2 - m\angle3$; similarly from ΔPBC, $y = 180° - m\angle4 - m\angle5$, from ΔPCD, $z = 180° - m\angle6 - m\angle7$ and from ΔPDA, $w = 180° - m\angle8 - m\angle1$. Use this to find the total measure $m\angle1 + m\angle2 + ... + m\angle8$, does it help you to arrive at the result? Remember $\angle x + \angle y + \angle z + \angle w = 360°$.

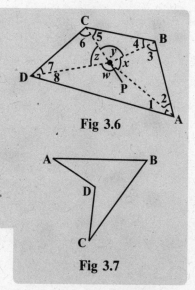

Fig 3.6

4. These quadrilaterals were convex. What would happen if the quadrilateral is not convex? Consider quadrilateral ABCD. Split it into two triangles and find the sum of the interior angles (Fig 3.7).

Fig 3.7

EXERCISE 3.1

1. Given here are some figures.

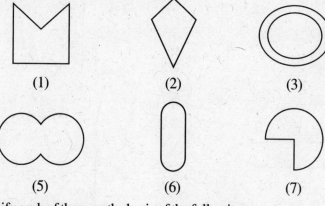

(1)   (2)   (3)   (4)

(5)   (6)   (7)   (8)

Classify each of them on the basis of the following.

    (a) Simple curve   (b) Simple closed curve   (c) Polygon

    (d) Convex polygon   (e) Concave polygon

2. How many diagonals does each of the following have?

    (a) A convex quadrilateral   (b) A regular hexagon   (c) A triangle

3. What is the sum of the measures of the angles of a convex quadrilateral? Will this property hold if the quadrilateral is not convex? (Make a non-convex quadrilateral and try!)

4. Examine the table. (Each figure is divided into triangles and the sum of the angles deduced from that.)

Figure				
Side	3	4	5	6
Angle sum	180°	$2 \times 180°$ $= (4-2) \times 180°$	$3 \times 180°$ $= (5-2) \times 180°$	$4 \times 180°$ $= (6-2) \times 180°$

What can you say about the angle sum of a convex polygon with number of sides?

(a) 7   (b) 8   (c) 10   (d) n

5. What is a regular polygon?

State the name of a regular polygon of

(i) 3 sides   (ii) 4 sides   (iii) 6 sides

6. Find the angle measure x in the following figures.

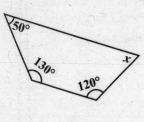

(a)

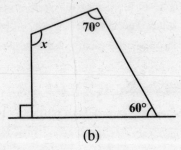

(b)

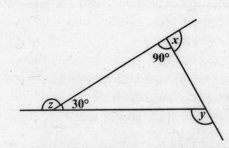

(c)

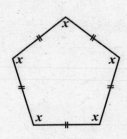

(d)

7.

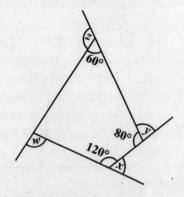

(a) Find $x + y + z$ (b) Find $x + y + z + w$

3.3 Sum of the Measures of the Exterior Angles of a Polygon

On many occasions a knowledge of exterior angles may throw light on the nature of interior angles and sides.

DO THIS

Draw a polygon on the floor, using a piece of chalk. (In the figure, a pentagon ABCDE is shown) (Fig 3.8).

We want to know the total measure of angles, i.e, $m\angle 1 + m\angle 2 + m\angle 3 + m\angle 4 + m\angle 5$. Start at A. Walk along $\overline{AB}$. On reaching B, you need to turn through an angle of $m\angle 1$, to walk along $\overline{BC}$. When you reach at C, you need to turn through an angle of $m\angle 2$ to walk along $\overline{CD}$. You continue to move in this manner, until you return to side AB. You would have in fact made one complete turn.

Therefore, $m\angle 1 + m\angle 2 + m\angle 3 + m\angle 4 + m\angle 5 = 360°$

This is true whatever be the number of sides of the polygon.

Therefore, *the sum of the measures of the external angles of any polygon is 360°.*

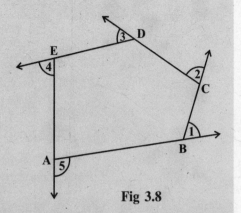

Fig 3.8

Example 1: Find measure x in Fig 3.9.

Solution:
$$x + 90° + 50° + 110° = 360° \quad \text{(Why?)}$$
$$x + 250° = 360°$$
$$x = 110°$$

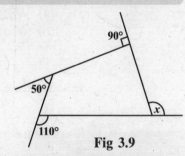

Fig 3.9

TRY THESE

Take a regular hexagon Fig 3.10.

1. What is the sum of the measures of its exterior angles x, y, z, p, q, r?
2. Is $x = y = z = p = q = r$? Why?
3. What is the measure of each?
   (i) exterior angle   (ii) interior angle
4. Repeat this activity for the cases of
   (i) a regular octagon   (ii) a regular 20-gon

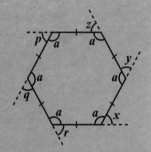

Fig 3.10

Example 2: Find the number of sides of a regular polygon whose each exterior angle has a measure of 45°.

Solution: Total measure of all exterior angles = 360°
Measure of each exterior angle = 45°

Therefore, the number of exterior angles = $\dfrac{360}{45} = 8$

The polygon has 8 sides.

EXERCISE 3.2

1. Find x in the following figures.

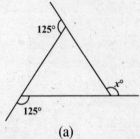

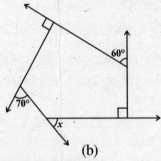

(a)   (b)

2. Find the measure of each exterior angle of a regular polygon of
   (i) 9 sides   (ii) 15 sides
3. How many sides does a regular polygon have if the measure of an exterior angle is 24°?
4. How many sides does a regular polygon have if each of its interior angles is 165°?
5. (a) Is it possible to have a regular polygon with measure of each exterior angle as 22°?
   (b) Can it be an interior angle of a regular polygon? Why?
6. (a) What is the minimum interior angle possible for a regular polygon? Why?
   (b) What is the maximum exterior angle possible for a regular polygon?

3.4 Kinds of Quadrilaterals

Based on the nature of the sides or angles of a quadrilateral, it gets special names.

3.4.1 Trapezium

Trapezium is a quadrilateral with a pair of parallel sides.

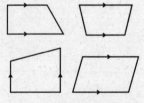

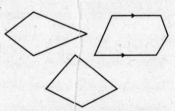

These are trapeziums   **These are not trapeziums**

Study the above figures and discuss with your friends why some of them are trapeziums while some are not. (**Note:** *The arrow marks indicate parallel lines*).

DO THIS

1. Take identical cut-outs of congruent triangles of sides 3 cm, 4 cm, 5 cm. Arrange them as shown (Fig 3.11).

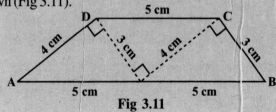

Fig 3.11

You get a trapezium. (Check it!) Which are the parallel sides here? Should the non-parallel sides be equal?

You can get two more trapeziums using the same set of triangles. Find them out and discuss their shapes.

2. Take four set-squares from your and your friend's instrument boxes. Use different numbers of them to place side-by-side and obtain different trapeziums.

If the non-parallel sides of a trapezium are of equal length, we call it an *isosceles trapezium*. Did you get an isoceles trapezium in any of your investigations given above?

3.4.2 Kite

Kite is a special type of a quadrilateral. The sides with the same markings in each figure are equal. For example AB = AD and BC = CD.

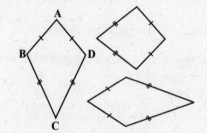

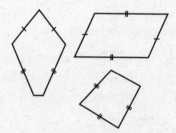

These are kites   **These are not kites**

Study these figures and try to describe what a kite is. Observe that

(i) A kite has 4 sides (It is a quadrilateral).

(ii) There are exactly two **distinct consecutive pairs** of sides of equal length.

Check whether a square is a kite.

DO THIS

Take a thick white sheet.
Fold the paper once.

Draw two line segments of different lengths as shown in Fig 3.12.

Cut along the line segments and open up.

You have the shape of a kite (Fig 3.13).

Has the kite any line symmetry?

Fold both the diagonals of the kite. Use the set-square to check if they cut at right angles. Are the diagonals equal in length?

Verify (by paper-folding or measurement) if the diagonals bisect each other.

By folding an angle of the kite on its opposite, check for angles of equal measure.

Observe the diagonal folds; do they indicate any diagonal being an angle bisector?

Share your findings with others and list them. A summary of these results are given elsewhere in the chapter for your reference.

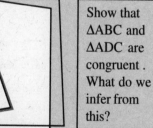

Fig 3.12

Show that ΔABC and ΔADC are congruent . What do we infer from this?

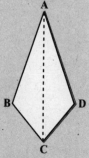

Fig 3.13

3.4.3 Parallelogram

A parallelogram is a quadrilateral. As the name suggests, it has something to do with parallel lines.

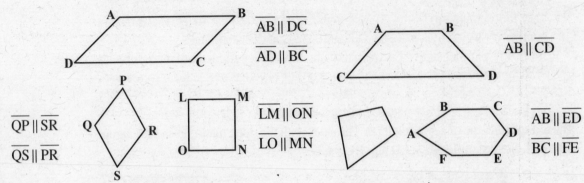

$$\overline{AB} \| \overline{DC}$$
$$\overline{AD} \| \overline{BC}$$

$$\overline{AB} \| \overline{CD}$$

$$\overline{QP} \| \overline{SR}$$
$$\overline{QS} \| \overline{PR}$$

$$\overline{LM} \| \overline{ON}$$
$$\overline{LO} \| \overline{MN}$$

$$\overline{AB} \| \overline{ED}$$
$$\overline{BC} \| \overline{FE}$$

These are parallelograms　　　　**These are not parallelograms**

Study these figures and try to describe in your own words what we mean by a parallelogram. Share your observations with your friends.

Check whether a rectangle is also a parallelogram.

DO THIS

Take two different rectangular cardboard strips of different widths (Fig 3.14).

Strip 1　　　**Fig 3.14**　　　**Strip 2**

Place one strip horizontally and draw lines along its edge as drawn in the figure (Fig 3.15).

Now place the other strip in a slant position over the lines drawn and use this to draw two more lines as shown (Fig 3.16).

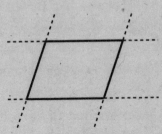

Fig 3.15

These four lines enclose a quadrilateral. This is made up of two pairs of parallel lines (Fig 3.17).

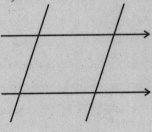

Fig 3.16　　　　　　　　　　**Fig 3.17**

It is a parallelogram.

A parallelogram is a quadrilateral whose opposite sides are parallel.

3.4.4 Elements of a parallelogram

There are four sides and four angles in a parallelogram. Some of these are equal. There are some terms associated with these elements that you need to remember.

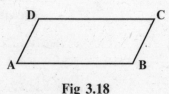

Fig 3.18

Given a parallelogram ABCD (Fig 3.18).

$\overline{AB}$ and $\overline{DC}$, are **opposite sides**. $\overline{AD}$ and $\overline{BC}$ form another pair of opposite sides.

∠A and ∠C are a pair of **opposite angles**; another pair of opposite angles would be ∠B and ∠D.

$\overline{AB}$ and $\overline{BC}$ are **adjacent sides**. This means, one of the sides starts where the other ends. Are $\overline{BC}$ and $\overline{CD}$ adjacent sides too? Try to find two more pairs of adjacent sides.

∠A and ∠B are **adjacent angles**. They are at the ends of the same side. ∠B and ∠C are also adjacent. Identify other pairs of adjacent angles of the parallelogram.

DO THIS

Take cut-outs of two identical parallelograms, say ABCD and A′B′C′D′ (Fig 3.19).

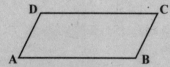 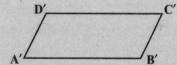

Fig 3.19

Here $\overline{AB}$ is same as $\overline{A'B'}$ except for the name. Similarly the other corresponding sides are equal too.

Place $\overline{A'B'}$ over $\overline{DC}$. Do they coincide? What can you now say about the lengths $\overline{AB}$ and $\overline{DC}$?

Similarly examine the lengths $\overline{AD}$ and $\overline{BC}$. What do you find?

You may also arrive at this result by measuring $\overline{AB}$ and $\overline{DC}$.

Property: *The opposite sides of a parallelogram are of equal length.*

TRY THESE

Take two identical set squares with angles 30° – 60° – 90° and place them adjacently to form a parallelogram as shown in Fig 3.20. Does this help you to verify the above property?

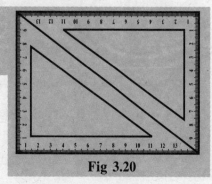

You can further strengthen this idea through a logical argument also.

Consider a parallelogram ABCD (Fig 3.21). Draw any one diagonal, say $\overline{AC}$.

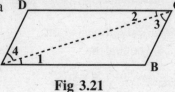

Fig 3.21

Fig 3.20

Looking at the angles,

$$\angle 1 = \angle 2 \quad \text{and} \quad \angle 3 = \angle 4 \quad \text{(Why?)}$$

Since in triangles ABC and ADC, $\angle 1 = \angle 2$, $\angle 3 = \angle 4$

and $\overline{AC}$ is common, so, by ASA congruency condition,

$$\Delta\, ABC \quad \cong \quad \Delta\, CDA \qquad \text{(How is ASA used here?)}$$

This gives $\quad\quad\quad\quad\quad\quad AB = DC \quad \text{and} \quad BC = AD.$

Example 3: Find the perimeter of the parallelogram PQRS (Fig 3.22).

Solution: In a parallelogram, the opposite sides have same length.

Therefore, PQ = SR = 12 cm and QR = PS = 7 cm

So, Perimeter = PQ + QR + RS + SP

$\quad\quad\quad\quad\quad\quad = 12\,\text{cm} + 7\,\text{cm} + 12\,\text{cm} + 7\,\text{cm} = 38\,\text{cm}$

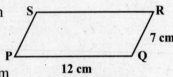

Fig 3.22

3.4.5 Angles of a parallelogram

We studied a property of parallelograms concerning the (opposite) sides. What can we say about the angles?

DO THIS

Let ABCD be a parallelogram (Fig 3.23). Copy it on a tracing sheet. Name this copy as A′B′C′D′. Place A′B′C′D′ on ABCD. Pin them together at the point where the diagonals meet. Rotate the transparent sheet by 180°. The parallelograms still concide; but you now find A′ lying exactly on C and vice-versa; similarly B′ lies on D and vice-versa.

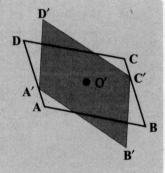

Fig 3.23

Does this tell you anything about the measures of the angles A and C? Examine the same for angles B and D. State your findings.

Property: *The opposite angles of a parallelogram are of equal measure.*

TRY THESE

Take two identical 30° – 60° – 90° set-squares and form a parallelogram as before. Does the figure obtained help you to confirm the above property?

You can further justify this idea through logical arguments.

If $\overline{AC}$ and $\overline{BD}$ are the diagonals of the parallelogram, (Fig 3.24) you find that

$$\angle 1 = \angle 2 \quad \text{and} \quad \angle 3 = \angle 4 \quad \text{(Why?)}$$

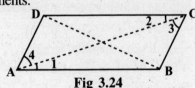

Fig 3.24

Studying △ABC and △ADC (Fig 3.25) separately, will help you to see that by ASA congruency condition,

$$\triangle ABC \quad \cong \quad \triangle CDA \qquad \text{(How?)}$$

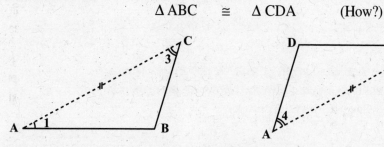

Fig 3.25

This shows that ∠B and ∠D have same measure. In the same way you can get $m\angle A = m\angle C$.

Alternatively, ∠1 = ∠2 and ∠3 = ∠4, we have, $m\angle A = \angle 1 + \angle 4 = \angle 2 + \angle C \ m\angle C$

Example 4: In Fig 3.26, BEST is a parallelogram. Find the values x, y and z.

Solution: S is opposite to B.

So, $\qquad x = 100°$ (opposite angles property)

$\qquad y = 100°$ (measure of angle corresponding to ∠x)

$\qquad z = 80°$ (since ∠y, ∠z is a linear pair)

We now turn our attention to adjacent angles of a parallelogram.
In parallelogram ABCD, (Fig 3.27).

∠A and ∠D are supplementary since

$\overline{DC} \parallel \overline{AB}$ and with transversal $\overline{DA}$, these two angles are interior opposite.

∠A and ∠B are also supplementary. Can you say 'why'?

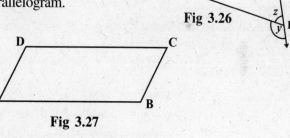

Fig 3.26

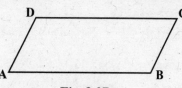

Fig 3.27

$\overline{AD} \parallel \overline{BC}$ and $\overline{BA}$ is a transversal, making ∠A and ∠B interior opposite.

Identify two more pairs of supplementary angles from the figure.

Property: *The adjacent angles in a parallelogram are supplementary.*

Example 5: In a parallelogram RING, (Fig 3.28) if $m\angle R = 70°$, find all the other angles.

Solution: Given $\quad m\angle R = 70°$

Then $\qquad\qquad m\angle N = 70°$

because ∠R and ∠N are opposite angles of a parallelogram.

Since ∠R and ∠I are supplementary,

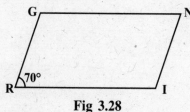

$$m\angle I = 180° - 70° = 110°$$

Fig 3.28

Also, $\qquad\qquad m\angle G = 110°$ since ∠G is opposite to ∠I

Thus, $\qquad\qquad m\angle R = m\angle N = 70°$ and $m\angle I = m\angle G = 110°$

THINK, DISCUSS AND WRITE

After showing $m\angle R = m\angle N = 70°$, can you find $m\angle I$ and $m\angle G$ by any other method?

3.4.6 Diagonals of a parallelogram

The diagonals of a parallelogram, in general, are not of equal length. (Did you check this in your earlier activity?) However, the diagonals of a parallelogram have an interesting property.

DO THIS

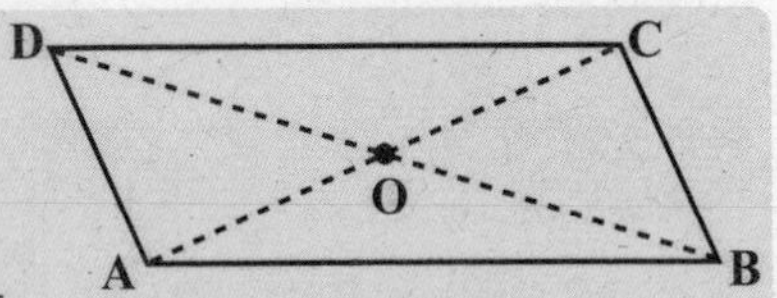

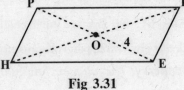

Take a cut-out of a parallelogram, say,

ABCD (Fig 3.29). Let its diagonals $\overline{AC}$ and $\overline{DB}$ meet at O.   **Fig 3.29**

Find the mid point of $\overline{AC}$ by a fold, placing C on A. Is the mid-point same as O?

Does this show that diagonal $\overline{DB}$ bisects the diagonal $\overline{AC}$ at the point O? Discuss it with your friends. Repeat the activity to find where the mid point of $\overline{DB}$ could lie.

Property: *The diagonals of a parallelogram bisect each other (at the point of their intersection, of course!)*

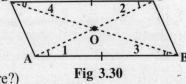

To argue and justify this property is not very difficult. From Fig 3.30, applying ASA criterion, it is easy to see that

$\Delta\,AOB \;\cong\; \Delta\,COD$ (How is ASA used here?)   **Fig 3.30**

This gives   AO = CO and   BO = DO

Example 6: In Fig 3.31 HELP is a parallelogram. (Lengths are in cms). Given that OE = 4 and HL is 5 more than PE? Find OH.

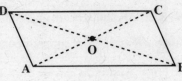

Solution : If   OE = 4 then OP also is 4 (Why?)

So   PE = 8,   (Why?)

Therefore   HL = 8 + 5 = 13

Fig 3.31

Hence $OH = \dfrac{1}{2} \times 13 = 6.5$ (cms)

EXERCISE 3.3

1. Given a parallelogram ABCD. Complete each statement along with the definition or property used.

(i)   AD = ...   (ii) $\angle$ DCB = ...

(iii) OC = ...   (iv) $m \angle$DAB + $m \angle$CDA = ...

2. Consider the following parallelograms. Find the values of the unknowns x, y, z.

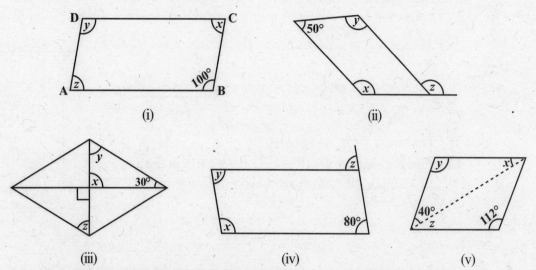

(i)   (ii)

(iii)   (iv)   (v)

3. Can a quadrilateral ABCD be a parallelogram if

    (i) $\angle D + \angle B = 180°$?   (ii)   AB = DC = 8 cm, AD = 4 cm and BC = 4.4 cm?

    (iii) $\angle A = 70°$ and $\angle C = 65°$?

4. Draw a rough figure of a quadrilateral that is not a parallelogram but has exactly two opposite angles of equal measure.

5. The measures of two adjacent angles of a parallelogram are in the ratio 3 : 2. Find the measure of each of the angles of the parallelogram.

6. Two adjacent angles of a parallelogram have equal measure. Find the measure of each of the angles of the parallelogram.

7. The adjacent figure HOPE is a parallelogram. Find the angle measures x, y and z. State the properties you use to find them.

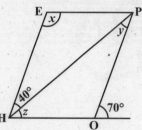

8. The following figures GUNS and RUNS are parallelograms. Find x and y. (Lengths are in cm)

(i)   (ii)

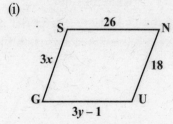   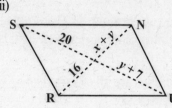

9.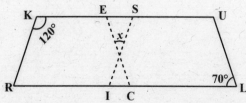

In the above figure both RISK and CLUE are parallelograms. Find the value of x.

10. Explain how this figure is a trapezium. Which of its two sides are parallel? (Fig 3.32)

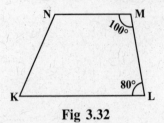

Fig 3.32

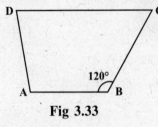

Fig 3.33

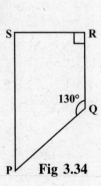

Fig 3.34

11. Find $m\angle C$ in Fig 3.33 if $\overline{AB} \parallel \overline{DC}$.

12. Find the measure of $\angle P$ and $\angle S$ if $\overline{SP} \parallel \overline{RQ}$ in Fig 3.34.
(If you find $m\angle R$, is there more than one method to find $m\angle P$?)

3.5 Some Special Parallelograms

3.5.1 Rhombus

We obtain a Rhombus (which, you will see, is a parallelogram) as a special case of kite (which is not a a parallelogram).

DO THIS

Recall the paper-cut kite you made earlier.

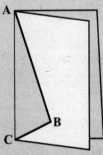

Kite-cut

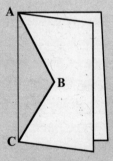

Rhombus-cut

When you cut along ABC and opened up, you got a kite. Here lengths AB and BC were different. If you draw AB = BC, then the kite you obtain is called a **rhombus**.

Note that the sides of rhombus are all of same length; this is not the case with the kite.

A rhombus is a quadrilateral with sides of equal length.

Since the opposite sides of a rhombus have the same length, it is also a parallelogram. So, *a rhombus has all the properties of a parallelogram and also that of a kite*. Try to list them out. You can then verify your list with the check list summarised in the book elsewhere.

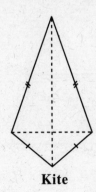

Kite

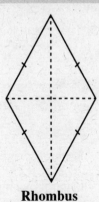

Rhombus

The most useful property of a rhombus is that of its diagonals.

Property: *The diagonals of a rhombus are perpendicular bisectors of one another.*

DO THIS

Take a copy of rhombus. By paper-folding verify if the point of intersection is the mid-point of each diagonal. You may also check if they intersect at right angles, using the corner of a set-square.

Here is an outline justifying this property using logical steps.

ABCD is a rhombus (Fig 3.35). Therefore it is a parallelogram too.

Since diagonals bisect each other,   OA = OC and OB = OD.

We have to show that $m\angle AOD = m\angle COD = 90°$

It can be seen that by SSS congruency criterion

Fig 3.35

$$\Delta\,AOD \quad \cong \quad \Delta\,COD$$

Therefore, $m\angle AOD = m\angle COD$

Since $\angle AOD$ and $\angle COD$ are a linear pair,

$$m\angle AOD = m\angle COD = 90°$$

Since AO = CO   (Why?)
    AD = CD   (Why?)
    OD = OD

Example 7:

RICE is a rhombus (Fig 3.36). Find x, y, z. Justify your findings.

Solution:

$x = OE$	$y = OR$	z = side of the rhombus
= OI (diagonals bisect)	= OC (diagonals bisect)	= 13 (all sides are equal)
= 5	= 12	

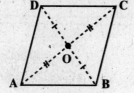

Fig 3.36

3.5.2 A rectangle

A rectangle is a parallelogram with equal angles (Fig 3.37).

What is the full meaning of this definition? Discuss with your friends.

If the rectangle is to be equiangular, what could be the measure of each angle?

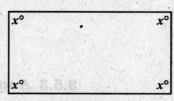

Fig 3.37

Let the measure of each angle be $x°$.

Then $4x° = 360°$ (Why)?

Therefore, $x° = 90°$

Thus each angle of a rectangle is a right angle.

So, a rectangle is a parallelogram in which every angle is a right angle.

   Being a parallelogram, the rectangle has opposite sides of equal length and its diagonals bisect each other.

In a parallelogram, the diagonals can be of different lengths. (Check this); but surprisingly the rectangle (being a special case) has diagonals of equal length.

Property: *The diagonals of a rectangle are of equal length.*

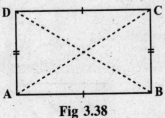
Fig 3.38

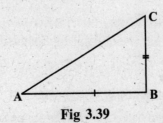
Fig 3.39

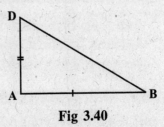
Fig 3.40

This is easy to justify. If ABCD is a rectangle (Fig 3.38), then looking at triangles ABC and ABD separately [(Fig 3.39) and (Fig 3.40) respectively], we have

$$\triangle ABC \cong \triangle ABD$$

This is because

AB = AB	(Common)
BC = AD	(Why?)
$m \angle A = m \angle B = 90°$	(Why?)

The congruency follows by SAS criterion.

Thus   AC = BD

and *in a rectangle the diagonals, besides being equal in length bisect each other* (Why?)

Example 8: RENT is a rectangle (Fig 3.41). Its diagonals meet at O. Find x, if OR = $2x + 4$ and OT = $3x + 1$.

Solution: $\overline{OT}$ is half of the diagonal $\overline{TE}$,

$\overline{OR}$ is half of the diagonal $\overline{RN}$.

Diagonals are equal here. (Why?)

So, their halves are also equal.

Therefore $3x + 1 = 2x + 4$
or $x = 3$

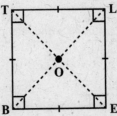
Fig 3.41

3.5.3 A square

A square is a rectangle with equal sides.

This means a square has all the properties of a rectangle with an additional requirement that all the sides have equal length.

The square, like the rectangle, has diagonals of equal length.

In a rectangle, there is no requirement for the diagonals to be perpendicular to one another, (Check this).

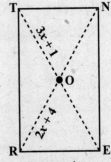

BELT is a square, BE = EL = LT = TB
∠B, ∠E, ∠L, ∠T are right angles.

BL = ET and $\overline{BL} \perp \overline{ET}$.

OB = OL and OE = OT.

In a square the diagonals.

(i) bisect one another   (square being a parallelogram)

(ii) are of equal length   (square being a rectangle) and

(iii) are perpendicular to one another.

Hence, we get the following property.

Property: *The diagonals of a square are perpendicular bisectors of each other.*

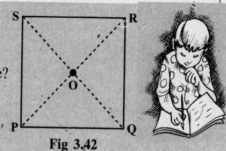

DO THIS

Take a square sheet, say PQRS (Fig 3.42).

Fold along both the diagonals. Are their mid-points the same?

Check if the angle at O is 90° by using a set-square.

This verifies the property stated above.

Fig 3.42

We can justify this also by arguing logically:

ABCD is a square whose diagonals meet at O (Fig 3.43).

$$OA = OC \quad \text{(Since the square is a parallelogram)}$$

By SSS congruency condition, we now see that

$$\Delta\, AOD \cong \Delta\, COD \quad \text{(How?)}$$

Therefore, $m\angle AOD = m\angle COD$

These angles being a linear pair, each is right angle.

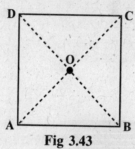

Fig 3.43

◤ EXERCISE 3.4

1. State whether True or False.

  (a) All rectangles are squares

  (b) All rhombuses are parallelograms

  (c) All squares are rhombuses and also rectangles

  (d) All squares are not parallelograms.

  (e) All kites are rhombuses.

  (f) All rhombuses are kites.

  (g) All parallelograms are trapeziums.

  (h) All squares are trapeziums.

2. Identify all the quadrilaterals that have.

  (a) four sides of equal length   (b) four right angles

3. Explain how a square is.

  (i) a quadrilateral   (ii) a parallelogram   (iii) a rhombus   (iv) a rectangle

4. Name the quadrilaterals whose diagonals.

  (i) bisect each other   (ii) are perpendicular bisectors of each other   (iii) are equal

5. Explain why a rectangle is a convex quadrilateral.

6. ABC is a right-angled triangle and O is the mid point of the side opposite to the right angle. Explain why O is equidistant from A, B and C. (The dotted lines are drawn additionally to help you).

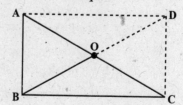

THINK, DISCUSS AND WRITE

1. A mason has made a concrete slab. He needs it to be rectangular. In what different ways can he make sure that it is rectangular?

2. A square was defined as a rectangle with all sides equal. Can we define it as rhombus with equal angles? Explore this idea.

3. Can a trapezium have all angles equal? Can it have all sides equal? Explain.

WHAT HAVE WE DISCUSSED?

Quadrilateral	Properties
Parallelogram: A quadrilateral with each pair of opposite sides parallel.	(1) Opposite sides are equal. (2) Opposite angles are equal. (3) Diagonals bisect one another.
Rhombus: A parallelogram with sides of equal length.	(1) All the properties of a parallelogram. (2) Diagonals are perpendicular to each other.
Rectangle: A parallelogram with a right angle.	(1) All the properties of a parallelogram. (2) Each of the angles is a right angle. (3) Diagonals are equal.
Square: A rectangle with sides of equal length.	All the properties of a parallelogram, rhombus and a rectangle.
Kite: A quadrilateral with exactly two pairs of equal consecutive sides	(1) The diagonals are perpendicular to one another (2) One of the diagonals bisects the other. (3) In the figure $m\angle B = m\angle D$ but $m\angle A \neq m\angle C$.

Practical Geometry

0852CH04

4.1 Introduction

You have learnt how to draw triangles in Class VII. We require three measurements (of sides and angles) to draw a unique triangle.

Since three measurements were enough to draw a triangle, a natural question arises whether four measurements would be sufficient to draw a unique four sided closed figure, namely, a quadrilateral.

DO THIS

Take a pair of sticks of equal lengths, say 10 cm. Take another pair of sticks of equal lengths, say, 8 cm. Hinge them up suitably to get a rectangle of length 10 cm and breadth 8 cm.

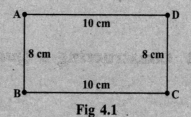

This rectangle has been created with the 4 available measurements.

Now just push along the breadth of the rectangle. Is the new shape obtained, still a rectangle (Fig 4.2)? Observe that the rectangle has now become a parallelogram. Have you altered the lengths of the sticks? No! The measurements of sides remain the same.

Give another push to the newly obtained shape in a different direction; what do you get? You again get a parallelogram, which is altogether different (Fig 4.3), yet the four measurements remain the same.

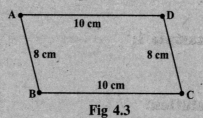

Fig 4.1

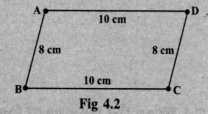

Fig 4.2

Fig 4.3

This shows that 4 measurements of a quadrilateral cannot determine it uniquely. Can 5 measurements determine a quadrilateral uniquely? Let us go back to the activity!

You have constructed a rectangle with two sticks each of length 10 cm and other two sticks each of length 8 cm. Now introduce another stick of length equal to BD (Fig 4.4). If you push the breadth now, does the shape change? No! It cannot, without making the figure open. The introduction of the fifth stick has fixed the rectangle uniquely, i.e., there is no other quadrilateral (with the given lengths of sides) possible now.

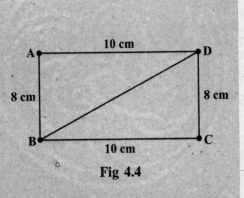

Fig 4.4

Thus, we observe that five measurements can determine a quadrilateral uniquely. But will any five measurements (of sides and angles) be sufficient to draw a unique quadrilateral?

THINK, DISCUSS AND WRITE

Arshad has five measurements of a quadrilateral ABCD. These are AB = 5 cm, ∠A = 50°, AC = 4 cm, BD = 5 cm and AD = 6 cm. Can he construct a unique quadrilateral? Give reasons for your answer.

4.2 Constructing a Quadrilateral

We shall learn how to construct a unique quadrilateral given the following measurements:

- When four sides and one diagonal are given.
- When two diagonals and three sides are given.
- When two adjacent sides and three angles are given.
- When three sides and two included angles are given.
- When other special properties are known.

Let us take up these constructions one-by-one.

4.2.1 When the lengths of four sides and a diagonal are given

We shall explain this construction through an example.

Example 1: Construct a quadrilateral PQRS where PQ = 4 cm, QR = 6 cm, RS = 5 cm, PS = 5.5 cm and PR = 7 cm.

Solution: [A rough sketch will help us in visualising the quadrilateral. We draw this first and mark the measurements.] (Fig 4.5)

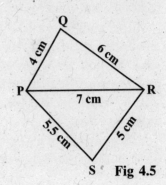

Fig 4.5

Step 1 From the rough sketch, it is easy to see that ΔPQR can be constructed using SSS construction condition. Draw ΔPQR (Fig 4.6).

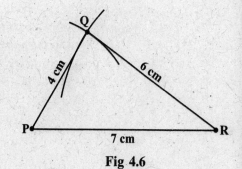

Fig 4.6

Step 2 Now, we have to locate the fourth point S. This 'S' would be on the side opposite to Q with reference to PR. For that, we have two measurements.

S is 5.5 cm away from P. So, with P as centre, draw an arc of radius 5.5 cm. (The point S is somewhere on this arc!) (Fig 4.7).

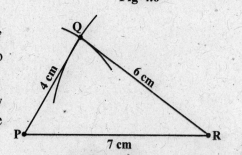

Fig 4.7

Step 3 S is 5 cm away from R. So with R as centre, draw an arc of radius 5 cm (The point S is somewhere on this arc also!) (Fig 4.8).

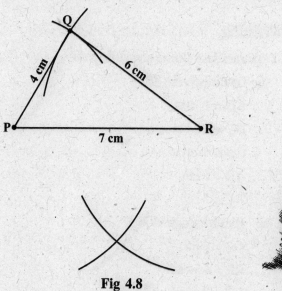

Fig 4.8

Step 4 S should lie on both the arcs drawn. So it is the point of intersection of the two arcs. Mark S and complete PQRS. PQRS is the required quadrilateral (Fig 4.9).

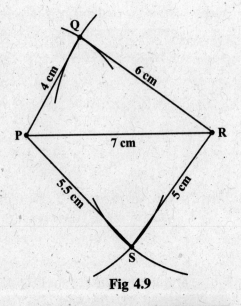

Fig 4.9

THINK, DISCUSS AND WRITE

(i) We saw that 5 measurements of a quadrilateral can determine a quadrilateral uniquely. Do you think any five measurements of the quadrilateral can do this?

(ii) Can you draw a parallelogram BATS where BA = 5 cm, AT = 6 cm and AS = 6.5 cm? Why?

(iii) Can you draw a rhombus ZEAL where ZE = 3.5 cm, diagonal EL = 5 cm? Why?

(iv) A student attempted to draw a quadrilateral PLAY where PL = 3 cm, LA = 4 cm, AY = 4.5 cm, PY = 2 cm and LY = 6 cm, but could not draw it. What is the reason?
[**Hint:** Discuss it using a rough sketch].

EXERCISE 4.1

1. Construct the following quadrilaterals.

   (i) Quadrilateral ABCD.

   AB = 4.5 cm

   BC = 5.5 cm

   CD = 4 cm

   AD = 6 cm

   AC = 7 cm

   (ii) Quadrilateral JUMP

   JU = 3.5 cm

   UM = 4 cm

   MP = 5 cm

   PJ = 4.5 cm

   PU = 6.5 cm

   (iii) Parallelogram MORE

   OR = 6 cm

   RE = 4.5 cm

   EO = 7.5 cm

   (iv) Rhombus BEST

   BE = 4.5 cm

   ET = 6 cm

4.2.2 When two diagonals and three sides are given

When four sides and a diagonal were given, we first drew a triangle with the available data and then tried to locate the fourth point. The same technique is used here.

Example 2: Construct a quadrilateral ABCD, given that BC = 4.5 cm, AD = 5.5 cm, CD = 5 cm the diagonal AC = 5.5 cm and diagonal BD = 7 cm.

Solution:

Here is the rough sketch of the quadrilateral ABCD (Fig 4.10). Studying this sketch, we can easily see that it is possible to draw △ ACD first (How?).

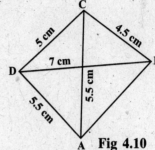

Fig 4.10

Step 1 Draw △ ACD using SSS construction (Fig 4.11). (We now need to find B at a distance of 4.5 cm from C and 7 cm from D).

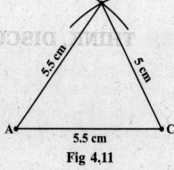

Fig 4.11

Step 2 With D as centre, draw an arc of radius 7 cm. (B is somewhere on this arc) (Fig 4.12).

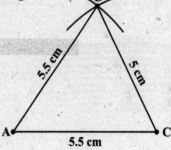

Fig 4.12

Step 3 With C as centre, draw an arc of radius 4.5 cm (B is somewhere on this arc also) (Fig 4.13).

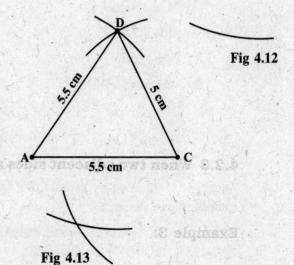

Fig 4.13

Step 4 Since B lies on both the arcs, B is the point intersection of the two arcs. Mark B and complete ABCD. ABCD is the required quadrilateral (Fig 4.14).

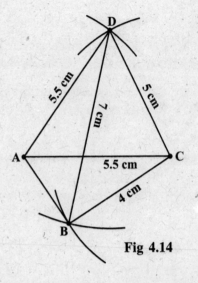

Fig 4.14

THINK, DISCUSS AND WRITE

1. In the above example, can we draw the quadrilateral by drawing △ABD first and then find the fourth point C?

2. Can you construct a quadrilateral PQRS with PQ = 3 cm, RS = 3 cm, PS = 7.5 cm, PR = 8 cm and SQ = 4 cm? Justify your answer.

EXERCISE 4.2

1. Construct the following quadrilaterals.

    (i)   quadrilateral LIFT

          LI = 4 cm

          IF = 3 cm

          TL = 2.5 cm

          LF = 4.5 cm

          IT = 4 cm

    (ii) Quadrilateral GOLD

          OL = 7.5 cm

          GL = 6 cm

          GD = 6 cm

          LD = 5 cm

          OD = 10 cm

    (iii) Rhombus BEND

          BN = 5.6 cm

          DE = 6.5 cm

4.2.3 When two adjacent sides and three angles are known

As before, we start with constructing a triangle and then look for the fourth point to complete the quadrilateral.

Example 3: Construct a quadrilateral MIST where MI = 3.5 cm, IS = 6.5 cm, ∠M = 75°, ∠I = 105° and ∠S = 120°.

Solution:

Here is a rough sketch that would help us in deciding our steps of construction. We give only hints for various steps (Fig 4.15).

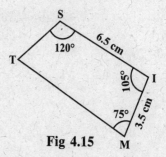

Fig 4.15

Step 1 How do you locate the points? What choice do you make for the base and what is the first step? (Fig 4.16)

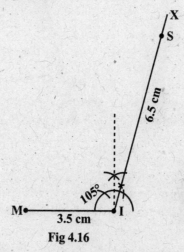

Fig 4.16

Step 2 Make ∠ISY = 120° at S (Fig 4.17).

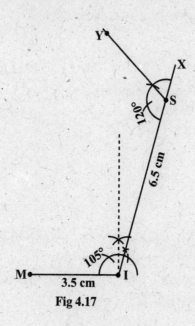

Fig 4.17

Step 3 Make ∠IMZ = 75° at M. (where will SY and MZ meet?) Mark that point as T. We get the required quadrilateral MIST (Fig 4.18).

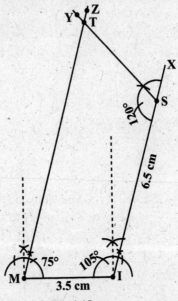

Fig 4.18

THINK, DISCUSS AND WRITE

1. Can you construct the above quadrilateral MIST if we have 100° at M instead of 75°?

2. Can you construct the quadrilateral PLAN if PL = 6 cm, LA = 9.5 cm, ∠P = 75°, ∠L = 150° and ∠A = 140°? (**Hint:** Recall angle-sum property).

3. In a parallelogram, the lengths of adjacent sides are known. Do we still need measures of the angles to construct as in the example above?

EXERCISE 4.3

1. Construct the following quadrilaterals.

   (i) Quadrilateral MORE
   MO = 6 cm
   OR = 4.5 cm
   ∠M = 60°
   ∠O = 105°
   ∠R = 105°

   (ii) Quadrilateral PLAN
   PL = 4 cm
   LA = 6.5 cm
   ∠P = 90°
   ∠A = 110°
   ∠N = 85°

   (iii) Parallelogram HEAR
   HE = 5 cm
   EA = 6 cm
   ∠R = 85°

   (iv) Rectangle OKAY
   OK = 7 cm
   KA = 5 cm

4.2.4 When three sides and two included angles are given

Under this type, when you draw a rough sketch, note carefully the "included" angles in particular.

Example 4: Construct a quadrilateral ABCD, where AB = 4 cm, BC = 5 cm, CD = 6.5 cm and ∠B = 105° and ∠C = 80°.

Fig 4.19

Solution:

We draw a rough sketch, as usual, to get an idea of how we can start off. Then we can devise a plan to locate the four points (Fig 4.19).

Step 1 Start with taking BC = 5 cm on B. Draw an angle of 105° along BX. Locate A 4 cm away on this. We now have B, C and A (Fig 4.20).

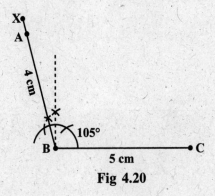

Fig 4.20

Step 2 The fourth point D is on CY which is inclined at 80° to BC. So make ∠BCY = 80° at C on BC (Fig 4.21).

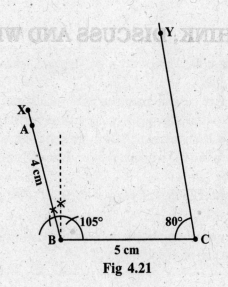

Fig 4.21

Step 3 D is at a distance of 6.5 cm on CY. With
C as centre, draw an arc of length 6.5 cm.
It cuts CY at D (Fig 4.22).

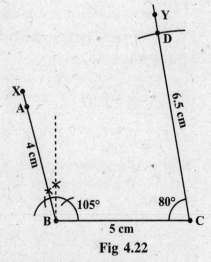

Fig 4.22

Step 4 Complete the quadrilateral ABCD. ABCD is the required quadrilateral (Fig 4.23).

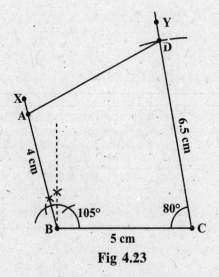

Fig 4.23

THINK, DISCUSS AND WRITE

1. In the above example, we first drew BC. Instead, what could have been be the other starting points?
2. We used some five measurements to draw quadrilaterals so far. Can there be different sets of five measurements (other than seen so far) to draw a quadrilateral? The following problems may help you in answering the question.
   (i) Quadrilateral ABCD with AB = 5 cm, BC = 5.5 cm, CD = 4 cm, AD = 6 cm and ∠B = 80°.
   (ii) Quadrilateral PQRS with PQ = 4.5 cm, ∠P = 70°, ∠Q = 100°, ∠R = 80° and ∠S = 110°.

Construct a few more examples of your own to find sufficiency/insufficiency of the data for construction of a quadrilateral.

EXERCISE 4.4

1. Construct the following quadrilaterals.

   (i) Quadrilateral DEAR

   DE = 4 cm

   EA = 5 cm

   AR = 4.5 cm

   ∠E = 60°

   ∠A = 90°

   (ii) Quadrilateral TRUE

   TR = 3.5 cm

   RU = 3 cm

   UE = 4 cm

   ∠R = 75°

   ∠U = 120°

4.3 Some Special Cases

To draw a quadrilateral, we used 5 measurements in our work. Is there any quadrilateral which can be drawn with less number of available measurements? The following examples examine such special cases.

Example 5: Draw a square of side 4.5 cm.

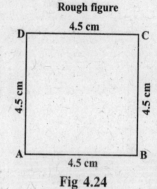

Rough figure

Fig 4.24

Solution: Initially it appears that only one measurement has been given. Actually we have many more details with us, because the figure is a special quadrilateral, namely a square. We now know that each of its angles is a right angle. (See the rough figure) (Fig 4.24)

This enables us to draw △ABC using SAS condition. Then D can be easily located. Try yourself now to draw the square with the given measurements.

Example 6: Is it possible to construct a rhombus ABCD where AC = 6 cm and BD = 7 cm? Justify your answer.

Solution: Only two (diagonal) measurements of the rhombus are given. However, since it is a rhombus, we can find more help from its properties.

The diagonals of a rhombus are perpendicular bisectors of one another.

So, first draw AC = 7 cm and then construct its perpendicular bisector. Let them meet at 0. Cut off 3 cm lengths on either side of the drawn bisector. You now get B and D.

Draw the rhombus now, based on the method described above (Fig 4.25).

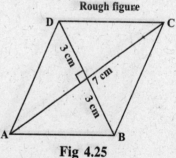

Rough figure

Fig 4.25

TRY THESE

1. How will you construct a rectangle PQRS if you know only the lengths PQ and QR?

2. Construct the kite EASY if AY = 8 cm, EY = 4 cm and SY = 6 cm (Fig 4.26). Which properties of the kite did you use in the process?

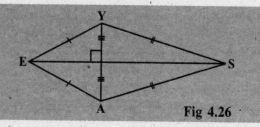

Fig 4.26

EXERCISE 4.5

Draw the following.

1. The square READ with RE = 5.1 cm.
2. A rhombus whose diagonals are 5.2 cm and 6.4 cm long.
3. A rectangle with adjacent sides of lengths 5 cm and 4 cm.
4. A parallelogram OKAY where OK = 5.5 cm and KA = 4.2 cm. Is it unique?

WHAT HAVE WE DISCUSSED?

1. Five measurements can determine a quadrilateral uniquely.
2. A quadrilateral can be constructed uniquely if the lengths of its four sides and a diagonal is given.
3. A quadrilateral can be constructed uniquely if its two diagonals and three sides are known.
4. A quadrilateral can be constructed uniquely if its two adjacent sides and three angles are known.
5. A quadrilateral can be constructed uniquely if its three sides and two included angles are given.

Data Handling

0852CH05

5.1 Looking for Information

In your day-to-day life, you might have come across information, such as:

(a) Runs made by a batsman in the last 10 test matches.

(b) Number of wickets taken by a bowler in the last 10 ODIs.

(c) Marks scored by the students of your class in the Mathematics unit test.

(d) Number of story books read by each of your friends etc.

The information collected in all such cases is called **data**. Data is usually collected in the context of a situation that we want to study. For example, a teacher may like to know the average height of students in her class. To find this, she will write the heights of all the students in her class, organise the data in a systematic manner and then interpret it accordingly.

Sometimes, data is represented **graphically** to give a clear idea of what it represents. Do you remember the different types of graphs which we have learnt in earlier classes?

1. **A Pictograph:** Pictorial representation of data using symbols.

	= 100 cars ← One symbol stands for 100 cars			
July	🚗 🚗 🚗	= 250	🚗	denotes $\frac{1}{2}$ of 100
August	🚗 🚗 🚗	= 300		
September	🚗 🚗 🚗 🚗	= ?		

(i)   How many cars were produced in the month of July?

(ii) In which month were maximum number of cars produced?

2. **A bar graph:** A display of information using bars of uniform width, their heights being proportional to the respective values.

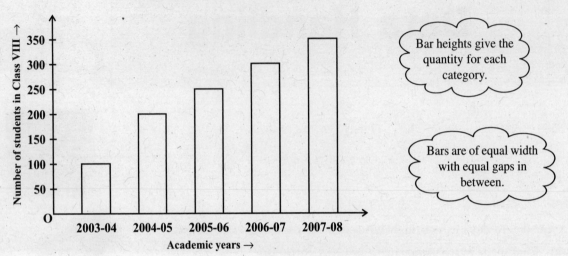

Bar heights give the quantity for each category.

Bars are of equal width with equal gaps in between.

(i) What is the information given by the bar graph?

(ii) In which year is the increase in the number of students maximum?

(iii) In which year is the number of students maximum?

(iv) State whether true or false:

'The number of students during 2005-06 is twice that of 2003-04.'

3. **Double Bar Graph:** A bar graph showing two sets of data simultaneously. It is useful for the comparison of the data.

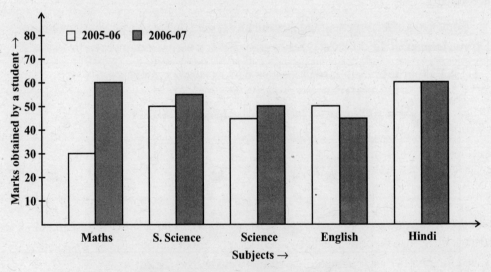

(i) What is the information given by the double bar graph?

(ii) In which subject has the performance improved the most?

(iii) In which subject has the performance deteriorated?

(iv) In which subject is the performance at par?

THINK, DISCUSS AND WRITE

If we change the position of any of the bars of a bar graph, would it change the information being conveyed? Why?

TRY THESE

Draw an appropriate graph to represent the given information.

1.

Month	July	August	September	October	November	December
Number of watches sold	1000	1500	1500	2000	2500	1500

2.

Children who prefer	School A	School B	School C
Walking	40	55	15
Cycling	45	25	35

3. Percentage wins in ODI by 8 top cricket teams.

Teams	From Champions Trophy to World Cup-06	Last 10 ODI in 07
South Africa	75%	78%
Australia	61%	40%
Sri Lanka	54%	38%
New Zealand	47%	50%
England	46%	50%
Pakistan	45%	44%
West Indies	44%	30%
India	43%	56%

5.2 Organising Data

Usually, data available to us is in an unorganised form called **raw data**. To draw meaningful inferences, we need to organise the data systematically. For example, a group of students was asked for their favourite subject. The results were as listed below:

Art, Mathematics, Science, English, Mathematics, Art, English, Mathematics, English, Art, Science, Art, Science, Science, Mathematics, Art, English, Art, Science, Mathematics, Science, Art.

Which is the most liked subject and the one least liked?

It is not easy to answer the question looking at the choices written haphazardly. We arrange the data in Table 5.1 using tally marks.

Table 5.1

Subject	Tally Marks	Number of Students
Art	~~卌~~ ‖	7
Mathematics	~~卌~~	5
Science	~~卌~~ ‖	6
English	‖‖	4

The number of tallies before each subject gives the number of students who like that particular subject.

This is known as the **frequency** of that subject.

Frequency gives the number of times that a particular entry occurs.

From Table 5.1,   Frequency of students who like English is 4

Frequency of students who like Mathematics is 5

The table made is known as **frequency distribution table** as it gives the number of times an entry occurs.

TRY THESE

1. A group of students were asked to say which animal they would like most to have as a pet. The results are given below:

dog, cat, cat, fish, cat, rabbit, dog, cat, rabbit, dog, cat, dog, dog, dog, cat, cow, fish, rabbit, dog, cat, dog, cat, cat, dog, rabbit, cat, fish, dog.

Make a frequency distribution table for the same.

5.3 Grouping Data

The data regarding choice of subjects showed the occurrence of each of the entries several times. For example, Art is liked by 7 students, Mathematics is liked by 5 students and so on (Table 5.1). This information can be displayed graphically using a pictograph or a bargraph. Sometimes, however, we have to deal with a large data. For example, consider the following marks (out of 50) obtained in Mathematics by 60 students of Class VIII:

21, 10, 30, 22, 33, 5, 37, 12, 25, 42, 15, 39, 26, 32, 18, 27, 28, 19, 29, 35, 31, 24, 36, 18, 20, 38, 22, 44, 16, 24, 10, 27, 39, 28, 49, 29, 32, 23, 31, 21, 34, 22, 23, 36, 24, 36, 33, 47, 48, 50, 39, 20, 7, 16, 36, 45, 47, 30, 22, 17.

If we make a frequency distribution table for each observation, then the table would be too long, so, for convenience, we make groups of observations say, 0-10, 10-20 and so on, and obtain a frequency distribution of the number of observations falling in each group. Thus, the frequency distribution table for the above data can be.

Table 5.2

Groups	Tally Marks	Frequency
0-10	II	2
10-20	ꟼNꟼ ꟼNꟼ	10
20-30	ꟼNꟼ ꟼNꟼ ꟼNꟼ ꟼNꟼ I	21
30-40	ꟼNꟼ ꟼNꟼ ꟼNꟼ IIII	19
40-50	ꟼNꟼ II	7
50-60	I	1
	Total	**60**

Data presented in this manner is said to be **grouped** and the distribution obtained is called **grouped frequency distribution**. It helps us to draw meaningful inferences like –

(1) Most of the students have scored between 20 and 40.

(2) Eight students have scored more than 40 marks out of 50 and so on.

Each of the groups 0-10, 10-20, 20-30, etc., is called a **Class Interval** (or briefly a class).

Observe that 10 occurs in both the classes, i.e., 0-10 as well as 10-20. Similarly, 20 occurs in classes 10-20 and 20-30. But it is not possible that an observation (say 10 or 20) can belong simultaneously to two classes. To avoid this, we adopt the convention that the common observation will belong to the higher class, i.e., 10 belongs to the class interval 10-20 (and not to 0-10). Similarly, 20 belongs to 20-30 (and not to 10-20). In the class interval, 10-20, 10 is called the **lower class limit** and 20 is called the **upper class limit**. Similarly, in the class interval 20-30, 20 is the lower class limit and 30 is the upper class limit. Observe that the difference between the upper class limit and lower class limit for each of the class intervals 0-10, 10-20, 20-30 etc., is equal, (10 in this case). This difference between the upper class limit and lower class limit is called the **width** or **size** of the class interval.

TRY THESE

1. Study the following frequency distribution table and answer the questions given below.

Frequency Distribution of Daily Income of 550 workers of a factory

Table 5.3

Class Interval (Daily Income in ₹)	Frequency (Number of workers)
100-125	45
125-150	25

150-175	55
175-200	125
200-225	140
225-250	55
250-275	35
275-300	50
300-325	20
Total	**550**

(i) What is the size of the class intervals?
(ii) Which class has the highest frequency?
(iii) Which class has the lowest frequency?
(iv) What is the upper limit of the class interval 250-275?
(v) Which two classes have the same frequency?

2. Construct a frequency distribution table for the data on weights (in kg) of 20 students of a class using intervals 30-35, 35-40 and so on.

   40, 38, 33, 48, 60, 53, 31, 46, 34, 36, 49, 41, 55, 49, 65, 42, 44, 47, 38, 39.

5.3.1 Bars with a difference

Let us again consider the grouped frequency distribution of the marks obtained by 60 students in Mathematics test. (Table 5.4)

Table 5.4

Class Interval	Frequency
0-10	2
10-20	10
20-30	21
30-40	19
40-50	7
50-60	1
Total	**60**

This is displayed graphically as in the adjoining graph (Fig 5.1).

Is this graph in any way different from the bar graphs which you have drawn in Class VII? Observe that, here we have represented the groups of observations (i.e., class intervals)

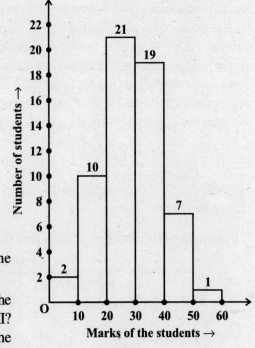

Fig 5.1

on the horizontal axis. The **height** of the bars show the **frequency** of the class-interval. Also, there is no gap between the bars as there is no gap between the class-intervals.

The graphical representation of data in this manner is called a **histogram**. The following graph is another histogram (Fig 5.2).

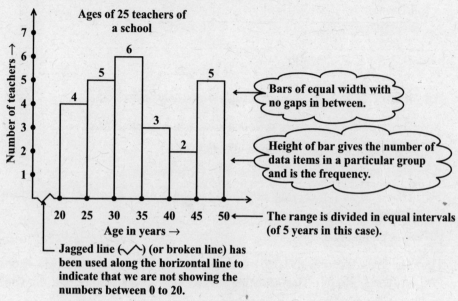

Fig 5.2

From the bars of this histogram, we can answer the following questions:
(i) How many teachers are of age 45 years or more but less than 50 years?
(ii) How many teachers are of age less than 35 years?

TRY THESE

1. Observe the histogram (Fig 5.3) and answer the questions given below.

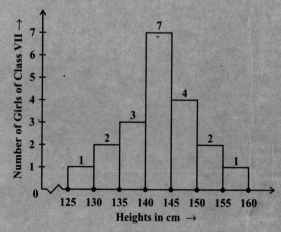

Fig 5.3

(i) What information is being given by the histogram?
(ii) Which group contains maximum girls?

(iii) How many girls have a height of 145 cms and more?

(iv) If we divide the girls into the following three categories, how many would there be in each?

150 cm and more — Group A

140 cm to less than 150 cm — Group B

Less than 140 cm — Group C

EXERCISE 5.1

1. For which of these would you use a histogram to show the data?

(a) The number of letters for different areas in a postman's bag.

(b) The height of competitors in an athletics meet.

(c) The number of cassettes produced by 5 companies.

(d) The number of passengers boarding trains from 7:00 a.m. to 7:00 p.m. at a station.

Give reasons for each.

2. The shoppers who come to a departmental store are marked as: man (M), woman (W), boy (B) or girl (G). The following list gives the shoppers who came during the first hour in the morning:

W W W G B W W M G G M M W W W W G B M W B G G M W W M M W W
W M W B W G M W W W W G W M M W W M W G W M G W M M B G G W

Make a frequency distribution table using tally marks. Draw a bar graph to illustrate it.

3. The weekly wages (in ₹) of 30 workers in a factory are.

830, 835, 890, 810, 835, 836, 869, 845, 898, 890, 820, 860, 832, 833, 855, 845, 804, 808, 812, 840, 885, 835, 835, 836, 878, 840, 868, 890, 806, 840

Using tally marks make a frequency table with intervals as 800–810, 810–820 and so on.

4. Draw a histogram for the frequency table made for the data in Question 3, and answer the following questions.

(i) Which group has the maximum number of workers?

(ii) How many workers earn ₹ 850 and more?

(iii) How many workers earn less than ₹ 850?

5. The number of hours for which students of a particular class watched television during holidays is shown through the given graph.

Answer the following.

(i) For how many hours did the maximum number of students watch TV?

(ii) How many students watched TV for less than 4 hours?

(iii) How many students spent more than 5 hours in watching TV?

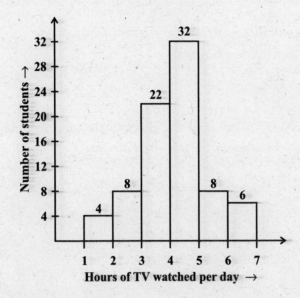

5.4 Circle Graph or Pie Chart

Have you ever come across data represented in circular form as shown (Fig 5.4)?

The time spent by a child during a day   Age groups of people in a town

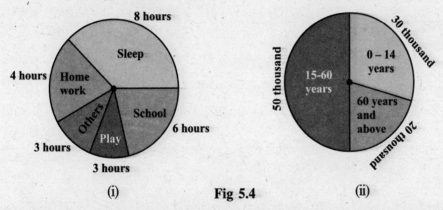

(i)   **Fig 5.4**   (ii)

These are called **circle graphs**. A circle graph shows the relationship between a whole and its parts. Here, the whole circle is divided into sectors. The size of each sector is proportional to the activity or information it represents.

For example, in the above graph, the proportion of the sector for hours spent in sleeping

$$= \frac{\text{number of sleeping hours}}{\text{whole day}} = \frac{8 \text{ hours}}{24 \text{ hours}} = \frac{1}{3}$$

So, this sector is drawn as $\frac{1}{3}$rd part of the circle. Similarly, the proportion of the sector

for hours spent in school $= \dfrac{\text{number of school hours}}{\text{whole day}} = \dfrac{6 \text{ hours}}{24 \text{ hours}} = \dfrac{1}{4}$

So this sector is drawn $\frac{1}{4}$ th of the circle. Similarly, the size of other sectors can be found.

Add up the fractions for all the activities. Do you get the total as one?

A circle graph is also called a **pie chart**.

TRY THESE

1. Each of the following pie charts (Fig 5.5) gives you a different piece of information about your class. Find the fraction of the circle representing each of these information.

(i)

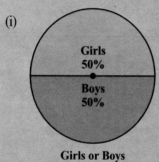

Girls or Boys

(ii)

Walk
40%

Bus or car
40%

Transport to school

(iii)

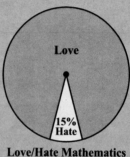

Love/Hate Mathematics

Fig 5.5

2. Answer the following questions based on the pie chart given (Fig 5.6).

   (i) Which type of programmes are viewed the most?

   (ii) Which two types of programmes have number of viewers equal to those watching sports channels?

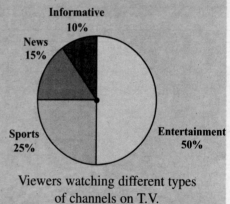

Viewers watching different types
of channels on T.V.

Fig 5.6

5.4.1 Drawing pie charts

The favourite flavours of ice-creams for students of a school is given in percentages as follows.

Flavours	Percentage of students Preferring the flavours
Chocolate	50%
Vanilla	25%
Other flavours	25%

Let us represent this data in a pie chart.

The total angle at the centre of a circle is 360°. The central angle of the sectors will be a fraction of 360°. We make a table to find the central angle of the sectors (Table 5.5).

Table 5.5

Flavours	Students in per cent preferring the flavours	In fractions	Fraction of 360°
Chocolate	50%	$\dfrac{50}{100} = \dfrac{1}{2}$	$\dfrac{1}{2}$ of 360° = 180°
Vanilla	25%	$\dfrac{25}{100} = \dfrac{1}{4}$	$\dfrac{1}{4}$ of 360° = 90°
Other flavours	25%	$\dfrac{25}{100} = \dfrac{1}{4}$	$\dfrac{1}{4}$ of 360° = 90°

1. Draw a circle with any convenient radius.
    Mark its centre (O) and a radius (OA).

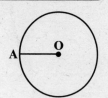

2. The angle of the sector for chocolate is 180°.
    Use the protractor to draw ∠AOB = 180°.

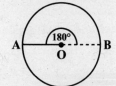

3. Continue marking the remaining sectors.

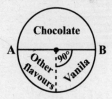

Example 1: Adjoining pie chart (Fig 5.7) gives the expenditure (in percentage) on various items and savings of a family during a month.

  (i)   On which item, the expenditure was maximum?
  (ii) Expenditure on which item is equal to the total savings of the family?
  (iii) If the monthly savings of the family is ₹ 3000, what is the monthly expenditure on clothes?

Solution:

  (i) Expenditure is maximum on food.
  (ii) Expenditure on Education of children is the same (i.e., 15%) as the savings of the family.

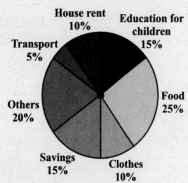

Fig 5.7

(iii)   15% represents ₹ 3000

Therefore, 10% represents ₹ $\frac{3000}{15} \times 10 = ₹\,2000$

Example 2: On a particular day, the sales (in rupees) of different items of a baker's shop are given below.

ordinary bread	: 320
fruit bread	: 80
cakes and pastries	: 160
biscuits	: 120
others	: 40
Total	**: 720**

Draw a pie chart for this data.

Solution: We find the central angle of each sector. Here the total sale = ₹ 720. We thus have this table.

Item	Sales (in ₹)	In Fraction	Central Angle
Ordinary Bread	320	$\frac{320}{720} = \frac{4}{9}$	$\frac{4}{9} \times 360° = 160°$
Biscuits	120	$\frac{120}{720} = \frac{1}{6}$	$\frac{1}{6} \times 360° = 60°$
Cakes and pastries	160	$\frac{160}{720} = \frac{2}{9}$	$\frac{2}{9} \times 360° = 80°$
Fruit Bread	80	$\frac{80}{720} = \frac{1}{9}$	$\frac{1}{9} \times 360° = 40°$
Others	40	$\frac{40}{720} = \frac{1}{18}$	$\frac{1}{18} \times 360° = 20°$

Now, we make the pie chart (Fig 5.8):

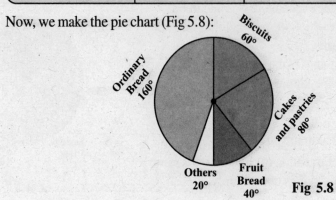

Fig 5.8

TRY THESE

Draw a pie chart of the data given below.

The time spent by a child during a day.

Sleep — 8 hours

School — 6 hours

Home work — 4 hours

Play — 4 hours

Others — 2 hours

THINK, DISCUSS AND WRITE

Which form of graph would be appropriate to display the following data.

1. **Production of food grains of a state.**

Year	2001	2002	2003	2004	2005	2006
Production (in lakh tons)	60	50	70	55	80	85

2. **Choice of food for a group of people.**

Favourite food	Number of people
North Indian	30
South Indian	40
Chinese	25
Others	25
Total	**120**

3. **The daily income of a group of a factory workers.**

Daily Income (in Rupees)	Number of workers (in a factory)
75-100	45
100-125	35
125-150	55
150-175	30
175-200	50
200-225	125
225-250	140
Total	**480**

EXERCISE 5.2

1. A survey was made to find the type of music that a certain group of young people liked in a city. Adjoining pie chart shows the findings of this survey.

    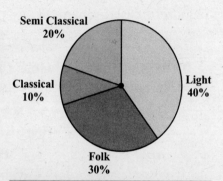

    From this pie chart answer the following:
    (i)   If 20 people liked classical music, how many young people were surveyed?
    (ii) Which type of music is liked by the maximum number of people?
    (iii) If a cassette company were to make 1000 CD's, how many of each type would they make?

2. A group of 360 people were asked to vote for their favourite season from the three seasons rainy, winter and summer.
    (i)   Which season got the most votes?
    (ii) Find the central angle of each sector.
    (iii) Draw a pie chart to show this information.

Season		No. of votes
Summer	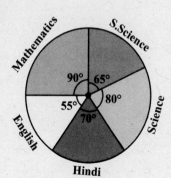	90
Rainy		120
Winter		150

3. Draw a pie chart showing the following information. The table shows the colours preferred by a group of people.

Colours	Number of people
Blue	18
Green	9
Red	6
Yellow	3
Total	**36**

Find the proportion of each sector. For example, Blue is $\dfrac{18}{36} = \dfrac{1}{2}$; Green is $\dfrac{9}{36} = \dfrac{1}{4}$ and so on. Use this to find the corresponding angles.

4. The adjoining pie chart gives the marks scored in an examination by a student in Hindi, English, Mathematics, Social Science and Science. If the total marks obtained by the students were 540, answer the following questions.
    (i)   In which subject did the student score 105 marks?
          (**Hint:** for 540 marks, the central angle = 360°. So, for 105 marks, what is the central angle?)
    (ii) How many more marks were obtained by the student in Mathematics than in Hindi?
    (iii) Examine whether the sum of the marks obtained in Social Science and Mathematics is more than that in Science and Hindi.
          (**Hint:** Just study the central angles).

    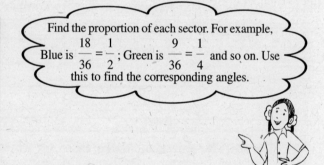

5. The number of students in a hostel, speaking different languages is given below. Display the data in a pie chart.

Language	Hindi	English	Marathi	Tamil	Bengali	Total
Number of students	40	12	9	7	4	72

5.5 Chance and Probability

Sometimes it happens that during rainy season, you carry a raincoat every day and it does not rain for many days. However, by chance, one day you forget to take the raincoat and it rains heavily on that day.

Sometimes it so happens that a student prepares 4 chapters out of 5, very well for a test. But a major question is asked from the chapter that she left unprepared.

Everyone knows that a particular train runs in time but the day you reach well in time it is late!

Oh! my raincoat.

You face a lot of situations such as these where you take a chance and it does not go the way you want it to. Can you give some more examples? These are examples where the chances of a certain thing happening or not happening are not equal. The chances of the train being in time or being late are not the same. When you buy a ticket which is wait listed, you do take a chance. You hope that it might get confirmed by the time you travel.

We however, consider here certain experiments whose results have an equal chance of occurring.

5.5.1 Getting a result

You might have seen that before a cricket match starts, captains of the two teams go out to toss a coin to decide which team will bat first.

What are the possible results you get when a coin is tossed? Of course, Head or Tail.

Imagine that you are the captain of one team and your friend is the captain of the other team. You toss a coin and ask your friend to make the call. Can you control the result of the toss? Can you get a head if you want one? Or a tail if you want that? No, that is not possible. Such an experiment is called a **random experiment**. Head or Tail are the two **outcomes** of this experiment.

TRY THESE

1. If you try to start a scooter, what are the possible outcomes?
2. When a die is thrown, what are the six possible outcomes?

3. When you spin the wheel shown, what are the possible outcomes? (Fig 5.9) List them.

    (Outcome here means the sector at which the pointer stops).

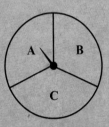

Fig 5.9

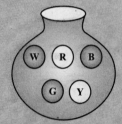

Fig 5.10

4. You have a bag with five identical balls of different colours and you are to pull out (draw) a ball without looking at it; list the outcomes you would get (Fig 5.10).

THINK, DISCUSS AND WRITE

In throwing a die:

• Does the first player have a greater chance of getting a six?

• Would the player who played after him have a lesser chance of getting a six?

• Suppose the second player got a six. Does it mean that the third player would not have a chance of getting a six?

5.5.2 Equally likely outcomes:

A coin is tossed several times and the number of times we get head or tail is noted. Let us look at the result sheet where we keep on increasing the tosses:

Number of tosses	Tally marks (H)	Number of heads	Tally mark (T)	Number of tails
50	NĮ NĮ NĮ NĮ NĮ II	27	NĮ NĮ NĮ NĮ III	23
60	NĮ NĮ NĮ NĮ NĮ III	28	NĮ NĮ NĮ NĮ NĮ NĮ II	32
70	...	33	...	37
80	...	38	...	42
90	...	44	...	46
100	...	48	...	52

Observe that as you increase the number of tosses more and more, the number of heads and the number of tails come closer and closer to each other.

This could also be done with a die, when tossed a large number of times. Number of each of the six outcomes become almost equal to each other.

In such cases, we may say that the different outcomes of the experiment are equally likely. This means that each of the outcomes has the same chance of occurring.

5.5.3 Linking chances to probability

Consider the experiment of tossing a coin once. What are the outcomes? There are only two outcomes – Head or Tail. Both the outcomes are equally likely. Likelihood of getting a head is one out of two outcomes, i.e., $\dfrac{1}{2}$. In other words, we say that the probability of getting a head $= \dfrac{1}{2}$. What is the probability of getting a tail?

Now take the example of throwing a die marked with 1, 2, 3, 4, 5, 6 on its faces (one number on one face). If you throw it once, what are the outcomes?

The outcomes are: 1, 2, 3, 4, 5, 6. Thus, there are six equally likely outcomes.

What is the probability of getting the outcome '2'?

It is $\dfrac{1}{6}$ ← Number of outcomes giving 2
← Number of equally likely outcomes.

What is the probability of getting the number 5? What is the probability of getting the number 7? What is the probability of getting a number 1 through 6?

5.5.4 Outcomes as events

Each outcome of an experiment or a collection of outcomes make an **event**.

For example in the experiment of tossing a coin, getting a Head is an event and getting a Tail is also an event.

In case of throwing a die, getting each of the outcomes 1, 2, 3, 4, 5 or 6 is an event.

Is getting an even number an event? Since an even number could be 2, 4 or 6, getting an even number is also an event. What will be the probability of getting an even number?

It is $\dfrac{3}{6}$ ← Number of outcomes that make the event

← Total number of outcomes of the experiment.

Example 3: A bag has 4 red balls and 2 yellow balls. (The balls are identical in all respects other than colour). A ball is drawn from the bag without looking into the bag. What is probability of getting a red ball? Is it more or less than getting a yellow ball?

Solution: There are in all (4 + 2 =) 6 outcomes of the event. Getting a red ball consists of 4 outcomes. (Why?)

Therefore, the probability of getting a red ball is $\dfrac{4}{6} = \dfrac{2}{3}$. In the same way the probability of getting a yellow ball $= \dfrac{2}{6} = \dfrac{1}{3}$ (Why?). Therefore, the probability of getting a red ball is more than that of getting a yellow ball.

TRY THESE

Suppose you spin the wheel

1. (i) List the number of outcomes of getting a green sector and not getting a green sector on this wheel (Fig 5.11).

   (ii) Find the probability of getting a green sector.

   (iii) Find the probability of not getting a green sector.

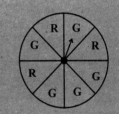

Fig 5.11

5.5.5 Chance and probability related to real life

We talked about the chance that it rains just on the day when we do not carry a rain coat.

What could you say about the chance in terms of probability? Could it be one in 10 days during a rainy season? The probability that it rains is then $\dfrac{1}{10}$. The probability that it does not rain $= \dfrac{9}{10}$. (Assuming raining or not raining on a day are equally likely)

The use of probability is made in various cases in real life.

1. To find characteristics of a large group by using a small part of the group.

   For example, during elections 'an exit poll' is taken. This involves asking the people whom they have voted for, when they come out after voting at the centres which are chosen off hand and distributed over the whole area. This gives an idea of chance of winning of each candidate and predictions are made based on it accordingly.

2. Metrological Department predicts weather by observing trends from the data over many years in the past.

EXERCISE 5.3

1. List the outcomes you can see in these experiments.

   (a) Spinning a wheel
   (b) Tossing two coins together

2. When a die is thrown, list the outcomes of an event of getting

   (i) (a) a prime number   (b) not a prime number.

   (ii) (a) a number greater than 5 (b) a number not greater than 5.

3. Find the.

   (a) Probability of the pointer stopping on D in (Question 1-(a))?

   (b) Probability of getting an ace from a well shuffled deck of 52 playing cards?

   (c) Probability of getting a red apple. (See figure below)

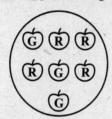

4. Numbers 1 to 10 are written on ten separate slips (one number on one slip), kept in a box and mixed well. One slip is chosen from the box without looking into it. What is the probability of .

   (i)   getting a number 6?

   (ii) getting a number less than 6?

   (iii) getting a number greater than 6?

   (iv) getting a 1-digit number?

5. If you have a spinning wheel with 3 green sectors, 1 blue sector and 1 red sector, what is the probability of getting a green sector? What is the probability of getting a non blue sector?

6. Find the probabilities of the events given in Question 2.

WHAT HAVE WE DISCUSSED?

1. Data mostly available to us in an unorganised form is called **raw data**.

2. In order to draw meaningful inferences from any data, we need to organise the data systematically.

3. **Frequency** gives the number of times that a particular entry occurs.

4. Raw data can be 'grouped' and presented systematically through 'grouped frequency distribution'.

5. Grouped data can be presented using **histogram**. Histogram is a type of bar diagram, where the class intervals are shown on the horizontal axis and the heights of the bars show the frequency of the class interval. Also, there is no gap between the bars as there is no gap between the class intervals.

6. Data can also presented using **circle graph** or **pie chart**. A circle graph shows the relationship between a whole and its part.

7. There are certain experiments whose outcomes have an equal chance of occurring.

8. A **random experiment** is one whose outcome cannot be predicted exactly in advance.

9. Outcomes of an experiment are **equally likely** if each has the same chance of occurring.

10. **Probability of an event** = $\dfrac{\text{Number of outcomes that make an event}}{\text{Total number of outcomes of the experiment}}$, when the outcomes are equally likely.

11. One or more outcomes of an experiment make an **event**.

12. Chances and probability are related to real life.

Squares and Square Roots

0852CH06

6.1 Introduction

You know that the area of a square = side × side (where 'side' means 'the length of a side'). Study the following table.

Side of a square (in cm)	Area of the square (in cm²)
1	$1 \times 1 = 1 = 1^2$
2	$2 \times 2 = 4 = 2^2$
3	$3 \times 3 = 9 = 3^2$
5	$5 \times 5 = 25 = 5^2$
8	$8 \times 8 = 64 = 8^2$
a	$a \times a = a^2$

What is special about the numbers 4, 9, 25, 64 and other such numbers?

Since, 4 can be expressed as $2 \times 2 = 2^2$, 9 can be expressed as $3 \times 3 = 3^2$, all such numbers can be expressed as the product of the number with itself.

Such numbers like 1, 4, 9, 16, 25, ... are known as **square numbers**.

In general, if a natural number m can be expressed as n^2, where n is also a natural number, then m is a **square number**. Is 32 a square number?

We know that $5^2 = 25$ and $6^2 = 36$. If 32 is a square number, it must be the square of a natural number between 5 and 6. But there is no natural number between 5 and 6.

Therefore 32 is not a square number.

Consider the following numbers and their squares.

Number	Square
1	$1 \times 1 = 1$
2	$2 \times 2 = 4$

3	$3 \times 3 = 9$
4	$4 \times 4 = 16$
5	$5 \times 5 = 25$
6	-----------
7	-----------
8	-----------
9	-----------
10	-----------

Can you complete it?

From the above table, can we enlist the square numbers between 1 and 100? Are there any natural square numbers upto 100 left out?

You will find that the rest of the numbers are not square numbers.

The numbers 1, 4, 9, 16 ... are square numbers. These numbers are also called **perfect squares**.

TRY THESE

1. Find the perfect square numbers between (i) 30 and 40 (ii) 50 and 60

6.2 Properties of Square Numbers

Following table shows the squares of numbers from 1 to 20.

Number	Square	Number	Square
1	1	11	121
2	4	12	144
3	9	13	169
4	16	14	196
5	25	15	225
6	36	16	256
7	49	17	289
8	64	18	324
9	81	19	361
10	100	20	400

Study the square numbers in the above table. What are the ending digits (that is, digits in the units place) of the square numbers? All these numbers end with 0, 1, 4, 5, 6 or 9 at units place. None of these end with 2, 3, 7 or 8 at unit's place.

Can we say that if a number ends in 0, 1, 4, 5, 6 or 9, then it must be a square number? Think about it.

TRY THESE

1. Can we say whether the following numbers are perfect squares? How do we know?
   (i) 1057   (ii) 23453   (iii) 7928   (iv) 222222
   (v) 1069   (vi) 2061

Write five numbers which you can decide by looking at their units digit that they are not square numbers.

2. Write five numbers which you cannot decide just by looking at their units digit (or units place) whether they are square numbers or not.

- Study the following table of some numbers and their squares and observe the one's place in both.

Table 1

Number	Square	Number	Square	Number	Square
1	1	11	121	21	441
2	4	12	144	22	484
3	9	13	169	23	529
4	16	14	196	24	576
5	25	15	225	25	625
6	36	16	256	30	900
7	49	17	289	35	1225
8	64	18	324	40	1600
9	81	19	361	45	2025
10	100	20	400	50	2500

The following square numbers end with digit 1.

Square	Number
1	1
81	9
121	11
361	19
441	21

TRY THESE

Which of 123^2, 77^2, 82^2, 161^2, 109^2 would end with digit 1?

Write the next two square numbers which end in 1 and their corresponding numbers.
You will see that if a number has 1 or 9 in the units place, then it's square ends in 1.

- Let us consider square numbers ending in 6.

Square	Number
16	4
36	6
196	14
256	16

TRY THESE

Which of the following numbers would have digit 6 at unit place.

(i) 19^2 (ii) 24^2 (iii) 26^2

(iv) 36^2 (v) 34^2

We can see that *when a square number ends in 6, the number whose square it is, will have either 4 or 6 in unit's place.*

Can you find more such rules by observing the numbers and their squares (Table 1)?

- Consider the following numbers and their squares.

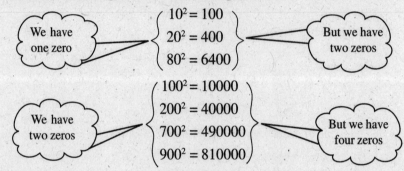

We have one zero
$$10^2 = 100$$
$$20^2 = 400$$
$$80^2 = 6400$$
But we have two zeros

We have two zeros
$$100^2 = 10000$$
$$200^2 = 40000$$
$$700^2 = 490000$$
$$900^2 = 810000$$
But we have four zeros

If a number contains 3 zeros at the end, how many zeros will its square have ?

What do you notice about the number of zeros at the end of the number and the number of zeros at the end of its square?

Can we say that square numbers can only have even number of zeros at the end?

- See Table 1 with numbers and their squares.

What can you say about the squares of even numbers and squares of odd numbers?

6.3 Some More Interesting Patterns

1. Adding triangular numbers.

Do you remember triangular numbers (numbers whose dot patterns can be arranged as triangles)?

```
                                                            *
                                            *             * *
                              *           * *           * * *
                *           * *         * * *         * * * *
  *           * *         * * *       * * * *       * * * * *
  1           3            6           10             15
```

If we combine two consecutive triangular numbers, we get a square number, like

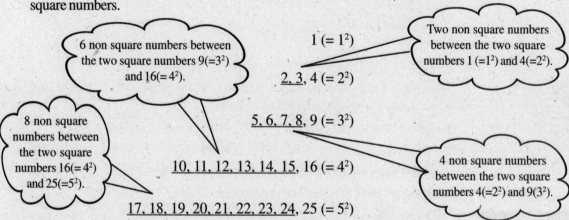

$1 + 3 = 4$ $3 + 6 = 9$ $6 + 10 = 16$

     $= 2^2$ $= 3^2$ $= 4^2$

2. Numbers between square numbers

Let us now see if we can find some interesting pattern between two consecutive square numbers.

> 6 non square numbers between the two square numbers 9(=3^2) and 16(= 4^2).

> Two non square numbers between the two square numbers 1 (=1^2) and 4(=2^2).

$1 (= 1^2)$

$\underline{2, 3}, 4 (= 2^2)$

$\underline{5, 6, 7, 8}, 9 (= 3^2)$

> 8 non square numbers between the two square numbers 16(= 4^2) and 25(=5^2).

$\underline{10, 11, 12, 13, 14, 15}, 16 (= 4^2)$

> 4 non square numbers between the two square numbers 4(=2^2) and 9(3^2).

$\underline{17, 18, 19, 20, 21, 22, 23, 24}, 25 (= 5^2)$

Between $1^2(=1)$ and $2^2(= 4)$ there are two (i.e., 2×1) non square numbers 2, 3.

Between $2^2(= 4)$ and $3^2(= 9)$ there are four (i.e., 2×2) non square numbers 5, 6, 7, 8.

Now, $3^2 = 9,$ $4^2 = 16$

Therefore, $4^2 - 3^2 = 16 - 9 = 7$

Between $9(=3^2)$ and $16(= 4^2)$ the numbers are 10, 11, 12, 13, 14, 15 that is, six non-square numbers which is 1 less than the difference of two squares.

We have $4^2 = 16$ and $5^2 = 25$

Therefore, $5^2 - 4^2 = 9$

Between $16(= 4^2)$ and $25(= 5^2)$ the numbers are 17, 18, ... , 24 that is, eight non square numbers which is 1 less than the difference of two squares.

Consider 7^2 and 6^2. Can you say how many numbers are there between 6^2 and 7^2? If we think of any natural number n and $(n + 1)$, then,

$$(n + 1)^2 - n^2 = (n^2 + 2n + 1) - n^2 = 2n + 1.$$

We find that between n^2 and $(n + 1)^2$ there are $2n$ numbers which is 1 less than the difference of two squares.

Thus, in general we can say that *there are 2n non perfect square numbers between the squares of the numbers n and (n + 1).* Check for $n = 5$, $n = 6$ etc., and verify.

1. How many natural numbers lie between 9^2 and 10^2 ? Between 11^2 and 12^2?
2. How many non square numbers lie between the following pairs of numbers
   (i) 100^2 and 101^2 (ii) 90^2 and 91^2 (iii) 1000^2 and 1001^2

3. **Adding odd numbers**

Consider the following

1 [one odd number]	$= 1 = 1^2$
$1 + 3$ [sum of first two odd numbers]	$= 4 = 2^2$
$1 + 3 + 5$ [sum of first three odd numbers]	$= 9 = 3^2$
$1 + 3 + 5 + 7$ [...]	$= 16 = 4^2$
$1 + 3 + 5 + 7 + 9$ [...]	$= 25 = 5^2$
$1 + 3 + 5 + 7 + 9 + 11$ [...]	$= 36 = 6^2$

So we can say that the *sum of first n odd natural numbers is n^2.*

Looking at it in a different way, we can say: 'If the number is a square number, it has to be the sum of successive **odd** numbers starting from 1.

Consider those numbers which are not perfect squares, say 2, 3, 5, 6, ... Can you express these numbers as a sum of successive odd natural numbers beginning from 1?

You will find that these numbers cannot be expressed in this form.

Consider the number 25. Successively subtract 1, 3, 5, 7, 9, ... from it

(i) $25 - 1 = 24$ (ii) $24 - 3 = 21$ (iii) $21 - 5 = 16$ (iv) $16 - 7 = 9$

(v) $9 - 9 = 0$

This means, $25 = 1 + 3 + 5 + 7 + 9$. Also, 25 is a perfect square.

Now consider another number 38, and again do as above.

(i) $38 - 1 = 37$ (ii) $37 - 3 = 34$ (iii) $34 - 5 = 29$ (iv) $29 - 7 = 22$

(v) $22 - 9 = 13$ (vi) $13 - 11 = 2$ (vii) $2 - 13 = -11$

This shows that we are not able to express 38 as the sum of consecutive odd numbers starting with 1. Also, 38 is not a perfect square.

So we can also say that *if a natural number cannot be expressed as a sum of successive odd natural numbers starting with 1, then it is not a perfect square.*

We can use this result to find whether a number is a perfect square or not.

Find whether each of the following numbers is a perfect square or not?

(i) 121   (ii) 55   (iii) 81

(iv) 49   (v) 69

4. **A sum of consecutive natural numbers**

Consider the following

First Number $= \dfrac{3^2 - 1}{2}$

$3^2 = 9 = 4 + 5$

$5^2 = 25 = 12 + 13$

$7^2 = 49 = 24 + 25$

Second Number $= \dfrac{3^2 + 1}{2}$

$9^2 = 81 = 40 + 41$

$11^2 = 121 = 60 + 61$

$15^2 = 225 = 112 + 113$

> Vow! we can express the square of any odd number as the sum of two consecutive positive integers.

TRY THESE

1. Express the following as the sum of two consecutive integers.

   (i) 21^2 (ii) 13^2 (iii) 11^2 (iv) 19^2

2. Do you think the reverse is also true, i.e., is the sum of any two consecutive positive integers is perfect square of a number? Give example to support your answer.

5. Product of two consecutive even or odd natural numbers

$11 \times 13 = 143 = 12^2 - 1$

Also $11 \times 13 = (12 - 1) \times (12 + 1)$

Therefore, $11 \times 13 = (12 - 1) \times (12 + 1) = 12^2 - 1$

Similarly, $13 \times 15 = (14 - 1) \times (14 + 1) = 14^2 - 1$

             $29 \times 31 = (30 - 1) \times (30 + 1) = 30^2 - 1$

             $44 \times 46 = (45 - 1) \times (45 + 1) = 45^2 - 1$

So in general we can say that $(a + 1) \times (a - 1) = a^2 - 1$.

6. Some more patterns in square numbers

Observe the squares of numbers; 1, 11, 111 ... etc. They give a beautiful pattern:

$1^2 =$ 1

$11^2 =$ 1   2   1

$111^2 =$ 1   2   3   2   1

$1111^2 =$ 1   2   3   4   3   2   1

$11111^2 =$ 1   2   3   4   5   4   3   2   1

$11111111^2 =$ 1   2   3   4   5   6   7   8   7   6   5   4   3   2   1

Another interesting pattern.

$$7^2 = 49$$
$$67^2 = 4489$$
$$667^2 = 444889$$
$$6667^2 = 44448889$$
$$66667^2 = 4444488889$$
$$666667^2 = 444444888889$$

The fun is in being able to find out why this happens. May be it would be interesting for you to explore and think about such questions even if the answers come some years later.

TRY THESE

Write the square, making use of the above pattern.

(i) 111111^2 (ii) 1111111^2

TRY THESE

Can you find the square of the following numbers using the above pattern?

(i) 6666667^2 (ii) 66666667^2

EXERCISE 6.1

1. What will be the unit digit of the squares of the following numbers?
   - (i) 81
   - (ii) 272
   - (iii) 799
   - (iv) 3853
   - (v) 1234
   - (vi) 26387
   - (vii) 52698
   - (viii) 99880
   - (ix) 12796
   - (x) 55555

2. The following numbers are obviously not perfect squares. Give reason.
   - (i) 1057
   - (ii) 23453
   - (iii) 7928
   - (iv) 222222
   - (v) 64000
   - (vi) 89722
   - (vii) 222000
   - (viii) 505050

3. The squares of which of the following would be odd numbers?
   - (i) 431
   - (ii) 2826
   - (iii) 7779
   - (iv) 82004

4. Observe the following pattern and find the missing digits.

$$11^2 = 121$$
$$101^2 = 10201$$
$$1001^2 = 1002001$$
$$100001^2 = 1 \ldots\ldots 2 \ldots\ldots 1$$
$$10000001^2 = \ldots\ldots\ldots\ldots\ldots\ldots$$

5. Observe the following pattern and supply the missing numbers.

$$11^2 = 1\ 2\ 1$$
$$101^2 = 1\ 0\ 2\ 0\ 1$$
$$10101^2 = 102030201$$
$$1010101^2 = \ldots\ldots\ldots\ldots\ldots\ldots$$
$$\ldots\ldots\ldots^2 = 10203040504030201$$

6. Using the given pattern, find the missing numbers.

$$1^2 + 2^2 + 2^2 = 3^2$$
$$2^2 + 3^2 + 6^2 = 7^2$$
$$3^2 + 4^2 + 12^2 = 13^2$$
$$4^2 + 5^2 + \_^2 = 21^2$$
$$5^2 + \_^2 + 30^2 = 31^2$$
$$6^2 + 7^2 + \_^2 = \_^2$$

   To find pattern
   Third number is related to first and second number. How?
   Fourth number is related to third number. How?

7. Without adding, find the sum.
   - (i) $1 + 3 + 5 + 7 + 9$
   - (ii) $1 + 3 + 5 + 7 + 9 + 11 + 13 + 15 + 17 + 19$
   - (iii) $1 + 3 + 5 + 7 + 9 + 11 + 13 + 15 + 17 + 19 + 21 + 23$

8. (i) Express 49 as the sum of 7 odd numbers.
   (ii) Express 121 as the sum of 11 odd numbers.

9. How many numbers lie between squares of the following numbers?
   - (i) 12 and 13
   - (ii) 25 and 26
   - (iii) 99 and 100

6.4 Finding the Square of a Number

Squares of small numbers like 3, 4, 5, 6, 7, ... etc. are easy to find. But can we find the square of 23 so quickly?

The answer is not so easy and we may need to multiply 23 by 23.

There is a way to find this without having to multiply 23×23.

We know $\qquad 23 = 20 + 3$

Therefore $\qquad 23^2 = (20 + 3)^2 = 20(20 + 3) + 3(20 + 3)$

$$= 20^2 + 20 \times 3 + 3 \times 20 + 3^2$$

$$= 400 + 60 + 60 + 9 = 529$$

Example 1: Find the square of the following numbers without actual multiplication.

(i) 39 $\qquad\qquad$ (ii) 42

Solution: (i) $\quad 39^2 = (30 + 9)^2 = 30(30 + 9) + 9(30 + 9)$

$$= 30^2 + 30 \times 9 + 9 \times 30 + 9^2$$

$$= 900 + 270 + 270 + 81 = 1521$$

(ii) $\quad 42^2 = (40 + 2)^2 = 40(40 + 2) + 2(40 + 2)$

$$= 40^2 + 40 \times 2 + 2 \times 40 + 2^2$$

$$= 1600 + 80 + 80 + 4 = 1764$$

6.4.1 Other patterns in squares

Consider the following pattern:

$25^2 = 625 = (2 \times 3) \text{ hundreds} + 25$

$35^2 = 1225 = (3 \times 4) \text{ hundreds} + 25$

$75^2 = 5625 = (7 \times 8) \text{ hundreds} + 25$

$125^2 = 15625 = (12 \times 13) \text{ hundreds} + 25$

Now can you find the square of 95?

> Consider a number with unit digit 5, i.e., $a5$
> $$(a5)^2 = (10a + 5)^2$$
> $$= 10a(10a + 5) + 5(10a + 5)$$
> $$= 100a^2 + 50a + 50a + 25$$
> $$= 100a(a + 1) + 25$$
> $$= a(a + 1) \text{ hundred} + 25$$

TRY THESE

Find the squares of the following numbers containing 5 in unit's place.

(i) 15 $\qquad$ (ii) 95 $\qquad$ (iii) 105 $\qquad$ (iv) 205

6.4.2 Pythagorean triplets

Consider the following

$$3^2 + 4^2 = 9 + 16 = 25 = 5^2$$

The collection of numbers 3, 4 and 5 is known as **Pythagorean triplet**. 6, 8, 10 is also a Pythagorean triplet, since

$$6^2 + 8^2 = 36 + 64 = 100 = 10^2$$

Again, observe that

$5^2 + 12^2 = 25 + 144 = 169 = 13^2$. The numbers 5, 12, 13 form another such triplet.

Can you find more such triplets?

For any natural number $m > 1$, we have $(2m)^2 + (m^2 - 1)^2 = (m^2 + 1)^2$. So, $2m$, $m^2 - 1$ and $m^2 + 1$ forms a Pythagorean triplet.

Try to find some more Pythagorean triplets using this form.

Example 2: Write a Pythagorean triplet whose smallest member is 8.

Solution: We can get Pythagorean triplets by using general form $2m, m^2 - 1, m^2 + 1$.

Let us first take $\qquad m^2 - 1 = 8$

So, $\qquad m^2 = 8 + 1 = 9$

which gives $\qquad m = 3$

Therefore, $\qquad 2m = 6 \quad$ and $\quad m^2 + 1 = 10$

The triplet is thus 6, 8, 10. But 8 is not the smallest member of this.

So, let us try $\qquad 2m = 8$

then $\qquad m = 4$

We get $\qquad m^2 - 1 = 16 - 1 = 15$

and $\qquad m^2 + 1 = 16 + 1 = 17$

The triplet is 8, 15, 17 with 8 as the smallest member.

Example 3: Find a Pythagorean triplet in which one member is 12.

Solution: If we take $\qquad m^2 - 1 = 12$

Then, $\qquad m^2 = 12 + 1 = 13$

Then the value of m will not be an integer.

So, we try to take $m^2 + 1 = 12$. Again $m^2 = 11$ will not give an integer value for m.

So, let us take $\qquad 2m = 12$

then $\qquad m = 6$

Thus, $\qquad m^2 - 1 = 36 - 1 = 35 \quad$ and $\quad m^2 + 1 = 36 + 1 = 37$

Therefore, the required triplet is 12, 35, 37.

Note: All Pythagorean triplets may not be obtained using this form. For example another triplet 5, 12, 13 also has 12 as a member.

◤ EXERCISE 6.2

1. Find the square of the following numbers.
    (i) 32 (ii) 35 (iii) 86 (iv) 93
    (v) 71 (vi) 46
2. Write a Pythagorean triplet whose one member is.
    (i) 6 (ii) 14 (iii) 16 (iv) 18

6.5 Square Roots

Study the following situations.

(a) Area of a square is 144 cm². What could be the side of the square?

We know that the area of a square = side^2

If we assume the length of the side to be 'a', then $144 = a^2$

To find the length of side it is necessary to find a number whose square is 144.

(b) What is the length of a diagonal of a square of side 8 cm (Fig 6.1)?

Can we use Pythagoras theorem to solve this?

We have, $AB^2 + BC^2 = AC^2$

i.e., $8^2 + 8^2 = AC^2$

or $64 + 64 = AC^2$

or $128 = AC^2$

Again to get AC we need to think of a number whose square is 128.

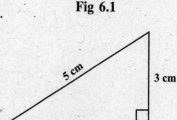

Fig 6.1

(c) In a right triangle the length of the hypotenuse and a side are respectively 5 cm and 3 cm (Fig 6.2).

Can you find the third side?

Let x cm be the length of the third side.

Using Pythagoras theorem $5^2 = x^2 + 3^2$

$25 - 9 = x^2$

$16 = x^2$

Fig 6.2

Again, to find x we need a number whose square is 16.

In all the above cases, we need to find a number whose square is known. Finding the number with the known square is known as finding the square root.

6.5.1 Finding square roots

The inverse (opposite) operation of addition is subtraction and the inverse operation of multiplication is division. Similarly, finding the square root is the inverse operation of squaring.

We have, $1^2 = 1$, therefore square root of 1 is 1

$2^2 = 4$, therefore square root of 4 is 2

$3^2 = 9$, therefore square root of 9 is 3

> Since $9^2 = 81$,
> and $(-9)^2 = 81$
> We say that square
> roots of 81 are 9 and -9.

TRY THESE

(i) $11^2 = 121$. What is the square root of 121?

(ii) $14^2 = 196$. What is the square root of 196?

THINK, DISCUSS AND WRITE

$(-1)^2 = 1$. Is -1, a square root of 1? $(-2)^2 = 4$. Is -2, a square root of 4?

$(-9)^2 = 81$. Is -9 a square root of 81?

From the above, you may say that there are two integral square roots of a perfect square number. In this chapter, we shall take up only positive square root of a natural number. Positive square root of a number is denoted by the symbol $\sqrt{}$.

For example: $\sqrt{4} = 2$ (not -2); $\sqrt{9} = 3$ (not -3) etc.

Statement	Inference		Statement	Inference
$1^2 = 1$	$\sqrt{1} = 1$		$6^2 = 36$	$\sqrt{36} = 6$
$2^2 = 4$	$\sqrt{4} = 2$		$7^2 = 49$	$\sqrt{49} = 7$
$3^2 = 9$	$\sqrt{9} = 3$		$8^2 = 64$	$\sqrt{64} = 8$
$4^2 = 16$	$\sqrt{16} = 4$		$9^2 = 81$	$\sqrt{81} = 9$
$5^2 = 25$	$\sqrt{25} = 5$		$10^2 = 100$	$\sqrt{100} = 10$

6.5.2 Finding square root through repeated subtraction

Do you remember that the sum of the first n odd natural numbers is n^2? That is, every square number can be expressed as a sum of successive odd natural numbers starting from 1.

Consider $\sqrt{81}$. Then,

(i) $81 - 1 = 80$ (ii) $80 - 3 = 77$ (iii) $77 - 5 = 72$ (iv) $72 - 7 = 65$

(v) $65 - 9 = 56$ (vi) $56 - 11 = 45$ (vii) $45 - 13 = 32$ (viii) $32 - 15 = 17$

(ix) $17 - 17 = 0$

From 81 we have subtracted successive odd numbers starting from 1 and obtained 0 at 9th step.

Therefore $\sqrt{81} = 9$.

Can you find the square root of 729 using this method? Yes, but it will be time consuming. Let us try to find it in a simpler way.

TRY THESE

By repeated subtraction of odd numbers starting from 1, find whether the following numbers are perfect squares or not? If the number is a perfect square then find its square root.

(i) 121
(ii) 55
(iii) 36
(iv) 49
(v) 90

6.5.3 Finding square root through prime factorisation

Consider the prime factorisation of the following numbers and their squares.

Prime factorisation of a Number	Prime factorisation of its Square
$6 = 2 \times 3$	$36 = 2 \times 2 \times 3 \times 3$
$8 = 2 \times 2 \times 2$	$64 = 2 \times 2 \times 2 \times 2 \times 2 \times 2$
$12 = 2 \times 2 \times 3$	$144 = 2 \times 2 \times 2 \times 2 \times 3 \times 3$
$15 = 3 \times 5$	$225 = 3 \times 3 \times 5 \times 5$

How many times does 2 occur in the prime factorisation of 6? Once. How many times does 2 occur in the prime factorisation of 36? Twice. Similarly, observe the occurrence of 3 in 6 and 36 of 2 in 8 and 64 etc.

You will find that each prime factor in the prime factorisation of the square of a number, occurs twice the number of times it occurs in the prime factorisation of the number itself. Let us use this to find the square root of a given square number, say 324.

We know that the prime factorisation of 324 is

$$324 = 2 \times 2 \times 3 \times 3 \times 3 \times 3$$

2	324
2	162
3	81
3	27
3	9
	3

By pairing the prime factors, we get

$$324 = \underline{2 \times 2} \times \underline{3 \times 3} \times \underline{3 \times 3} = 2^2 \times 3^2 \times 3^2 = (2 \times 3 \times 3)^2$$

So, $\sqrt{324} = 2 \times 3 \times 3 = 18$

Similarly can you find the square root of 256? Prime factorisation of 256 is

$$256 = 2 \times 2 \times 2 \times 2 \times 2 \times 2 \times 2 \times 2$$

By pairing the prime factors we get,

$$256 = \underline{2 \times 2} \times \underline{2 \times 2} \times \underline{2 \times 2} \times \underline{2 \times 2} = (2 \times 2 \times 2 \times 2)^2$$

Therefore, $\sqrt{256} = 2 \times 2 \times 2 \times 2 = 16$

Is 48 a perfect square?

We know $48 = \underline{2 \times 2} \times \underline{2 \times 2} \times 3$

Since all the factors are not in pairs so 48 is not a perfect square.

2	256
2	128
2	64
2	32
2	16
2	8
2	4
	2

Suppose we want to find the smallest multiple of 48 that is a perfect square, how should we proceed? Making pairs of the prime factors of 48 we see that 3 is the only factor that does not have a pair. So we need to multiply by 3 to complete the pair.

Hence $48 \times 3 = 144$ is a perfect square.

Can you tell by which number should we divide 48 to get a perfect square?

The factor 3 is not in pair, so if we divide 48 by 3 we get $48 \div 3 = 16 = \underline{2 \times 2} \times \underline{2 \times 2}$ and this number 16 is a perfect square too.

Example 4: Find the square root of 6400.

Solution: Write $6400 = \underline{2 \times 2} \times \underline{2 \times 2} \times \underline{2 \times 2} \times \underline{2 \times 2} \times \underline{5 \times 5}$

Therefore $\sqrt{6400} = 2 \times 2 \times 2 \times 2 \times 5 = 80$

2	6400
2	3200
2	1600
2	800
2	400
2	200
2	100
2	50
5	25
	5

Example 5: Is 90 a perfect square?

Solution: We have $90 = 2 \times 3 \times 3 \times 5$

2	90
3	45
3	15
	5

The prime factors 2 and 5 do not occur in pairs. Therefore, 90 is not a perfect square. That 90 is not a perfect square can also be seen from the fact that it has only one zero.

Example 6: Is 2352 a perfect square? If not, find the smallest multiple of 2352 which is a perfect square. Find the square root of the new number.

Solution: We have $2352 = \underline{2 \times 2} \times \underline{2 \times 2} \times 3 \times \underline{7 \times 7}$

As the prime factor 3 has no pair, 2352 is not a perfect square.

If 3 gets a pair then the number will become perfect square. So, we multiply 2352 by 3 to get,

$$2352 \times 3 = \underline{2 \times 2} \times \underline{2 \times 2} \times \underline{3 \times 3} \times \underline{7 \times 7}$$

2	2352
2	1176
2	588
2	294
3	147
7	49
	7

Now each prime factor is in a pair. Therefore, $2352 \times 3 = 7056$ is a perfect square. Thus the required smallest multiple of 2352 is 7056 which is a perfect square.

And, $\sqrt{7056} = 2 \times 2 \times 3 \times 7 = 84$

Example 7: Find the smallest number by which 9408 must be divided so that the quotient is a perfect square. Find the square root of the quotient.

Solution: We have, $9408 = \underline{2 \times 2} \times \underline{2 \times 2} \times \underline{2 \times 2} \times 3 \times \underline{7 \times 7}$

If we divide 9408 by the factor 3, then

$9408 \div 3 = 3136 = \underline{2 \times 2} \times \underline{2 \times 2} \times \underline{2 \times 2} \times \underline{7 \times 7}$ which is a perfect square. (Why?)

Therefore, the required smallest number is 3.

And, $\qquad\qquad\qquad\qquad \sqrt{3136} = 2 \times 2 \times 2 \times 7 = 56$.

2	6, 9, 15
3	3, 9, 15
3	1, 3, 5
5	1, 1, 5
	1, 1, 1

Example 8: Find the smallest square number which is divisible by each of the numbers 6, 9 and 15.

Solution: This has to be done in two steps. First find the smallest common multiple and then find the square number needed. The least number divisible by each one of 6, 9 and 15 is their LCM. The LCM of 6, 9 and 15 is $2 \times 3 \times 3 \times 5 = 90$.

Prime factorisation of 90 is $90 = 2 \times \underline{3 \times 3} \times 5$.

We see that prime factors 2 and 5 are not in pairs. Therefore 90 is not a perfect square.

In order to get a perfect square, each factor of 90 must be paired. So we need to make pairs of 2 and 5. Therefore, 90 should be multiplied by 2×5, i.e., 10.

Hence, the required square number is $90 \times 10 = 900$.

EXERCISE 6.3

1. What could be the possible 'one's' digits of the square root of each of the following numbers?
   - (i) 9801
   - (ii) 99856
   - (iii) 998001
   - (iv) 657666025

2. Without doing any calculation, find the numbers which are surely not perfect squares.
   - (i) 153
   - (ii) 257
   - (iii) 408
   - (iv) 441

3. Find the square roots of 100 and 169 by the method of repeated subtraction.

4. Find the square roots of the following numbers by the Prime Factorisation Method.
   - (i) 729
   - (ii) 400
   - (iii) 1764
   - (iv) 4096
   - (v) 7744
   - (vi) 9604
   - (vii) 5929
   - (viii) 9216
   - (ix) 529
   - (x) 8100

5. For each of the following numbers, find the smallest whole number by which it should be multiplied so as to get a perfect square number. Also find the square root of the square number so obtained.
   - (i) 252
   - (ii) 180
   - (iii) 1008
   - (iv) 2028
   - (v) 1458
   - (vi) 768

6. For each of the following numbers, find the smallest whole number by which it should be divided so as to get a perfect square. Also find the square root of the square number so obtained.
   - (i) 252
   - (ii) 2925
   - (iii) 396
   - (iv) 2645
   - (v) 2800
   - (vi) 1620

7. The students of Class VIII of a school donated ₹ 2401 in all, for Prime Minister's National Relief Fund. Each student donated as many rupees as the number of students in the class. Find the number of students in the class.

8. 2025 plants are to be planted in a garden in such a way that each row contains as many plants as the number of rows. Find the number of rows and the number of plants in each row.

9. Find the smallest square number that is divisible by each of the numbers 4, 9 and 10.

10. Find the smallest square number that is divisible by each of the numbers 8, 15 and 20.

6.5.4 Finding square root by division method

When the numbers are large, even the method of finding square root by prime factorisation becomes lengthy and difficult. To overcome this problem we use Long Division Method.

For this we need to determine the number of digits in the square root.
See the following table:

Number	Square	
10	100	which is the smallest 3-digit perfect square
31	961	which is the greatest 3-digit perfect square
32	1024	which is the smallest 4-digit perfect square
99	9801	which is the greatest 4-digit perfect square

So, what can we say about the number of digits in the square root if a perfect square is a 3-digit or a 4-digit number? We can say that, if a perfect square is a 3-digit or a 4-digit number, then its square root will have 2-digits.

Can you tell the number of digits in the square root of a 5-digit or a 6-digit perfect square?

The smallest 3-digit perfect square number is 100 which is the square of 10 and the greatest 3-digit perfect square number is 961 which is the square of 31. The smallest 4-digit square number is 1024 which is the square of 32 and the greatest 4-digit number is 9801 which is the square of 99.

THINK, DISCUSS AND WRITE

Can we say that if a perfect square is of n-digits, then its square root will have $\dfrac{n}{2}$ digits if n is even or $\dfrac{(n+1)}{2}$ if n is odd?

The use of the number of digits in square root of a number is useful in the following method:

● Consider the following steps to find the square root of 529.

Can you estimate the number of digits in the square root of this number?

Step 1 Place a bar over every pair of digits starting from the digit at one's place. If the number of digits in it is odd, then the left-most single digit too will have a bar.

Thus we have, $\overline{5}\,\overline{29}$.

Step 2 Find the largest number whose square is less than or equal to the number under the extreme left bar ($2^2 < 5 < 3^2$). Take this number as the divisor and the quotient with the number under the extreme left bar as the dividend (here 5). Divide and get the remainder (1 in this case).

$$
\begin{array}{r}
2 \\
2\;{\overline{\smash{\big)}\,5\,29}} \\
\underline{-4} \\
1
\end{array}
$$

$$
\begin{array}{r|l}
2 \\
2\ \overline{\ }\ \overline{5\,29} \\
-4 \\
\hline
1\,29
\end{array}
$$

Step 3 Bring down the number under the next bar (i.e., 29 in this case) to the right of the remainder. So the new dividend is 129.

Step 4 Double the quotient and enter it with a blank on its right.

$$
\begin{array}{r|l}
2 \\
2\ \overline{\ }\ \overline{5\,29} \\
-4 \\
\hline
4\_\ \ \ 1\,29
\end{array}
$$

Step 5 Guess a largest possible digit to fill the blank which will also become the new digit in the quotient, such that when the new divisor is multiplied to the new quotient the product is less than or equal to the dividend.

In this case $42 \times 2 = 84$.

As $43 \times 3 = 129$ so we choose the new digit as 3. Get the remainder.

$$
\begin{array}{r|l}
2\,3 \\
2\ \overline{\ }\ \overline{5\,29} \\
-4 \\
\hline
43\ \ 1\,29 \\
-1\,29 \\
\hline
0
\end{array}
$$

Step 6 Since the remainder is 0 and no digits are left in the given number, therefore, $\sqrt{529} = 23$.

- Now consider $\sqrt{4096}$

Step 1 Place a bar over every pair of digits starting from the one's digit. ($\overline{40}\ \overline{96}$).

$$
\begin{array}{r|l}
6 \\
6\ \overline{\ }\ \overline{40\,96} \\
-36 \\
\hline
4
\end{array}
$$

Step 2 Find the largest number whose square is less than or equal to the number under the left-most bar ($6^2 < 40 < 7^2$). Take this number as the divisor and the number under the left-most bar as the dividend. Divide and get the remainder i.e., 4 in this case.

$$
\begin{array}{r|l}
6 \\
6\ \overline{\ }\ \overline{40\,96} \\
-36 \\
\hline
496
\end{array}
$$

Step 3 Bring down the number under the next bar (i.e., 96) to the right of the remainder. The new dividend is 496.

Step 4 Double the quotient and enter it with a blank on its right.

$$
\begin{array}{r|l}
6 \\
6\ \overline{\ }\ \overline{40\,96} \\
-36 \\
\hline
12\_\ \ 496
\end{array}
$$

Step 5 Guess a largest possible digit to fill the blank which also becomes the new digit in the quotient such that when the new digit is multiplied to the new quotient the product is less than or equal to the dividend. In this case we see that $124 \times 4 = 496$.

So the new digit in the quotient is 4. Get the remainder.

$$
\begin{array}{r|l}
6\,4 \\
6\ \overline{\ }\ \overline{40\,96} \\
-36 \\
\hline
124\ \ 496 \\
-496 \\
\hline
0
\end{array}
$$

Step 6 Since the remainder is 0 and no bar left, therefore, $\sqrt{4096} = 64$.

Estimating the number

We use bars to find the number of digits in the square root of a perfect square number.

$$\sqrt{529} = 23 \qquad \text{and} \qquad \sqrt{4096} = 64$$

In both the numbers 529 and 4096 there are two bars and the number of digits in their square root is 2. Can you tell the number of digits in the square root of 14400?

By placing bars we get $\overline{1}\,\overline{44}\,\overline{00}$. Since there are 3 bars, the square root will be of 3 digit.

TRY THESE

Without calculating square roots, find the number of digits in the square root of the following numbers.

  (i) 25600   (ii) 100000000   (iii) 36864

Example 9: Find the square root of : (i) 729   (ii) 1296

Solution:

(i)
```
            27
      ┌──────────
   2  │  7̄ 2̄9̄
      │  − 4
      ├──────────
  47  │   329
      │   329
      ├──────────
      │     0
```
Therefore $\sqrt{729} = 27$

(ii)
```
            36
      ┌──────────
   3  │  1̄2̄ 9̄6̄
      │  − 9
      ├──────────
  66  │   396
      │   396
      ├──────────
      │     0
```
Therefore $\sqrt{1296} = 36$

Example 10: Find the least number that must be subtracted from 5607 so as to get a perfect square. Also find the square root of the perfect square.

Solution: Let us try to find $\sqrt{5607}$ by long division method. We get the remainder 131. It shows that 74^2 is less than 5607 by 131.

This means if we subtract the remainder from the number, we get a perfect square.

Therefore, the required perfect square is $5607 - 131 = 5476$. And, $\sqrt{5476} = 74$.

```
            74
      ┌──────────
   7  │  5607
      │  − 49
      ├──────────
 144  │   707
      │  −576
      ├──────────
      │   131
```

Example 11: Find the greatest 4-digit number which is a perfect square.

Solution: Greatest number of 4-digits = 9999. We find $\sqrt{9999}$ by long division method. The remainder is 198. This shows 99^2 is less than 9999 by 198.

This means if we subtract the remainder from the number, we get a perfect square. Therefore, the required perfect square is $9999 - 198 = 9801$.

And, $\sqrt{9801} = 99$

```
            99
      ┌──────────
   9  │  9999
      │  − 81
      ├──────────
 189  │  1899
      │ −1701
      ├──────────
      │   198
```

Example 12: Find the least number that must be added to 1300 so as to get a perfect square. Also find the square root of the perfect square.

Solution: We find $\sqrt{1300}$ by long division method. The remainder is 4.

This shows that $36^2 < 1300$.

Next perfect square number is $37^2 = 1369$.

Hence, the number to be added is $37^2 - 1300 = 1369 - 1300 = 69$.

```
            36
      ┌──────────
   3  │  1300
      │  − 9
      ├──────────
  66  │   400
      │  − 396
      ├──────────
      │     4
```

6.6 Square Roots of Decimals

Consider $\sqrt{17.64}$

Step 1   To find the square root of a decimal number we put bars on the integral part (i.e., 17) of the number in the usual manner. And place bars on the decimal part

$$\begin{array}{r} 4 \\ 4\ \overline{\smash{\big)}\ \overline{17.64}} \\ \underline{-16} \\ 1 \end{array}$$

Step 2 (i.e., 64) on every pair of digits beginning with the first decimal place. Proceed as usual. We get $\overline{17}.\overline{64}$.

Now proceed in a similar manner. The left most bar is on 17 and $4^2 < 17 < 5^2$. Take this number as the divisor and the number under the left-most bar as the dividend, i.e., 17. Divide and get the remainder.

$$\begin{array}{r} 4 \\ 4\ \overline{\smash{\big)}\ \overline{17}.\overline{64}} \\ \underline{-16} \\ 8\_\ \quad 1\ 64 \end{array}$$

Step 3 The remainder is 1. Write the number under the next bar (i.e., 64) to the right of this remainder, to get 164.

$$\begin{array}{r} 4. \\ 4\ \overline{\smash{\big)}\ 17.64} \\ \underline{-16} \\ 82\ \quad 164 \end{array}$$

Step 4 Double the divisor and enter it with a blank on its right.

Since 64 is the decimal part so put a decimal point in the quotient.

Step 5 We know $82 \times 2 = 164$, therefore, the new digit is 2. Divide and get the remainder.

$$\begin{array}{r} 4.2 \\ 4\ \overline{\smash{\big)}\ 17.64} \\ \underline{-16} \\ 82\ \quad 164 \\ \underline{-\ 164} \\ 0 \end{array}$$

Step 6 Since the remainder is 0 and no bar left, therefore $\sqrt{17.64} = 4.2$.

Example 13: Find the square root of 12.25.

Solution:

$$\begin{array}{r} 3.5 \\ 3\ \overline{\smash{\big)}\ \overline{12}.\overline{25}} \\ \underline{-9} \\ 65\ \quad 325 \\ \quad 325 \\ \underline{} \\ 0 \end{array}$$

Therefore, $\sqrt{12.25} = 3.5$

Which way to move

Consider a number 176.341. Put bars on both integral part and decimal part. In what way is putting bars on decimal part different from integral part? Notice for 176 we start from the unit's place close to the decimal and move towards left. The first bar is over 76 and the second bar over 1. For .341, we start from the decimal and move towards right. First bar is over 34 and for the second bar we put 0 after 1 and make $.\overline{34}\overline{10}$.

Example 14: Area of a square plot is 2304 m². Find the side of the square plot.

$$\begin{array}{r} 48 \\ 4\ \overline{\smash{\big)}\ \overline{23}\overline{04}} \\ \underline{-16} \\ 88\ \quad 704 \\ \quad 704 \\ \underline{} \\ 0 \end{array}$$

Solution: Area of square plot = 2304 m²

Therefore, side of the square plot = $\sqrt{2304}$ m

We find that, $\sqrt{2304} = 48$

Thus, the side of the square plot is 48 m.

Example 15: There are 2401 students in a school. P.T. teacher wants them to stand in rows and columns such that the number of rows is equal to the number of columns. Find the number of rows.

Solution: Let the number of rows be x

So, the number of columns = x

Therefore, number of students = $x \times x = x^2$

Thus, $x^2 = 2401$ gives $x = \sqrt{2401} = 49$

The number of rows = 49.

$$
\begin{array}{r|l}
 & 49 \\
\hline
4 & \overline{24}\,\overline{01} \\
 & -16 \\
\hline
89 & 801 \\
 & 801 \\
\hline
 & 0
\end{array}
$$

6.7 Estimating Square Root

Consider the following situations:

1. Deveshi has a square piece of cloth of area 125 cm². She wants to know whether she can make a handkerchief of side 15 cm. If that is not possible she wants to know what is the maximum length of the side of a handkerchief that can be made from this piece.

2. Meena and Shobha played a game. One told a number and other gave its square root. Meena started first. She said 25 and Shobha answered quickly as 5. Then Shobha said 81 and Meena answered 9. It went on, till at one point Meena gave the number 250. And Shobha could not answer. Then Meena asked Shobha if she could atleast tell a number whose square is closer to 250.

In all such cases we need to *estimate* the square root.

We know that $100 < 250 < 400$ and $\sqrt{100} = 10$ and $\sqrt{400} = 20$.

So $\qquad 10 < \sqrt{250} < 20$

But still we are not very close to the square number.

We know that $15^2 = 225$ and $16^2 = 256$

Therefore, $\qquad 15 < \sqrt{250} < 16$ and 256 is much closer to 250 than 225.

So, $\qquad \sqrt{250}$ is approximately 16.

TRY THESE

Estimate the value of the following to the nearest whole number.

(i) $\sqrt{80}$ (ii) $\sqrt{1000}$ (iii) $\sqrt{350}$ (iv) $\sqrt{500}$

EXERCISE 6.4

1. Find the square root of each of the following numbers by Division method.

   (i) 2304 (ii) 4489 (iii) 3481 (iv) 529

   (v) 3249 (vi) 1369 (vii) 5776 (viii) 7921

   (ix) 576 (x) 1024 (xi) 3136 (xii) 900

2. Find the number of digits in the square root of each of the following numbers (without any calculation).

   (i) 64 (ii) 144 (iii) 4489 (iv) 27225

   (v) 390625

3. Find the square root of the following decimal numbers.
   (i) 2.56   (ii) 7.29   (iii) 51.84   (iv) 42.25
   (v) 31.36

4. Find the least number which must be subtracted from each of the following numbers so as to get a perfect square. Also find the square root of the perfect square so obtained.
   (i) 402   (ii) 1989   (iii) 3250   (iv) 825
   (v) 4000

5. Find the least number which must be added to each of the following numbers so as to get a perfect square. Also find the square root of the perfect square so obtained.
   (i) 525   (ii) 1750   (iii) 252   (iv) 1825
   (v) 6412

6. Find the length of the side of a square whose area is 441 m^2.

7. In a right triangle ABC, $\angle$B = 90°.
   (a) If AB = 6 cm, BC = 8 cm, find AC   (b) If AC = 13 cm, BC = 5 cm, find AB

8. A gardener has 1000 plants. He wants to plant these in such a way that the number of rows and the number of columns remain same. Find the minimum number of plants he needs more for this.

9. There are 500 children in a school. For a P.T. drill they have to stand in such a manner that the number of rows is equal to number of columns. How many children would be left out in this arrangement.

WHAT HAVE WE DISCUSSED?

1. If a natural number m can be expressed as n^2, where n is also a natural number, then m is a **square number**.

2. All square numbers end with 0, 1, 4, 5, 6 or 9 at units place.

3. Square numbers can only have even number of zeros at the end.

4. **Square root** is the inverse operation of square.

5. There are two integral square roots of a perfect square number.

   Positive square root of a number is denoted by the symbol $\sqrt{}$.

   For example, $3^2 = 9$ gives $\sqrt{9} = 3$

Cubes and Cube Roots

CHAPTER 7

0852CH07

7.1 Introduction

This is a story about one of India's great mathematical geniuses, S. Ramanujan. Once another famous mathematician Prof. G.H. Hardy came to visit him in a taxi whose number was 1729. While talking to Ramanujan, Hardy described this number "a dull number". Ramanujan quickly pointed out that 1729 was indeed interesting. He said it is the smallest number that can be expressed as a sum of two cubes in two different ways:

$$1729 = 1728 + 1 = 12^3 + 1^3$$
$$1729 = 1000 + 729 = 10^3 + 9^3$$

1729 has since been known as the Hardy – Ramanujan Number, even though this feature of 1729 was known more than 300 years before Ramanujan.

> **Hardy – Ramanujan Number**
>
> 1729 is the smallest Hardy–Ramanujan Number. There are an infinitely many such numbers. Few are 4104 (2, 16; 9, 15), 13832 (18, 20; 2, 24), Check it with the numbers given in the brackets.

How did Ramanujan know this? Well, he loved numbers. All through his life, he experimented with numbers. He probably found numbers that were expressed as the sum of two squares and sum of two cubes also.

There are many other interesting patterns of cubes. Let us learn about cubes, cube roots and many other interesting facts related to them.

7.2 Cubes

You know that the word 'cube' is used in geometry. A cube is a solid figure which has all its sides equal. How many cubes of side 1 cm will make a cube of side 2 cm?

How many cubes of side 1 cm will make a cube of side 3 cm?

Consider the numbers 1, 8, 27, ...

These are called **perfect cubes or cube numbers**. Can you say why they are named so? Each of them is obtained when a number is multiplied by taking it three times.

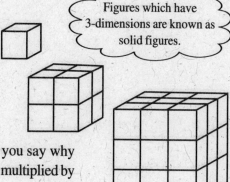

Figures which have 3-dimensions are known as solid figures.

We note that $1 = 1 \times 1 \times 1 = 1^3$; $8 = 2 \times 2 \times 2 = 2^3$; $27 = 3 \times 3 \times 3 = 3^3$.

Since $5^3 = 5 \times 5 \times 5 = 125$, therefore 125 is a cube number.

Is 9 a cube number? No, as $9 = 3 \times 3$ and there is no natural number which multiplied by taking three times gives 9. We can see also that $2 \times 2 \times 2 = 8$ and $3 \times 3 \times 3 = 27$. This shows that 9 is not a perfect cube.

The following are the cubes of numbers from 1 to 10.

Table 1

Number	Cube
1	$1^3 = 1$
2	$2^3 = 8$
3	$3^3 = 27$
4	$4^3 = 64$
5	$5^3 = \underline{\quad}$
6	$6^3 = \underline{\quad}$
7	$7^3 = \underline{\quad}$
8	$8^3 = \underline{\quad}$
9	$9^3 = \underline{\quad}$
10	$10^3 = \underline{\quad}$

> The numbers 729, 1000, 1728 are also perfect cubes.

> Complete it.

There are only ten perfect cubes from 1 to 1000. (Check this). How many perfect cubes are there from 1 to 100?

Observe the cubes of even numbers. Are they all even? What can you say about the cubes of odd numbers?

Following are the cubes of the numbers from 11 to 20.

Table 2

Number	Cube
11	1331
12	1728
13	2197
14	2744
15	3375
16	4096
17	4913
18	5832
19	6859
20	8000

> We are even, so are our cubes

> We are odd so are our cubes

Consider a few numbers having 1 as the one's digit (or unit's). Find the cube of each of them. What can you say about the one's digit of the cube of a number having 1 as the one's digit?

Similarly, explore the one's digit of cubes of numbers ending in 2, 3, 4, ... , etc.

TRY THESE

Find the one's digit of the cube of each of the following numbers.

(i) 3331   (ii) 8888   (iii) 149   (iv) 1005

(v) 1024   (vi) 77   (vii) 5022   (viii) 53

7.2.1 Some interesting patterns

1. Adding consecutive odd numbers

Observe the following pattern of sums of odd numbers.

$$1 = 1 = 1^3$$
$$3 + 5 = 8 = 2^3$$
$$7 + 9 + 11 = 27 = 3^3$$
$$13 + 15 + 17 + 19 = 64 = 4^3$$
$$21 + 23 + 25 + 27 + 29 = 125 = 5^3$$

Is it not interesting? How many consecutive odd numbers will be needed to obtain the sum as 10^3?

TRY THESE

Express the following numbers as the sum of odd numbers using the above pattern?

(a) 6^3 (b) 8^3 (c) 7^3

Consider the following pattern.

$$2^3 - 1^3 = 1 + 2 \times 1 \times 3$$
$$3^3 - 2^3 = 1 + 3 \times 2 \times 3$$
$$4^3 - 3^3 = 1 + 4 \times 3 \times 3$$

Using the above pattern, find the value of the following.

(i) $7^3 - 6^3$ (ii) $12^3 - 11^3$ (iii) $20^3 - 19^3$ (iv) $51^3 - 50^3$

2. Cubes and their prime factors

Consider the following prime factorisation of the numbers and their cubes.

Prime factorisation of a number	Prime factorisation of its cube
$4 = 2 \times 2$	$4^3 = 64 = 2 \times 2 \times 2 \times 2 \times 2 \times 2 = 2^3 \times 2^3$
$6 = 2 \times 3$	$6^3 = 216 = 2 \times 2 \times 2 \times 3 \times 3 \times 3 = 2^3 \times 3^3$
$15 = 3 \times 5$	$15^3 = 3375 = 3 \times 3 \times 3 \times 5 \times 5 \times 5 = 3^3 \times 5^3$
$12 = 2 \times 2 \times 3$	$12^3 = 1728 = 2 \times 2 \times 2 \times 2 \times 2 \times 2 \times 3 \times 3 \times 3$
	$= 2^3 \times 2^3 \times 3^3$

each prime factor appears three times in its cubes

2	216
2	108
2	54
3	27
3	9
3	3
	1

Observe that each prime factor of a number appears three times in the prime factorisation of its cube.

In the prime factorisation of any number, if each factor appears three times, then, is the number a perfect cube? Think about it. Is 216 a perfect cube?

By prime factorisation, $216 = 2 \times 2 \times 2 \times 3 \times 3 \times 3$

Each factor appears 3 times. $216 = 2^3 \times 3^3 = (2 \times 3)^3$

$= 6^3$ which is a perfect cube!

> Do you remember that $a^m \times b^m = (a \times b)^m$

> factors can be grouped in triples

Is 729 a perfect cube? $729 = \underline{3 \times 3 \times 3} \times \underline{3 \times 3 \times 3}$

Yes, 729 is a perfect cube.

Now let us check for 500.

Prime factorisation of 500 is $2 \times 2 \times \underline{5 \times 5 \times 5}$.

So, 500 is not a perfect cube.

Example 1: Is 243 a perfect cube?

> There are three 5's in the product but only two 2's.

Solution: $243 = \underline{3 \times 3 \times 3} \times 3 \times 3$

In the above factorisation 3×3 remains after grouping the 3's in triplets. Therefore, 243 is not a perfect cube.

TRY THESE

Which of the following are perfect cubes?

1.	400	2.	3375	3.	8000	4.	15625
5.	9000	6.	6859	7.	2025	8.	10648

7.2.2 Smallest multiple that is a perfect cube

Raj made a cuboid of plasticine. Length, breadth and height of the cuboid are 15 cm, 30 cm, 15 cm respectively.

Anu asks how many such cuboids will she need to make a perfect cube? Can you tell?

Raj said, Volume of cuboid is $15 \times 30 \times 15 = 3 \times 5 \times 2 \times 3 \times 5 \times 3 \times 5$

$$= 2 \times \underline{3 \times 3 \times 3} \times \underline{5 \times 5 \times 5}$$

Since there is only one 2 in the prime factorisation. So we need 2×2, i.e., 4 to make it a perfect cube. Therefore, we need 4 such cuboids to make a cube.

Example 2: Is 392 a perfect cube? If not, find the smallest natural number by which 392 must be multiplied so that the product is a perfect cube.

Solution: $392 = \underline{2 \times 2 \times 2} \times 7 \times 7$

The prime factor 7 does not appear in a group of three. Therefore, 392 is not a perfect cube. To make its a cube, we need one more 7. In that case

$$392 \times 7 = \underline{2 \times 2 \times 2} \times \underline{7 \times 7 \times 7} = 2744 \quad \text{which is a perfect cube.}$$

Hence the smallest natural number by which 392 should be multiplied to make a perfect cube is 7.

Example 3: Is 53240 a perfect cube? If not, then by which smallest natural number should 53240 be divided so that the quotient is a perfect cube?

Solution: $53240 = \underline{2 \times 2 \times 2} \times \underline{11 \times 11 \times 11} \times 5$

The prime factor 5 does not appear in a group of three. So, 53240 is not a perfect cube. In the factorisation 5 appears only one time. If we divide the number by 5, then the prime factorisation of the quotient will not contain 5.

So, $53240 \div 5 = \underline{2 \times 2 \times 2} \times \underline{11 \times 11 \times 11}$

Hence the smallest number by which 53240 should be divided to make it a perfect cube is 5.

The perfect cube in that case is = 10648.

Example 4: Is 1188 a perfect cube? If not, by which smallest natural number should 1188 be divided so that the quotient is a perfect cube?

Solution: $1188 = 2 \times 2 \times \underline{3 \times 3 \times 3} \times 11$

The primes 2 and 11 do not appear in groups of three. So, 1188 is not a perfect cube. In the factorisation of 1188 the prime 2 appears only two times and the prime 11 appears once. So, if we divide 1188 by $2 \times 2 \times 11 = 44$, then the prime factorisation of the quotient will not contain 2 and 11.

Hence the smallest natural number by which 1188 should be divided to make it a perfect cube is 44.

And the resulting perfect cube is $1188 \div 44 = 27 \,(= 3^3)$.

Example 5: Is 68600 a perfect cube? If not, find the smallest number by which 68600 must be multiplied to get a perfect cube.

Solution: We have, $68600 = 2 \times 2 \times 2 \times 5 \times 5 \times 7 \times 7 \times 7$. In this factorisation, we find that there is no triplet of 5.

So, 68600 is not a perfect cube. To make it a perfect cube we multiply it by 5.

Thus, $68600 \times 5 = 2 \times 2 \times 2 \times 5 \times 5 \times 5 \times 7 \times 7 \times 7$
                                  $= 343000$, which is a perfect cube.

Observe that 343 is a perfect cube. From Example 5 we know that 343000 is also perfect cube.

◤ THINK, DISCUSS AND WRITE ◢

Check which of the following are perfect cubes. (i) 2700 (ii) 16000 (iii) 64000 (iv) 900 (v) 125000 (vi) 36000 (vii) 21600 (viii) 10,000 (ix) 27000000 (x) 1000. What pattern do you observe in these perfect cubes?

EXERCISE 7.1

1. Which of the following numbers are not perfect cubes?
   (i) 216   (ii) 128   (iii) 1000   (iv) 100
   (v) 46656

2. Find the smallest number by which each of the following numbers must be multiplied to obtain a perfect cube.
   (i) 243   (ii) 256   (iii) 72   (iv) 675
   (v) 100

3. Find the smallest number by which each of the following numbers must be divided to obtain a perfect cube.
   (i) 81   (ii) 128   (iii) 135   (iv) 192
   (v) 704

4. Parikshit makes a cuboid of plasticine of sides 5 cm, 2 cm, 5 cm. How many such cuboids will he need to form a cube?

7.3 Cube Roots

If the volume of a cube is 125 cm³, what would be the length of its side? To get the length of the side of the cube, we need to know a number whose cube is 125.

Finding the square root, as you know, is the inverse operation of squaring. Similarly, finding the cube root is the inverse operation of finding cube.

We know that $2^3 = 8$; so we say that the cube root of 8 is 2.

We write $\sqrt[3]{8} = 2$. **The symbol $\sqrt[3]{}$ denotes 'cube-root.'**

Consider the following:

Statement	Inference	Statement	Inference
$1^3 = 1$	$\sqrt[3]{1} = 1$	$6^3 = 216$	$\sqrt[3]{216} = 6$
$2^3 = 8$	$\sqrt[3]{8} = \sqrt[3]{2^3} = 2$	$7^3 = 343$	$\sqrt[3]{343} = 7$
$3^3 = 27$	$\sqrt[3]{27} = \sqrt[3]{3^3} = 3$	$8^3 = 512$	$\sqrt[3]{512} = 8$
$4^3 = 64$	$\sqrt[3]{64} = 4$	$9^3 = 729$	$\sqrt[3]{729} = 9$
$5^3 = 125$	$\sqrt[3]{125} = 5$	$10^3 = 1000$	$\sqrt[3]{1000} = 10$

7.3.1 Cube root through prime factorisation method

Consider 3375. We find its cube root by prime factorisation:

$$3375 = \underline{3 \times 3 \times 3} \times \underline{5 \times 5 \times 5} = 3^3 \times 5^3 = (3 \times 5)^3$$

Therefore, cube root of 3375 = $\sqrt[3]{3375} = 3 \times 5 = 15$

Similarly, to find $\sqrt[3]{74088}$, we have,

$$74088 = \underline{2 \times 2 \times 2} \times \underline{3 \times 3 \times 3} \times \underline{7 \times 7 \times 7} = 2^3 \times 3^3 \times 7^3 = (2 \times 3 \times 7)^3$$

Therefore, $\sqrt[3]{74088} = 2 \times 3 \times 7 = 42$

Example 6: Find the cube root of 8000.

Solution: Prime factorisation of 8000 is $\underline{2 \times 2 \times 2} \times \underline{2 \times 2 \times 2} \times \underline{5 \times 5 \times 5}$

So, $\sqrt[3]{8000} = 2 \times 2 \times 5 = 20$

Example 7: Find the cube root of 13824 by prime factorisation method.

Solution:

$$13824 = \underline{2 \times 2 \times 2} \times \underline{2 \times 2 \times 2} \times \underline{2 \times 2 \times 2} \times \underline{3 \times 3 \times 3} = 2^3 \times 2^3 \times 2^3 \times 3^3.$$

Therefore, $\sqrt[3]{13824} = 2 \times 2 \times 2 \times 3 = 24$

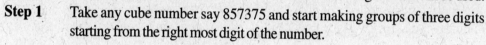

◣ **THINK, DISCUSS AND WRITE** ◢

State true or false: for any integer m, $m^2 < m^3$. Why?

7.3.2 Cube root of a cube number

If you know that the given number is a cube number then following method can be used.

Step 1   Take any cube number say 857375 and start making groups of three digits starting from the right most digit of the number.

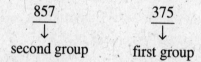

$$\underset{\underset{\text{second group}}{\downarrow}}{857} \qquad \underset{\underset{\text{first group}}{\downarrow}}{375}$$

We can estimate the cube root of a given cube number through a step by step process.

We get 375 and 857 as two groups of three digits each.

Step 2   First group, i.e., 375 will give you the one's (or unit's) digit of the required cube root.

The number 375 ends with 5. We know that 5 comes at the unit's place of a number only when it's cube root ends in 5.

So, we get 5 at the unit's place of the cube root.

Step 3   Now take another group, i.e., 857.

We know that $9^3 = 729$ and $10^3 = 1000$. Also, $729 < 857 < 1000$. We take the one's place, of the smaller number 729 as the ten's place of the required cube root. So, we get $\sqrt[3]{857375} = 95$.

Example 8: Find the cube root of 17576 through estimation.

Solution: The given number is 17576.

Step 1   Form groups of three starting from the rightmost digit of 17576.

17 576. In this case one group i.e., 576 has three digits whereas 17 has only two digits.

Step 2   Take 576.

The digit 6 is at its one's place.

We take the one's place of the required cube root as 6.

Step 3   Take the other group, i.e., 17.
Cube of 2 is 8 and cube of 3 is 27. 17 lies between 8 and 27.
The smaller number among 2 and 3 is 2.

The one's place of 2 is 2 itself. Take 2 as ten's place of the cube root of 17576.

Thus, $\sqrt[3]{17576} = 26$ (Check it!)

EXERCISE 7.2

1. Find the cube root of each of the following numbers by prime factorisation method.

    (i) 64   (ii) 512   (iii) 10648   (iv) 27000

    (v) 15625   (vi) 13824   (vii) 110592   (viii) 46656

    (ix) 175616   (x) 91125

2. State true or false.

    (i) Cube of any odd number is even.

    (ii) A perfect cube does not end with two zeros.

    (iii) If square of a number ends with 5, then its cube ends with 25.

    (iv) There is no perfect cube which ends with 8.

    (v) The cube of a two digit number may be a three digit number.

    (vi) The cube of a two digit number may have seven or more digits.

    (vii) The cube of a single digit number may be a single digit number.

3. You are told that 1,331 is a perfect cube. Can you guess without factorisation what is its cube root? Similarly, guess the cube roots of 4913, 12167, 32768.

WHAT HAVE WE DISCUSSED?

1. Numbers like 1729, 4104, 13832, are known as Hardy – Ramanujan Numbers. They can be expressed as sum of two cubes in two different ways.

2. Numbers obtained when a number is multiplied by itself three times are known as **cube numbers**. For example 1, 8, 27, ... etc.

3. If in the prime factorisation of any number each factor appears three times, then the number is a perfect cube.

4. The symbol $\sqrt[3]{}$ denotes cube root. For example $\sqrt[3]{27} = 3$.

Comparing Quantities

8

0852CH08

8.1 Recalling Ratios and Percentages

We know, ratio means comparing two quantities.

A basket has two types of fruits, say, 20 apples and 5 oranges.

Then, the ratio of the number of oranges to the number of apples = 5 : 20.

The comparison can be done by using fractions as, $\dfrac{5}{20} = \dfrac{1}{4}$

The number of oranges is $\dfrac{1}{4}$ th the number of apples. In terms of ratio, this is

1 : 4, read as, "1 is to 4"

OR

Number of apples to number of oranges = $\dfrac{20}{5} = \dfrac{4}{1}$ which means, the number of apples

is 4 times the number of oranges. This comparison can also be done using percentages.

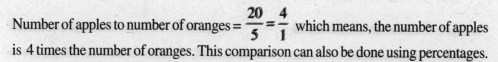

<table>
<tr>
<td>
There are 5 oranges out of 25 fruits.
So percentage of oranges is

$\dfrac{5}{25} \times \dfrac{4}{4} = \dfrac{20}{100} = 20\%$

[Denominator made 100].
</td>
<td>OR</td>
<td>
By unitary method:
Out of 25 fruits, number of oranges are 5.
So out of 100 fruits, number of oranges

$= \dfrac{5}{25} \times 100 = 20.$
</td>
</tr>
</table>

Since contains only apples and oranges,

So,　　percentage of apples + percentage of oranges = 100

or　　percentage of apples + 20 = 100

or　　percentage of apples = 100 − 20 = 80

Thus the basket has 20% oranges and 80% apples.

Example 1: A picnic is being planned in a school for Class VII. Girls are 60% of the total number of students and are 18 in number.

The picnic site is 55 km from the school and the transport company is charging at the rate of ₹ 12 per km. The total cost of refreshments will be ₹ 4280.

Can you tell.

1. The ratio of the number of girls to the number of boys in the class?
2. The cost per head if two teachers are also going with the class?
3. If their first stop is at a place 22 km from the school, what per cent of the total distance of 55 km is this? What per cent of the distance is left to be covered?

Solution:

1. To find the ratio of girls to boys.

   Ashima and John came up with the following answers.

   They needed to know the number of boys and also the total number of students.

Ashima did this		John used the unitary method
Let the total number of students be x. 60% of x is girls.		There are 60 girls out of 100 students.
Therefore, 60% of x = 18		There is one girl out of $\dfrac{100}{60}$ students.
$\dfrac{60}{100} \times x = 18$	OR	So, 18 girls are out of how many students?
or, $x = \dfrac{18 \times 100}{60} = 30$		Number of students = $\dfrac{100}{60} \times 18$
Number of students = 30.		= 30

   So, the number of boys = 30 – 18 = 12.

   Hence, ratio of the number of girls to the number of boys is 18 : 12 or $\dfrac{18}{12} = \dfrac{3}{2}$.

   $\dfrac{3}{2}$ is written as 3 : 2 and read as 3 is to 2.

2. To find the cost per person.

   Transportation charge = Distance both ways × Rate

   $\qquad = ₹ (55 \times 2) \times 12$

   $\qquad = ₹ 110 \times 12 = ₹ 1320$

   Total expenses = Refreshment charge

   $\qquad\qquad\quad + \text{Transportation charge}$

   $\qquad = ₹ 4280 + ₹ 1320$

   $\qquad = ₹ 5600$

   Total number of persons = 18 girls + 12 boys + 2 teachers

   $\qquad = 32 \text{ persons}$

   Ashima and John then used unitary method to find the cost per head.

   For 32 persons, amount spent would be ₹ 5600.

   The amount spent for 1 person = ₹ $\dfrac{5600}{32}$ = ₹ 175.

3. The distance of the place where first stop was made = 22 km.

To find the percentage of distance:

<table>
<tr><td>

Ashima used this method:

$$\frac{22}{55} = \frac{22}{55} \times \frac{100}{100} = 40\%$$

She is multiplying

the ratio by $\frac{100}{100} = 1$

and converting to

percentage.

</td><td>

OR

</td><td>

John used the unitary method:

Out of 55 km, 22 km are travelled.

Out of 1 km, $\frac{22}{55}$ km are travelled.

Out of 100 km, $\frac{22}{55} \times 100$ km are travelled.

That is 40% of the total distance is travelled.

</td></tr>
</table>

Both came out with the same answer that the distance from their school of the place where they stopped at was 40% of the total distance they had to travel.

Therefore, the percent distance left to be travelled = 100% – 40% = 60%.

TRY THESE

In a primary school, the parents were asked about the number of hours they spend per day in helping their children to do homework. There were 90 parents who helped for $\frac{1}{2}$ hour to $1\frac{1}{2}$ hours. The distribution of parents according to the time for which, they said they helped is given in the adjoining figure ; 20% helped for more than $1\frac{1}{2}$ hours per day;

30% helped for $\frac{1}{2}$ hour to $1\frac{1}{2}$ hours; 50% did not help at all.

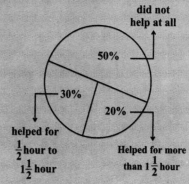

Using this, answer the following:
(i)   How many parents were surveyed?
(ii) How many said that they did not help?
(iii) How many said that they helped for more than $1\frac{1}{2}$ hours?

EXERCISE 8.1

1. Find the ratio of the following.
    (a) Speed of a cycle 15 km per hour to the speed of scooter 30 km per hour.
    (b) 5 m to 10 km   (c) 50 paise to ₹ 5
2. Convert the following ratios to percentages.
    (a) 3 : 4   (b) 2 : 3
3. 72% of 25 students are interested in mathematics. How many are not interested in mathematics?
4. A football team won 10 matches out of the total number of matches they played. If their win percentage was 40, then how many matches did they play in all?
5. If Chameli had ₹ 600 left after spending 75% of her money, how much did she have in the beginning?

6. If 60% people in a city like cricket, 30% like football and the remaining like other games, then what per cent of the people like other games? If the total number of people is 50 lakh, find the exact number who like each type of game.

8.2 Finding the Increase or Decrease Per cent

We often come across such information in our daily life as.

  (i) 25% off on marked prices   (ii) 10% hike in the price of petrol

Let us consider a few such examples.

Example 2: The price of a scooter was ₹ 34,000 last year. It has increased by 20% this year. What is the price now?

Solution:

Amita said that she would first find the increase in the price, which is 20% of ₹ 34,000, and then find the new price.

$$20\% \text{ of } ₹\ 34000 = ₹\ \frac{20}{100} \times 34000$$
$$= ₹\ 6800$$

New price = Old price + Increase
$$= ₹\ 34,000 + ₹\ 6,800$$
$$= ₹\ 40,800$$

OR

Sunita used the unitary method. 20% increase means, ₹ 100 increased to ₹ 120. So, ₹ 34,000 will increase to?

$$\text{Increased price} = ₹\frac{120}{100} \times 34000$$
$$= ₹\ 40,800$$

Similarly, a percentage decrease in price would imply finding the actual decrease followed by its subtraction the from original price.

Suppose in order to increase its sale, the price of scooter was decreased by 5%. Then let us find the price of scooter.

$$\text{Price of scooter} = ₹\ 34000$$
$$\text{Reduction} = 5\% \text{ of } ₹\ 34000$$
$$= ₹\ \frac{5}{100} \times 34000 = ₹\ 1700$$
$$\text{New price} = \text{Old price} - \text{Reduction}$$
$$= ₹\ 34000 - ₹\ 1700 = ₹\ 32300$$

We will also use this in the next section of the chapter.

8.3 Finding Discounts

Discount is a reduction given on the Marked Price (MP) of the article.

    This is generally given to attract customers to buy goods or to promote sales of the goods. You can find the discount by subtracting its sale price from its marked price.

So, Discount = Marked price – Sale price

Example 3: An item marked at ₹ 840 is sold for ₹ 714. What is the discount and discount %?

Solution:
$$\text{Discount} = \text{Marked Price} - \text{Sale Price}$$
$$= ₹\ 840 - ₹\ 714$$
$$= ₹\ 126$$

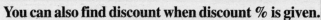

Since discount is on marked price, we will have to use marked price as the base.

On marked price of ₹ 840, the discount is ₹ 126.
On MP of ₹ 100, how much will the discount be?

$$\text{Discount} = \frac{126}{840} \times 100\% = 15\%$$

You can also find discount when discount % is given.

Example 4: The list price of a frock is ₹ 220.
A discount of 20% is announced on sales. What is the amount
of discount on it and its sale price.

Solution: Marked price is same as the list price.
20% discount means that on ₹ 100 (MP), the discount is ₹ 20.

By unitary method, on ₹1 the discount will be ₹ $\frac{20}{100}$.

20% off

Rs 220

On ₹ 220, discount = ₹ $\frac{20}{100} \times 220 = ₹ 44$

The sale price = (₹ 220 – ₹ 44) or ₹ 176

Rehana found the sale price like this —
A discount of 20% means for a MP of ₹ 100, discount is ₹ 20. Hence the sale price is
₹ 80. Using unitary method, when MP is ₹ 100, sale price is ₹ 80;

When MP is ₹ 1, sale price is ₹ $\frac{80}{100}$.

Hence when MP is ₹ 220, sale price = ₹ $\frac{80}{100} \times 220 = ₹ 176$.

Even though the discount was not found, I could find the sale price directly.

TRY THESE

1. A shop gives 20% discount. What would the sale price of each of these be?
   (a) A dress marked at ₹ 120   (b) A pair of shoes marked at ₹ 750
   (c) A bag marked at ₹ 250
2. A table marked at ₹ 15,000 is available for ₹ 14,400. Find the discount given and the discount per cent.
3. An almirah is sold at ₹ 5,225 after allowing a discount of 5%. Find its marked price.

8.3.1 Estimation in percentages

Your bill in a shop is ₹ 577.80 and the shopkeeper gives a discount of 15%. How would you estimate the amount to be paid?

(i) Round off the bill to the nearest tens of ₹ 577.80, i.e., to ₹ 580.

(ii) Find 10% of this, i.e., ₹ $\frac{10}{100} \times 580 = ₹ 58$.

(iii) Take half of this, i.e., $\frac{1}{2} \times 58 = ₹ 29$.

(iv) Add the amounts in (ii) and (iii) to get ₹ 87.

You could therefore reduce your bill amount by ₹ 87 or by about ₹ 85, which will be ₹ 495 approximately.

1. Try estimating 20% of the same bill amount.   2. Try finding 15% of ₹ 375.

8.4 Prices Related to Buying and Selling (Profit and Loss)

For the school fair (mela) I am going to put a stall of lucky dips. I will charge ₹ 10 for one lucky dip but I will buy items which are worth ₹ 5.

So you are making a profit of 100%.

No, I will spend ₹ 3 on paper to wrap the gift and tape. So my expenditure is ₹ 8.

This gives me a profit of ₹ 2, which is, $\frac{2}{8} \times 100\% = 25\%$ only.

Sometimes when an article is bought, some additional expenses are made while buying or before selling it. These expenses have to be included in the cost price.

These expenses are sometimes referred to as **overhead charges**. These may include expenses like amount spent on repairs, labour charges, transportation etc.

8.4.1 Finding cost price/selling price, profit %/loss%

Example 5: Sohan bought a second hand refrigerator for ₹ 2,500, then spent ₹ 500 on its repairs and sold it for ₹ 3,300. Find his loss or gain per cent.

Solution: Cost Price (CP) = ₹ 2500 + ₹ 500 (overhead expenses are added to give CP)

= ₹ 3000

Sale Price (SP) = ₹ 3300

As SP > CP, he made a profit = ₹ 3300 – ₹ 3000 = ₹ 300

His profit on ₹ 3,000, is ₹ 300. How much would be his profit on ₹ 100?

Profit $= \frac{300}{3000} \times 100\% = \frac{30}{3}\% = 10\%$ $\boxed{P\% = \frac{P}{CP} \times 100}$

TRY THESE

1. Find selling price (SP) if a profit of 5% is made on
   (a) a cycle of ₹ 700 with ₹ 50 as overhead charges.
   (b) a lawn mower bought at ₹ 1150 with ₹ 50 as transportation charges.
   (c) a fan bought for ₹ 560 and expenses of ₹ 40 made on its repairs.

Example 6: A shopkeeper purchased 200 bulbs for ₹ 10 each. However 5 bulbs were fused and had to be thrown away. The remaining were sold at ₹ 12 each. Find the gain or loss %.

Solution: Cost price of 200 bulbs = ₹ 200 × 10 = ₹ 2000

5 bulbs were fused. Hence, number of bulbs left = 200 – 5 = 195

These were sold at ₹ 12 each.

The SP of 195 bulbs = ₹ 195 × 12 = ₹ 2340

He obviously made a profit (as SP > CP).

Profit = ₹ 2340 – ₹ 2000 = ₹ 340

CP is ₹ 10

On ₹ 2000, the profit is ₹ 340. How much profit is made on ₹ 100? Profit

$$= \frac{340}{2000} \times 100\% = 17\%.$$

SP is ₹ 12

Example 7: Meenu bought two fans for ₹ 1200 each. She sold one at a loss of 5% and the other at a profit of 10%. Find the selling price of each. Also find out the total profit or loss.

Solution: Overall CP of each fan = ₹ 1200. One is sold at a loss of 5%.

This means if CP is ₹ 100, SP is ₹ 95.

Therefore, when CP is ₹ 1200, then SP = ₹ $\frac{95}{100} \times 1200$ = ₹ 1140

Also second fan is sold at a profit of 10%.

It means, if CP is ₹ 100, SP is ₹ 110.

Therefore, when CP is ₹ 1200, then SP = ₹ $\frac{110}{100} \times 1200$ = ₹ 1320

Was there an overall loss or gain?

We need to find the combined CP and SP to say whether there was an overall profit or loss.

Total CP = ₹ 1200 + ₹ 1200 = ₹ 2400

Total SP = ₹ 1140 + ₹ 1320 = ₹ 2460

Since total SP > total CP, a profit of ₹ (2460 – 2400) or ₹ 60 has been made.

TRY THESE

1. A shopkeeper bought two TV sets at ₹ 10,000 each. He sold one at a profit 10% and the other at a loss of 10%. Find whether he made an overall profit or loss.

8.5 Sales Tax/Value Added Tax/Goods and Services Tax

The teacher showed the class a bill in which the following heads were written.

Bill No.			Date	
Menu				
S.No.	Item	Quantity	Rate	Amount
		Bill amount + ST (5%)		
	Total			

Sales tax (ST) is charged by the government on the sale of an item. It is collected by the shopkeeper from the customer and given to the government. This is, therefore, always on the selling price of an item and is added to the value of the bill. There is another type of tax which is included in the prices known as **Value Added Tax (VAT)**.

From July 1, 2017, Government of India introduced GST which stands for Goods and Services Tax which is levied on supply of goods or services or both.

Example 8: (**Finding Sales Tax**) The cost of a pair of roller skates at a shop was ₹ 450. The sales tax charged was 5%. Find the bill amount.

Solution: On ₹ 100, the tax paid was ₹ 5.

$$\text{On ₹ 450, the tax paid would be} = ₹ \ \frac{5}{100} \times 450$$

$$= ₹ \ 22.50$$

Bill amount = Cost of item + Sales tax = ₹ 450 + ₹ 22.50 = ₹ 472.50.

Example 9: (**Value Added Tax (VAT)**) Waheeda bought an air cooler for ₹ 3300 including a tax of 10%. Find the price of the air cooler before VAT was added.

Solution: The price includes the VAT, i.e., the value added tax. Thus, a 10% VAT means if the price without VAT is ₹ 100 then price including VAT is ₹ 110.

Now, when price including VAT is ₹ 110, original price is ₹ 100.

Hence when price including tax is ₹ 3300, the original price = $₹ \frac{100}{110} \times 3300 = ₹ \ 3000$.

Example 10: Salim bought an article for ₹ 784 which included GST of 12%. What is the price of the article before GST was added?

Solution: Let original price of the article be ₹ 100. GST = 12%.

Price after GST is included = ₹ (100+12) = ₹ 112

When the selling price is ₹ 112 then original price = ₹ 100.

When the selling price is ₹ 784, then original price = $₹ \frac{100}{12} \times 784 = ₹ \ 700$

THINK, DISCUSS AND WRITE

1. Two times a number is a 100% increase in the number. If we take half the number what would be the decrease in per cent?
2. By what per cent is ₹ 2,000 less than ₹ 2,400? Is it the same as the per cent by which ₹ 2,400 is more than ₹ 2,000?

EXERCISE 8.2

1. A man got a 10% increase in his salary. If his new salary is ₹ 1,54,000, find his original salary.

2. On Sunday 845 people went to the Zoo. On Monday only 169 people went. What is the per cent decrease in the people visiting the Zoo on Monday?

3. A shopkeeper buys 80 articles for ₹ 2,400 and sells them for a profit of 16%. Find the selling price of one article.

4. The cost of an article was ₹ 15,500. ₹ 450 were spent on its repairs. If it is sold for a profit of 15%, find the selling price of the article.

5. A VCR and TV were bought for ₹ 8,000 each. The shopkeeper made a loss of 4% on the VCR and a profit of 8% on the TV. Find the gain or loss percent on the whole transaction.

6. During a sale, a shop offered a discount of 10% on the marked prices of all the items. What would a customer have to pay for a pair of jeans marked at ₹ 1450 and two shirts marked at ₹ 850 each?

7. A milkman sold two of his buffaloes for ₹ 20,000 each. On one he made a gain of 5% and on the other a loss of 10%. Find his overall gain or loss. (**Hint:** Find CP of each)

8. The price of a TV is ₹ 13,000. The sales tax charged on it is at the rate of 12%. Find the amount that Vinod will have to pay if he buys it.

9. Arun bought a pair of skates at a sale where the discount given was 20%. If the amount he pays is ₹ 1,600, find the marked price.

10. I purchased a hair-dryer for ₹ 5,400 including 8% VAT. Find the price before VAT was added.

11. An article was purchased for ₹ 1239 including GST of 18%. Find the price of the article before GST was added?

8.6 Compound Interest

You might have come across statements like "one year interest for FD (fixed deposit) in the bank @ 9% per annum" or 'Savings account with interest @ 5% per annum'.

Interest is the extra money paid by institutions like banks or post offices on money deposited (kept) with them. Interest is also paid by people when they borrow money. We already know how to calculate **Simple Interest**.

Example 10: A sum of ₹ 10,000 is borrowed at a rate of interest 15% per annum for 2 years. Find the simple interest on this sum and the amount to be paid at the end of 2 years.

Solution: On ₹ 100, interest charged for 1 year is ₹ 15.

So, on ₹ 10,000, interest charged $= \dfrac{15}{100} \times 10000 = ₹\ 1500$

Interest for 2 years = ₹ 1500 × 2 = ₹ 3000

Amount to be paid at the end of 2 years = Principal + Interest

$= ₹\ 10000 + ₹\ 3000 = ₹\ 13000$

TRY THESE

Find interest and amount to be paid on ₹ 15000 at 5% per annum after 2 years.

My father has kept some money in the post office for 3 years. Every year the money increases as more than the previous year.

We have some money in the bank. Every year some interest is added to it, which is shown in the passbook. This interest is not the same, each year it increases.

Normally, the interest paid or charged is never simple. The interest is calculated on the amount of the previous year. This is known as interest compounded or **Compound Interest** (C.I.).

Let us take an example and find the interest year by year. Each year our sum or principal changes.

Calculating Compound Interest

A sum of ₹ 20,000 is borrowed by Heena for 2 years at an interest of 8% compounded annually. Find the Compound Interest (C.I.) and the amount she has to pay at the end of 2 years.

Aslam asked the teacher whether this means that they should find the interest year by year. The teacher said 'yes', and asked him to use the following steps :

1. Find the Simple Interest (S.I.) for one year.

    Let the principal for the first year be P_1. Here, P_1 = ₹ 20,000

    $$SI_1 = \text{SI at 8\% p.a. for 1st year} = ₹\ \frac{20000 \times 8}{100} = ₹\ 1600$$

2. Then find the amount which will be paid or received. This becomes principal for the next year.

    Amount at the end of 1st year = $P_1 + SI_1$ = ₹ 20000 + ₹ 1600

    $= ₹\ 21600 = P_2$ (Principal for 2nd year)

3. Again find the interest on this sum for another year.

$$SI_2 = \text{SI at 8\% p.a. for 2nd year} = ₹ \frac{21600 \times 8}{100}$$

$$= ₹ \, 1728$$

4. Find the amount which has to be paid or received at the end of second year.

$$\text{Amount at the end of 2nd year} = P_2 + SI_2$$

$$= ₹ \, 21600 + ₹ \, 1728$$

$$= ₹ \, 23328$$

$$\text{Total interest given} = ₹ \, 1600 + ₹ \, 1728$$

$$= ₹ \, 3328$$

Reeta asked whether the amount would be different for simple interest. The teacher told her to find the interest for two years and see for herself.

$$\text{SI for 2 years} = ₹ \, \frac{20000 \times 8 \times 2}{100} = ₹ \, 3200$$

Reeta said that when compound interest was used Heena would pay ₹ 128 more.

Let us look at the difference between simple interest and compound interest. We start with ₹ 100. Try completing the chart.

		Under Simple Interest	Under Compound Interest
First year	Principal	₹ 100.00	₹ 100.00
	Interest at 10%	₹ 10.00	₹ 10.00
	Year-end amount	₹ 110.00	₹ 110.00
Second year	Principal	₹ 100.00	₹ 110.00
	Interest at 10%	₹ 10.00	₹ 11.00
	Year-end amount	₹(110 + 10) = ₹ 120	₹ 121.00
Third year	Principal	₹ 100.00	₹ 121.00
	Interest at 10%	₹ 10.00	₹ 12.10
	Year-end amount	₹(120 + 10) = ₹ 130	₹ 133.10

Which means you pay interest on the interest accumulated till then!

Note that in 3 years,

Interest earned by Simple Interest = ₹ (130 − 100) = ₹ 30, whereas,

Interest earned by Compound Interest = ₹ (133.10 − 100) = ₹ 33.10

Note also that the Principal remains the same under Simple Interest, while it changes year after year under compound interest.

8.7 Deducing a Formula for Compound Interest

Zubeda asked her teacher, 'Is there an easier way to find compound interest?' The teacher said 'There is a shorter way of finding compound interest. Let us try to find it.'

Suppose P_1 is the sum on which interest is compounded annually at a rate of R% per annum.

Let $P_1 = ₹ 5000$ and R = 5. Then by the steps mentioned above

1. $SI_1 = ₹ \dfrac{5000 \times 5 \times 1}{100}$ or $SI_1 = ₹ \dfrac{P_1 \times R \times 1}{100}$

so, $A_1 = ₹ 5000 + \dfrac{5000 \times 5 \times 1}{100}$ or $A_1 = P_1 + SI_1 = P_1 + \dfrac{P_1 R}{100}$

$= ₹ 5000 \left(1 + \dfrac{5}{100}\right) = P_2$ $= P_1 \left(1 + \dfrac{R}{100}\right) = P_2$

2. $SI_2 = ₹ 5000 \left(1 + \dfrac{5}{100}\right) \times \dfrac{5 \times 1}{100}$ or $SI_2 = \dfrac{P_2 \times R \times 1}{100}$

$= ₹ \dfrac{5000 \times 5}{100} \left(1 + \dfrac{5}{100}\right)$ $= P_1 \left(1 + \dfrac{R}{100}\right) \times \dfrac{R}{100}$

$= \dfrac{P_1 R}{100} \left(1 + \dfrac{R}{100}\right)$

$A_2 = ₹ 5000 \left(1 + \dfrac{5}{100}\right) + ₹ \dfrac{5000 \times 5}{100} \left(1 + \dfrac{5}{100}\right)$ $A_2 = P_2 + SI_2$

$= ₹ 5000 \left(1 + \dfrac{5}{100}\right) \left(1 + \dfrac{5}{100}\right)$ $= P_1 \left(1 + \dfrac{R}{100}\right) + P_1 \dfrac{R}{100} \left(1 + \dfrac{R}{100}\right)$

$= ₹ 5000 \left(1 + \dfrac{5}{100}\right)^2 = P_3$ $= P_1 \left(1 + \dfrac{R}{100}\right) \left(1 + \dfrac{R}{100}\right)$

$= P_1 \left(1 + \dfrac{R}{100}\right)^2 = P_3$

Proceeding in this way the amount at the end of n years will be

$$A_n = P_1 \left(1 + \dfrac{R}{100}\right)^n$$

Or, we can say $A = P \left(1 + \dfrac{R}{100}\right)^n$

So, Zubeda said, but using this we get only the formula for the amount to be paid at the end of *n* years, and not the formula for compound interest.

Aruna at once said that we know CI = A – P, so we can easily find the compound interest too.

Example 11: Find CI on ₹ 12600 for 2 years at 10% per annum compounded annually.

Solution: We have, $A = P\left(1 + \dfrac{R}{100}\right)^n$, where Principal (P) = ₹ 12600, Rate (R) = 10,

Number of years (*n*) = 2

$$= ₹\ 12600\left(1 + \frac{10}{100}\right)^2 = ₹\ 12600\left(\frac{11}{10}\right)^2$$

$$= ₹\ 12600 \times \frac{11}{10} \times \frac{11}{10} = ₹\ 15246$$

CI = A – P = ₹ 15246 – ₹ 12600 = ₹ 2646

> **TRY THESE**
>
> 1. Find CI on a sum of ₹ 8000 for 2 years at 5% per annum compounded annually.

8.8 Rate Compounded Annually or Half Yearly (Semi Annually)

You may want to know why 'compounded annually' was mentioned after 'rate'. Does it mean anything?

It does, because we can also have interest rates compounded half yearly or quarterly. Let us see what happens to ₹ 100 over a period of one year if an interest is compounded annually or half yearly.

> **Time period and rate when interest not compounded annually**
>
> The time period after which the interest is added each time to form a new principal is called the **conversion period**. When the interest is compounded half yearly, there are two conversion periods in a year each after 6 months. In such situations, the half yearly rate will be half of the annual rate. What will happen if interest is compounded quarterly? In this case, there are 4 conversion periods in a year and the quarterly rate will be one-fourth of the annual rate.

P = ₹ 100 at 10% per annum compounded annually	P = ₹ 100 at 10% per annum compounded half yearly
The time period taken is 1 year	The time period is 6 months or $\dfrac{1}{2}$ year
$I = ₹\ \dfrac{100 \times 10 \times 1}{100} = \text{Rs } 10$	$I = ₹\ \dfrac{100 \times \boxed{10 \times \dfrac{1}{2}}}{100} = ₹\ 5$
A = ₹ 100 + ₹ 10 = ₹ 110	A = ₹ 100 + ₹ 5 = ₹ 105 Now for next 6 months the P = ₹ 105
	So, $I = ₹\ \dfrac{105 \times 10 \times \dfrac{1}{2}}{100} = ₹\ 5.25$ and A = ₹ 105 + ₹ 5.25 = ₹ 110.25

Rate becomes half

Do you see that, if interest is compounded half yearly, we compute the interest two times. So time period becomes twice and rate is taken half.

TRY THESE

Find the time period and rate for each .

1. A sum taken for $1\frac{1}{2}$ years at 8% per annum is compounded half yearly.
2. A sum taken for 2 years at 4% per annum compounded half yearly.

THINK, DISCUSS AND WRITE

A sum is taken for one year at 16% p.a. If interest is compounded after every three months, how many times will interest be charged in one year?

Example 12: What amount is to be repaid on a loan of ₹ 12000 for $1\frac{1}{2}$ years at 10% per annum compounded half yearly.

Solution:

Principal for first 6 months = ₹ 12,000	**Principal for first 6 months = ₹ 12,000**
There are 3 half years in $1\frac{1}{2}$ years. Therefore, compounding has to be done 3 times. Rate of interest = half of 10% $\quad$ = 5% half yearly $A = P\left(1+\dfrac{R}{100}\right)^n$ $= ₹\ 12000\left(1+\dfrac{5}{100}\right)^3$ $= ₹\ 12000\times\dfrac{21}{20}\times\dfrac{21}{20}\times\dfrac{21}{20}$ $= ₹\ 13{,}891.50$	Time = 6 months = $\dfrac{6}{12}$ year = $\dfrac{1}{2}$ year Rate = 10% $I = ₹\ \dfrac{12000\times10\times\frac{1}{2}}{100} = ₹\ 600$ $A = P + I = ₹\ 12000 + ₹\ 600$ $\quad = ₹12600$. It is principal for next 6 months. $I = ₹\ \dfrac{12600\times10\times\frac{1}{2}}{100} = ₹\ 630$ Principal for third period = ₹ 12600 + ₹ 630 $\quad\quad = ₹\ 13{,}230.$ $I = ₹\ \dfrac{13230\times10\times\frac{1}{2}}{100} = ₹\ 661.50$ $A = P + I = ₹\ 13230 + ₹\ 661.50$ $\quad = ₹\ 13{,}891.50$

TRY THESE

Find the amount to be paid

1. At the end of 2 years on ₹ 2,400 at 5% per annum compounded annually.
2. At the end of 1 year on ₹ 1,800 at 8% per annum compounded quarterly.

Example 13: Find CI paid when a sum of ₹ 10,000 is invested for 1 year and

3 months at $8\frac{1}{2}$ % per annum compounded annually.

Solution: Mayuri first converted the time in years.

$$1 \text{ year } 3 \text{ months} = 1\frac{3}{12} \text{ year} = 1\frac{1}{4} \text{ years}$$

Mayuri tried putting the values in the known formula and came up with:

$$A = ₹ \, 10000 \left(1 + \frac{17}{200}\right)^{1\frac{1}{4}}$$

Now she was stuck. She asked her teacher how would she find a power which is fractional? The teacher then gave her a hint:

Find the amount for the whole part, i.e., 1 year in this case. Then use this as principal

to get simple interest for $\frac{1}{4}$ year more. Thus,

$$A = ₹ \, 10000 \left(1 + \frac{17}{200}\right)$$

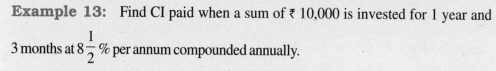

$$= ₹ \, 10000 \times \frac{217}{200} = ₹ \, 10,850$$

Now this would act as principal for the next $\frac{1}{4}$ year. We find the SI on ₹ 10,850

for $\frac{1}{4}$ year.

$$SI = ₹ \, \frac{10850 \times \dfrac{1}{4} \times 17}{100 \times 2}$$

$$= ₹ \, \frac{10850 \times 1 \times 17}{800} = ₹ \, 230.56$$

Interest for first year = ₹ 10850 – ₹ 10000 = ₹ 850

And, interest for the next $\frac{1}{4}$ year = ₹ 230.56

Therefore, total compound Interest = 850 + 230.56 = ₹ 1080.56.

8.9 Applications of Compound Interest Formula

There are some situations where we could use the formula for calculation of amount in CI. Here are a few.

(i) Increase (or decrease) in population.

(ii) The growth of a bacteria if the rate of growth is known.

(iii) The value of an item, if its price increases or decreases in the intermediate years.

Example 14: The population of a city was 20,000 in the year 1997. It increased at the rate of 5% p.a. Find the population at the end of the year 2000.

Solution: There is 5% increase in population every year, so every new year has new population. Thus, we can say it is increasing in compounded form.

Population in the beginning of 1998 = 20000 (we treat this as the principal for the 1st year)

Increase at 5% = $\frac{5}{100} \times 20000 = 1000$

Population in 1999 = 20000 + 1000 = 21000 ◁ Treat as the Principal for the 2nd year.

Increase at 5% = $\frac{5}{100} \times 21000 = 1050$

Population in 2000 = 21000 + 1050

= 22050 ◁ Treat as the Principal for the 3rd year.

Increase at 5% = $\frac{5}{100} \times 22050$

= 1102.5

At the end of 2000 the population = 22050 + 1102.5 = 23152.5

or, Population at the end of 2000 = $20000 \left(1 + \frac{5}{100}\right)^3$

= $20000 \times \frac{21}{20} \times \frac{21}{20} \times \frac{21}{20}$

= 23152.5

So, the estimated population = 23153.

Aruna asked what is to be done if there is a decrease. The teacher then considered the following example.

Example 15: A TV was bought at a price of ₹ 21,000. After one year the value of the TV was depreciated by 5% (Depreciation means reduction of value due to use and age of the item). Find the value of the TV after one year.

Solution:

Principal = ₹ 21,000

Reduction = 5% of ₹ 21000 per year

$$= ₹ \frac{21000 \times 5 \times 1}{100} = ₹ 1050$$

value at the end of 1 year = ₹ 21000 – ₹ 1050 = ₹ 19,950

Alternately, We may directly get this as follows:

$$\text{value at the end of 1 year} = ₹ 21000 \left(1 - \frac{5}{100}\right)$$

$$= ₹ 21000 \times \frac{19}{20} = ₹ 19,950$$

TRY THESE

1. A machinery worth ₹ 10,500 depreciated by 5%. Find its value after one year.
2. Find the population of a city after 2 years, which is at present 12 lakh, if the rate of increase is 4%.

EXERCISE 8.3

1. Calculate the amount and compound interest on

   (a) ₹ 10,800 for 3 years at $12\frac{1}{2}$ % per annum compounded annually.

   (b) ₹ 18,000 for $2\frac{1}{2}$ years at 10% per annum compounded annually.

   (c) ₹ 62,500 for $1\frac{1}{2}$ years at 8% per annum compounded half yearly.

   (d) ₹ 8,000 for 1 year at 9% per annum compounded half yearly.
   (You could use the year by year calculation using SI formula to verify).

   (e) ₹ 10,000 for 1 year at 8% per annum compounded half yearly.

2. Kamala borrowed ₹ 26,400 from a Bank to buy a scooter at a rate of 15% p.a. compounded yearly. What amount will she pay at the end of 2 years and 4 months to clear the loan?

   (**Hint:** Find A for 2 years with interest is compounded yearly and then find SI on the 2nd year amount for $\frac{4}{12}$ years).

3. Fabina borrows ₹ 12,500 at 12% per annum for 3 years at simple interest and Radha borrows the same amount for the same time period at 10% per annum, compounded annually. Who pays more interest and by how much?

4. I borrowed ₹ 12,000 from Jamshed at 6% per annum simple interest for 2 years. Had I borrowed this sum at 6% per annum compound interest, what extra amount would I have to pay?

5. Vasudevan invested ₹ 60,000 at an interest rate of 12% per annum compounded half yearly. What amount would he get

   (i)   after 6 months?

   (ii) after 1 year?

6. Arif took a loan of ₹ 80,000 from a bank. If the rate of interest is 10% per annum, find the difference in amounts he would be paying after $1\frac{1}{2}$ years if the interest is

   (i)   compounded annually.

   (ii) compounded half yearly.

7. Maria invested ₹ 8,000 in a business. She would be paid interest at 5% per annum compounded annually. Find

   (i)   The amount credited against her name at the end of the second year.

   (ii) The interest for the 3rd year.

8. Find the amount and the compound interest on ₹ 10,000 for $1\frac{1}{2}$ years at 10% per annum, compounded half yearly. Would this interest be more than the interest he would get if it was compounded annually?

9. Find the amount which Ram will get on ₹ 4096, if he gave it for 18 months at $12\frac{1}{2}\%$ per annum, interest being compounded half yearly.

10. The population of a place increased to 54,000 in 2003 at a rate of 5% per annum

    (i)   find the population in 2001.

    (ii) what would be its population in 2005?

11. In a Laboratory, the count of bacteria in a certain experiment was increasing at the rate of 2.5% per hour. Find the bacteria at the end of 2 hours if the count was initially 5, 06,000.

12. A scooter was bought at ₹ 42,000. Its value depreciated at the rate of 8% per annum. Find its value after one year.

WHAT HAVE WE DISCUSSED?

1. **Discount** is a reduction given on marked price.

   Discount = Marked Price – Sale Price.

2. Discount can be calculated when discount percentage is given.

   Discount = Discount % of Marked Price

3. Additional expenses made after buying an article are included in the cost price and are known as **overhead expenses**.

   CP = Buying price + Overhead expenses

4. Sales tax is charged on the sale of an item by the government and is added to the Bill Amount.

   Sales tax = Tax% of Bill Amount

5. GST stands for Goods and Services Tax and is levied on supply of goods or services or both.

6. Compound interest is the interest calculated on the previous year's amount $(A = P + I)$

7. (i) Amount when interest is compounded annually

   $$= P\left(1 + \frac{R}{100}\right)^n; \quad P \text{ is principal, } R \text{ is rate of interest, } n \text{ is time period}$$

   (ii) Amount when interest is compounded half yearly

   $$= P\left(1 + \frac{R}{200}\right)^{2n} \quad \begin{cases} \dfrac{R}{2} \text{ is half yearly rate and} \\ 2n = \text{number of 'half-years'} \end{cases}$$

NOTES

Algebraic Expressions and Identities

0852CH09

9.1 What are Expressions?

In earlier classes, we have already become familiar with what algebraic expressions (or simply expressions) are. Examples of expressions are:

$$x + 3, \ 2y - 5, \ 3x^2, \ 4xy + 7 \text{ etc.}$$

You can form many more expressions. As you know expressions are formed from variables and constants. The expression $2y - 5$ is formed from the variable y and constants 2 and 5. The expression $4xy + 7$ is formed from variables x and y and constants 4 and 7.

We know that, the value of y in the expression, $2y - 5$, may be anything. It can be $2, 5, -3, 0, \dfrac{5}{2}, -\dfrac{7}{3}$ etc.; actually countless different values. The value of an expression changes with the value chosen for the variables it contains. Thus as y takes on different values, the value of $2y - 5$ goes on changing. When $y = 2, 2y - 5 = 2(2) - 5 = -1$; when $y = 0, 2y - 5 = 2 \times 0 - 5 = -5$, etc. Find the value of the expression $2y - 5$ for the other given values of y.

Number line and an expression:

Consider the expression $x + 5$. Let us say the variable x has a position X on the number line;

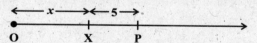

X may be anywhere on the number line, but it is definite that the value of $x + 5$ is given by a point P, 5 units to the right of X. Similarly, the value of $x - 4$ will be 4 units to the left of X and so on.

What about the position of $4x$ and $4x + 5$?

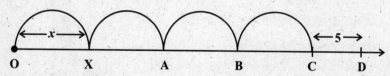

The position of $4x$ will be point C; the distance of C from the origin will be four times the distance of X from the origin. The position D of $4x + 5$ will be 5 units to the right of C.

1. Give five examples of expressions containing one variable and five examples of expressions containing two variables.
2. Show on the number line x, $x - 4$, $2x + 1$, $3x - 2$.

9.2 Terms, Factors and Coefficients

Take the expression $4x + 5$. This expression is made up of two terms, $4x$ and 5. **Terms are added to form expressions**. **Terms** themselves **can be** formed as **the product of factors**. The term $4x$ is the product of its factors 4 and x. The term 5 is made up of just one factor, i.e., 5.

TRY THESE

Identify the coefficient of each term in the expression $x^2y^2 - 10x^2y + 5xy^2 - 20$.

The expression $7xy - 5x$ has two terms $7xy$ and $-5x$. The term $7xy$ is a product of factors 7, x and y. The numerical factor of a term is called its **numerical coefficient or simply coefficient**. The coefficient in the term $7xy$ is 7 and the coefficient in the term $-5x$ is -5.

9.3 Monomials, Binomials and Polynomials

Expression that contains only one term is called a **monomial**. Expression that contains two terms is called a **binomial**. An expression containing three terms is a **trinomial** and so on. In general, an expression containing, one or more terms with non-zero coefficient (with variables having non negative integers as exponents) is called a **polynomial**. A polynomial may contain any number of terms, one or more than one.

Examples of monomials: $4x^2$, $3xy$, $-7z$, $5xy^2$, $10y$, -9, $82mnp$, etc.
Examples of binomials: $a + b$, $4l + 5m$, $a + 4$, $5 - 3xy$, $z^2 - 4y^2$, etc.
Examples of trinomials: $a + b + c$, $2x + 3y - 5$, $x^2y - xy^2 + y^2$, etc.
Examples of polynomials: $a + b + c + d$, $3xy$, $7xyz - 10$, $2x + 3y + 7z$, etc.

TRY THESE

1. Classify the following polynomials as monomials, binomials, trinomials.
   $-z + 5$, $x + y + z$, $y + z + 100$, $ab - ac$, 17
2. Construct
   (a) 3 binomials with only x as a variable;
   (b) 3 binomials with x and y as variables;
   (c) 3 monomials with x and y as variables;
   (d) 2 polynomials with 4 or more terms.

9.4 Like and Unlike Terms

Look at the following expressions:
$7x$, $14x$, $-13x$, $5x^2$, $7y$, $7xy$, $-9y^2$, $-9x^2$, $-5yx$
Like terms from these are:
(i) $7x$, $14x$, $-13x$ are like terms.
(ii) $5x^2$ and $-9x^2$ are like terms.

(iii) $7xy$ and $-5yx$ are like terms.

Why are $7x$ and $7y$ not like?

Why are $7x$ and $7xy$ not like?

Why are $7x$ and $5x^2$ not like?

TRY THESE

Write two terms which are like

(i) $7xy$ (ii) $4mn^2$ (iii) $2l$

9.5 Addition and Subtraction of Algebraic Expressions

In the earlier classes, we have also learnt how to add and subtract algebraic expressions. For example, to add $7x^2 - 4x + 5$ and $9x - 10$, we do

$$
\begin{array}{r}
7x^2 - 4x + 5 \\
+ \quad\quad 9x - 10 \\
\hline
7x^2 + 5x - 5
\end{array}
$$

Observe how we do the addition. We write each expression to be added in a separate row. While doing so we write like terms one below the other, and add them, as shown. Thus $5 + (-10) = 5 - 10 = -5$. Similarly, $-4x + 9x = (-4 + 9)x = 5x$. Let us take some more examples.

Example 1: Add: $7xy + 5yz - 3zx$, $4yz + 9zx - 4y$, $-3xz + 5x - 2xy$.

Solution: Writing the three expressions in separate rows, with like terms one below the other, we have

$$
\begin{array}{l}
\quad\; 7xy + 5yz - 3zx \\[4pt]
+ \quad\quad\quad 4yz + 9zx \quad\quad - 4y \\
+ \;\; -2xy \quad\quad\quad - 3zx + 5x \quad\quad\quad \text{(Note } xz \text{ is same as } zx) \\
\hline
\quad\; 5xy + 9yz + 3zx + 5x - 4y
\end{array}
$$

Thus, the sum of the expressions is $5xy + 9yz + 3zx + 5x - 4y$. Note how the terms, $-4y$ in the second expression and $5x$ in the third expression, are carried over as they are, since they have no like terms in the other expressions.

Example 2: Subtract $5x^2 - 4y^2 + 6y - 3$ from $7x^2 - 4xy + 8y^2 + 5x - 3y$.

Solution:

$$
\begin{array}{r}
7x^2 - 4xy + 8y^2 + 5x - 3y \\[4pt]
5x^2 \quad\quad - 4y^2 \quad\quad + 6y - 3 \\
(-) \quad\quad\quad\quad (+) \quad\quad (-) \ (+) \\
\hline
2x^2 - 4xy + 12y^2 + 5x - 9y + 3
\end{array}
$$

Note that subtraction of a number is the same as addition of its additive inverse. Thus subtracting –3 is the same as adding +3. Similarly, subtracting $6y$ is the same as adding – $6y$; subtracting – $4y^2$ is the same as adding $4y^2$ and so on. The signs in the third row written below each term in the second row help us in knowing which operation has to be performed.

EXERCISE 9.1

1. Identify the terms, their coefficients for each of the following expressions.

    (i) $5xyz^2 - 3zy$ (ii) $1 + x + x^2$ (iii) $4x^2y^2 - 4x^2y^2z^2 + z^2$

    (iv) $3 - pq + qr - rp$ (v) $\dfrac{x}{2} + \dfrac{y}{2} - xy$ (vi) $0.3a - 0.6ab + 0.5b$

2. Classify the following polynomials as monomials, binomials, trinomials. Which polynomials do not fit in any of these three categories?

    $x + y$, 1000, $x + x^2 + x^3 + x^4$, $7 + y + 5x$, $2y - 3y^2$, $2y - 3y^2 + 4y^3$, $5x - 4y + 3xy$, $4z - 15z^2$, $ab + bc + cd + da$, pqr, $p^2q + pq^2$, $2p + 2q$

3. Add the following.

    (i) $ab - bc$, $bc - ca$, $ca - ab$ (ii) $a - b + ab$, $b - c + bc$, $c - a + ac$

    (iii) $2p^2q^2 - 3pq + 4$, $5 + 7pq - 3p^2q^2$ (iv) $l^2 + m^2$, $m^2 + n^2$, $n^2 + l^2$,

    $2lm + 2mn + 2nl$

4. (a) Subtract $4a - 7ab + 3b + 12$ from $12a - 9ab + 5b - 3$

    (b) Subtract $3xy + 5yz - 7zx$ from $5xy - 2yz - 2zx + 10xyz$

    (c) Subtract $4p^2q - 3pq + 5pq^2 - 8p + 7q - 10$ from

    $18 - 3p - 11q + 5pq - 2pq^2 + 5p^2q$

9.6 Multiplication of Algebraic Expressions: Introduction

(i) Look at the following patterns of dots.

Pattern of dots	Total number of dots
	4×9
	5×7

$$n$$

$$m \times n$$

$$m \times n$$

To find the number of dots we have to multiply the expression for the number of rows by the expression for the number of columns.

$$n + 3$$

$$m + 2$$

$$(m + 2) \times (n + 3)$$

Here the number of rows is increased by 2, i.e., $m + 2$ and number of columns increased by 3, i.e., $n + 3$.

(ii) Can you now think of similar other situations in which two algebraic expressions have to be multiplied?

Ameena gets up. She says, "We can think of area of a rectangle." The area of a rectangle is $l \times b$, where l is the length, and b is breadth. If the length of the rectangle is increased by 5 units, i.e., $(l + 5)$ and breadth is decreased by 3 units , i.e., $(b - 3)$ units, the area of the new rectangle will be $(l + 5) \times (b - 3)$.

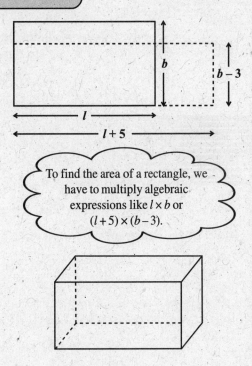

To find the area of a rectangle, we have to multiply algebraic expressions like $l \times b$ or $(l + 5) \times (b - 3)$.

(iii) Can you think about volume? (The volume of a rectangular box is given by the product of its length, breadth and height).

(iv) Sarita points out that when we buy things, we have to carry out multiplication. For example, if

$$\text{price of bananas per dozen} = ₹\, p$$

and for the school picnic bananas needed = z dozens,

$$\text{then we have to pay} = ₹\, p \times z$$

Suppose, the price per dozen was less by ₹ 2 and the bananas needed were less by 4 dozens.

Then,   price of bananas per dozen = ₹ $(p - 2)$

and   bananas needed = $(z - 4)$ dozens,

Therefore, we would have to pay   = ₹ $(p - 2) \times (z - 4)$

TRY THESE

Can you think of two more such situations, where we may need to multiply algebraic expressions?

[**Hint:** • Think of speed and time;
• Think of interest to be paid, the principal and the rate of simple interest; etc.]

In all the above examples, we had to carry out multiplication of two or more quantities. If the quantities are given by algebraic expressions, we need to find their product. This means that we should know how to obtain this product. Let us do this systematically. To begin with we shall look at the multiplication of two monomials.

9.7 Multiplying a Monomial by a Monomial

9.7.1 Multiplying two monomials

We begin with

$$4 \times x = x + x + x + x = 4x \text{ as seen earlier.}$$

Similarly, $4 \times (3x) = 3x + 3x + 3x + 3x = 12x$

Now, observe the following products.

(i) $\quad x \times 3y = x \times 3 \times y = 3 \times x \times y = 3xy$

(ii) $\quad 5x \times 3y = 5 \times x \times 3 \times y = 5 \times 3 \times x \times y = 15xy$

(iii) $\quad 5x \times (-3y) = 5 \times x \times (-3) \times y$
$$= 5 \times (-3) \times x \times y = -15xy$$

> Notice that all the three products of monomials, $3xy$, $15xy$, $-15xy$, are also monomials.

Some more useful examples follow.

(iv) $\quad 5x \times 4x^2 = (5 \times 4) \times (x \times x^2)$
$$= 20 \times x^3 = 20x^3$$

(v) $\quad 5x \times (-4xyz) = (5 \times -4) \times (x \times xyz)$
$$= -20 \times (x \times x \times yz) = -20x^2yz$$

Observe how we collect the powers of different variables in the algebraic parts of the two monomials. While doing so, we use the rules of exponents and powers.

> Note that $\quad 5 \times 4 = 20$
> i.e., coefficient of product = coefficient of first monomial × coefficient of second monomial;
> and $\quad x \times x^2 = x^3$
> i.e., algebraic factor of product = algebraic factor of first monomial × algebraic factor of second monomial.

9.7.2 Multiplying three or more monomials

Observe the following examples.

(i) $\quad 2x \times 5y \times 7z = (2x \times 5y) \times 7z = 10xy \times 7z = 70xyz$

(ii) $\quad 4xy \times 5x^2y^2 \times 6x^3y^3 = (4xy \times 5x^2y^2) \times 6x^3y^3 = 20x^3y^3 \times 6x^3y^3 = 120x^3y^3 \times x^3y^3$
$$= 120\,(x^3 \times x^3) \times (y^3 \times y^3) = 120x^6 \times y^6 = 120x^6y^6$$

It is clear that we first multiply the first two monomials and then multiply the resulting monomial by the third monomial. This method can be extended to the product of any number of monomials.

TRY THESE

Find $4x \times 5y \times 7z$
First find $4x \times 5y$ and multiply it by $7z$;
or first find $5y \times 7z$ and multiply it by $4x$.
Is the result the same? What do you observe?
Does the order in which you carry out the multiplication matter?

We can find the product in other way also.
$4xy \times 5x^2y^2 \times 6x^3\,y^3$
$= (4 \times 5 \times 6) \times (x \times x^2 \times x^3) \times (y \times y^2 \times y^3)$
$= 120\ x^6y^6$

Example 3: Complete the table for area of a rectangle with given length and breadth.

Solution:

length	breadth	area
$3x$	$5y$	$3x \times 5y = 15xy$
$9y$	$4y^2$	....
$4ab$	$5bc$	....
$2l^2m$	$3lm^2$	....

Example 4: Find the volume of each rectangular box with given length, breadth and height.

	length	breadth	height
(i)	$2ax$	$3by$	$5cz$
(ii)	m^2n	n^2p	p^2m
(iii)	$2q$	$4q^2$	$8q^3$

Solution: Volume = length × breadth × height

Hence, for   (i)   volume $= (2ax) \times (3by) \times (5cz)$

$= 2 \times 3 \times 5 \times (ax) \times (by) \times (cz) = 30abcxyz$

for   (ii)   volume $= m^2n \times n^2p \times p^2m$

$= (m^2 \times m) \times (n \times n^2) \times (p \times p^2) = m^3n^3p^3$

for   (iii)   volume $= 2q \times 4q^2 \times 8q^3$

$= 2 \times 4 \times 8 \times q \times q^2 \times q^3 = 64q^6$

EXERCISE 9.2

1. Find the product of the following pairs of monomials.

   (i) $4, 7p$ (ii) $-4p, 7p$ (iii) $-4p, 7pq$ (iv) $4p^3, -3p$
   (v) $4p, 0$

2. Find the areas of rectangles with the following pairs of monomials as their lengths and breadths respectively.

   (p, q); $(10m, 5n)$; $(20x^2, 5y^2)$; $(4x, 3x^2)$; $(3mn, 4np)$

3. Complete the table of products.

First monomial → Second monomial ↓	$2x$	$-5y$	$3x^2$	$-4xy$	$7x^2y$	$-9x^2y^2$
$2x$	$4x^2$	...	...	...	...	...
$-5y$	...	...	$-15x^2y$	...	...	...
$3x^2$	...	...	...	...	...	...
$-4xy$	...	...	...	...	...	...
$7x^2y$	...	...	...	...	...	...
$-9x^2y^2$	...	...	...	...	...	...

4. Obtain the volume of rectangular boxes with the following length, breadth and height respectively.

    (i) $5a, 3a^2, 7a^4$ (ii) $2p, 4q, 8r$ (iii) $xy, 2x^2y, 2xy^2$ (iv) $a, 2b, 3c$

5. Obtain the product of

    (i) xy, yz, zx (ii) $a, -a^2, a^3$ (iii) $2, 4y, 8y^2, 16y^3$

    (iv) $a, 2b, 3c, 6abc$ (v) $m, -mn, mnp$

9.8 Multiplying a Monomial by a Polynomial

9.8.1 Multiplying a monomial by a binomial

Let us multiply the monomial $3x$ by the binomial $5y + 2$, i.e., find $3x \times (5y + 2) = ?$

Recall that $3x$ and $(5y + 2)$ represent numbers. Therefore, using the distributive law,

$3x \times (5y + 2) = (3x \times 5y) + (3x \times 2) = 15xy + 6x$

"Product of monomial and binomial is binomial."

> We commonly use distributive law in our calculations. For example:
>
> $7 \times 106 = 7 \times (100 + 6)$
> $\qquad\qquad = 7 \times 100 + 7 \times 6 \qquad$ (Here, we used distributive law)
> $\qquad\qquad = 700 + 42 = 742$
> $7 \times 38 = 7 \times (40 - 2)$
> $\qquad\qquad = 7 \times 40 - 7 \times 2 \qquad$ (Here, we used distributive law)
> $\qquad\qquad = 280 - 14 = 266$

Similarly, $(-3x) \times (-5y + 2) = (-3x) \times (-5y) + (-3x) \times (2) = 15xy - 6x$

and $5xy \times (y^2 + 3) = (5xy \times y^2) + (5xy \times 3) = 5xy^3 + 15xy.$

What about a binomial × monomial? For example, $(5y + 2) \times 3x = ?$

We may use commutative law as : $7 \times 3 = 3 \times 7$; or in general $a \times b = b \times a$

Similarly, $(5y + 2) \times 3x = 3x \times (5y + 2) = 15xy + 6x$ as before.

TRY THESE

Find the product   (i) $2x (3x + 5xy)$ (ii) $a^2 (2ab - 5c)$

9.8.2 Multiplying a monomial by a trinomial

Consider $3p \times (4p^2 + 5p + 7)$. As in the earlier case, we use distributive law;

$$3p \times (4p^2 + 5p + 7) = (3p \times 4p^2) + (3p \times 5p) + (3p \times 7)$$
$$= 12p^3 + 15p^2 + 21p$$

Multiply each term of the trinomial by the monomial and add products.

> Observe, by using the distributive law, we are able to carry out the multiplication term by term.

TRY THESE

Find the product:

$(4p^2 + 5p + 7) \times 3p$

Example 5: Simplify the expressions and evaluate them as directed:

(i) $x(x - 3) + 2$ for $x = 1$,
(ii) $3y(2y - 7) - 3(y - 4) - 63$ for $y = -2$

Solution:

(i) $x(x - 3) + 2 = x^2 - 3x + 2$

For $x = 1$, $x^2 - 3x + 2 = (1)^2 - 3(1) + 2$
$$= 1 - 3 + 2 = 3 - 3 = 0$$

(ii) $3y(2y - 7) - 3(y - 4) - 63 = 6y^2 - 21y - 3y + 12 - 63$
$$= 6y^2 - 24y - 51$$

For $y = -2$, $6y^2 - 24y - 51 = 6(-2)^2 - 24(-2) - 51$
$$= 6 \times 4 + 24 \times 2 - 51$$
$$= 24 + 48 - 51 = 72 - 51 = 21$$

Example 6: Add

(i) $5m(3 - m)$ and $6m^2 - 13m$
(ii) $4y(3y^2 + 5y - 7)$ and $2(y^3 - 4y^2 + 5)$

Solution:

(i) First expression $= 5m(3 - m) = (5m \times 3) - (5m \times m) = 15m - 5m^2$

Now adding the second expression to it, $15m - 5m^2 + 6m^2 - 13m = m^2 + 2m$

(ii) The first expression $= 4y(3y^2 + 5y - 7) = (4y \times 3y^2) + (4y \times 5y) + (4y \times (-7))$
$$= 12y^3 + 20y^2 - 28y$$

The second expression $= 2(y^3 - 4y^2 + 5) = 2y^3 + 2 \times (-4y^2) + 2 \times 5$
$$= 2y^3 - 8y^2 + 10$$

Adding the two expressions,

	$12y^3$	+	$20y^2 - 28y$	
+	$2y^3$	−	$8y^2$	+ 10
	$14y^3$	+	$12y^2 - 28y$	+ 10

Example 7: Subtract $3pq(p - q)$ from $2pq(p + q)$.

Solution: We have $3pq(p - q) = 3p^2q - 3pq^2$ and
$$2pq(p + q) = 2p^2q + 2pq^2$$

Subtracting,

	$2p^2q$	+	$2pq^2$
	$3p^2q$	−	$3pq^2$
	−		+
	$-p^2q$	+	$5pq^2$

EXERCISE 9.3

1. Carry out the multiplication of the expressions in each of the following pairs.

   (i) $4p, q + r$ (ii) $ab, a - b$ (iii) $a + b, 7a^2b^2$ (iv) $a^2 - 9, 4a$

   (v) $pq + qr + rp, 0$

2. Complete the table.

	First expression	Second expression	Product
(i)	a	$b + c + d$	...
(ii)	$x + y - 5$	$5xy$	...
(iii)	p	$6p^2 - 7p + 5$	...
(iv)	$4p^2q^2$	$p^2 - q^2$	...
(v)	$a + b + c$	abc	...

3. Find the product.

   (i) $(a^2) \times (2a^{22}) \times (4a^{26})$ (ii) $\left(\dfrac{2}{3} xy\right) \times \left(\dfrac{-9}{10} x^2 y^2\right)$

   (iii) $\left(-\dfrac{10}{3} pq^3\right) \times \left(\dfrac{6}{5} p^3 q\right)$ (iv) $x \times x^2 \times x^3 \times x^4$

4. (a) Simplify $3x (4x - 5) + 3$ and find its values for (i) $x = 3$ (ii) $x = \dfrac{1}{2}$.

   (b) Simplify $a (a^2 + a + 1) + 5$ and find its value for (i) $a = 0$, (ii) $a = 1$
   (iii) $a = -1$.

5. (a) Add: $p (p - q), q (q - r)$ and $r (r - p)$

   (b) Add: $2x (z - x - y)$ and $2y (z - y - x)$

   (c) Subtract: $3l (l - 4 m + 5 n)$ from $4l (10 n - 3 m + 2 l)$

   (d) Subtract: $3a (a + b + c) - 2 b (a - b + c)$ from $4c (-a + b + c)$

9.9 Multiplying a Polynomial by a Polynomial

9.9.1 Multiplying a binomial by a binomial

Let us multiply one binomial $(2a + 3b)$ by another binomial, say $(3a + 4b)$. We do this step-by-step, as we did in earlier cases, following the distributive law of multiplication,

$$(3a + 4b) \times (2a + 3b) = 3a \times (2a + 3b) + 4b \times (2a + 3b)$$

> Observe, every term in one binomial multiplies every term in the other binomial.

$$= (3a \times 2a) + (3a \times 3b) + (4b \times 2a) + (4b \times 3b)$$
$$= 6a^2 + 9ab + 8ba + 12b^2$$
$$= 6a^2 + 17ab + 12b^2 \qquad \text{(Since } ba = ab\text{)}$$

When we carry out term by term multiplication, we expect $2 \times 2 = 4$ terms to be present. But two of these are like terms, which are combined, and hence we get 3 terms. **In multiplication of polynomials with polynomials, we should always look for like terms, if any, and combine them.**

Example 8: Multiply

(i) $(x - 4)$ and $(2x + 3)$ (ii) $(x - y)$ and $(3x + 5y)$

Solution:

(i) $(x - 4) \times (2x + 3) = x \times (2x + 3) - 4 \times (2x + 3)$
$= (x \times 2x) + (x \times 3) - (4 \times 2x) - (4 \times 3) = 2x^2 + 3x - 8x - 12$
$= 2x^2 - 5x - 12$ (Adding like terms)

(ii) $(x - y) \times (3x + 5y) = x \times (3x + 5y) - y \times (3x + 5y)$
$= (x \times 3x) + (x \times 5y) - (y \times 3x) - (y \times 5y)$
$= 3x^2 + 5xy - 3yx - 5y^2 = 3x^2 + 2xy - 5y^2$ (Adding like terms)

Example 9: Multiply

(i) $(a + 7)$ and $(b - 5)$ (ii) $(a^2 + 2b^2)$ and $(5a - 3b)$

Solution:

(i) $(a + 7) \times (b - 5) = a \times (b - 5) + 7 \times (b - 5)$
$= ab - 5a + 7b - 35$

Note that there are no like terms involved in this multiplication.

(ii) $(a^2 + 2b^2) \times (5a - 3b) = a^2 (5a - 3b) + 2b^2 \times (5a - 3b)$
$= 5a^3 - 3a^2b + 10ab^2 - 6b^3$

9.9.2 Multiplying a binomial by a trinomial

In this multiplication, we shall have to multiply each of the three terms in the trinomial by each of the two terms in the binomial. We shall get in all $3 \times 2 = 6$ terms, which may reduce to 5 or less, if the term by term multiplication results in like terms. Consider

$$\underbrace{(a + 7)}_{\text{binomial}} \times \underbrace{(a^2 + 3a + 5)}_{\text{trinomial}} = a \times (a^2 + 3a + 5) + 7 \times (a^2 + 3a + 5)$$

                              [using the distributive law]

$= a^3 + 3a^2 + 5a + 7a^2 + 21a + 35$
$= a^3 + (3a^2 + 7a^2) + (5a + 21a) + 35$
$= a^3 + 10a^2 + 26a + 35$ (Why are there only 4 terms in the final result?)

Example 10: Simplify $(a + b)(2a - 3b + c) - (2a - 3b)c$.

Solution: We have

$(a + b)(2a - 3b + c) = a(2a - 3b + c) + b(2a - 3b + c)$
$= 2a^2 - 3ab + ac + 2ab - 3b^2 + bc$
$= 2a^2 - ab - 3b^2 + bc + ac$ (Note, $-3ab$ and $2ab$ are like terms)

and $(2a - 3b)c = 2ac - 3bc$

Therefore,

$(a + b)(2a - 3b + c) - (2a - 3b)c = 2a^2 - ab - 3b^2 + bc + ac - (2ac - 3bc)$
$= 2a^2 - ab - 3b^2 + bc + ac - 2ac + 3bc$
$= 2a^2 - ab - 3b^2 + (bc + 3bc) + (ac - 2ac)$
$= 2a^2 - 3b^2 - ab + 4bc - ac$

EXERCISE 9.4

1. Multiply the binomials.
   (i) $(2x + 5)$ and $(4x - 3)$ (ii) $(y - 8)$ and $(3y - 4)$
   (iii) $(2.5l - 0.5m)$ and $(2.5l + 0.5m)$ (iv) $(a + 3b)$ and $(x + 5)$
   (v) $(2pq + 3q^2)$ and $(3pq - 2q^2)$
   (vi) $\left(\dfrac{3}{4}a^2 + 3b^2\right)$ and $4\left(a^2 - \dfrac{2}{3}b^2\right)$

2. Find the product.
   (i) $(5 - 2x)(3 + x)$ (ii) $(x + 7y)(7x - y)$
   (iii) $(a^2 + b)(a + b^2)$ (iv) $(p^2 - q^2)(2p + q)$

3. Simplify.
   (i) $(x^2 - 5)(x + 5) + 25$ (ii) $(a^2 + 5)(b^3 + 3) + 5$
   (iii) $(t + s^2)(t^2 - s)$
   (iv) $(a + b)(c - d) + (a - b)(c + d) + 2(ac + bd)$
   (v) $(x + y)(2x + y) + (x + 2y)(x - y)$ (vi) $(x + y)(x^2 - xy + y^2)$
   (vii) $(1.5x - 4y)(1.5x + 4y + 3) - 4.5x + 12y$
   (viii) $(a + b + c)(a + b - c)$

9.10 What is an Identity?

Consider the equality $(a + 1)(a + 2) = a^2 + 3a + 2$

We shall evaluate both sides of this equality for some value of a, say $a = 10$.

For $a = 10$,   LHS $= (a + 1)(a + 2) = (10 + 1)(10 + 2) = 11 \times 12 = 132$
             RHS $= a^2 + 3a + 2 = 10^2 + 3 \times 10 + 2 = 100 + 30 + 2 = 132$

Thus, the values of the two sides of the equality are equal for $a = 10$.

Let us now take $a = -5$

         LHS $= (a + 1)(a + 2) = (-5 + 1)(-5 + 2) = (-4) \times (-3) = 12$
         RHS $= a^2 + 3a + 2 = (-5)^2 + 3(-5) + 2$
              $= 25 - 15 + 2 = 10 + 2 = 12$

Thus, for $a = -5$, also LHS = RHS.

We shall find that for any value of a, LHS = RHS. **Such an equality, true for every value of the variable in it, is called an identity**. Thus,

       $(a + 1)(a + 2) = a^2 + 3a + 2$ is an identity.

An equation is true for only certain values of the variable in it. It is not true for all values of the variable. For example, consider the equation

           $a^2 + 3a + 2 = 132$

It is true for $a = 10$, as seen above, but it is not true for $a = -5$ or for $a = 0$ etc.

Try it: Show that $a^2 + 3a + 2 = 132$ is not true for $a = -5$ and for $a = 0$.

9.11 Standard Identities

We shall now study three identities which are very useful in our work. These identities are obtained by multiplying a binomial by another binomial.

Let us first consider the product $(a + b) (a + b)$ or $(a + b)^2$.

$$(a + b)^2 = (a + b) (a + b)$$
$$= a(a + b) + b (a + b)$$
$$= a^2 + ab + ba + b^2$$
$$= a^2 + 2ab + b^2 \qquad \text{(since } ab = ba\text{)}$$

Thus

$$\boxed{(a + b)^2 = a^2 + 2ab + b^2} \qquad \text{(I)}$$

Clearly, this is an identity, since the expression on the RHS is obtained from the LHS by actual multiplication. One may verify that for any value of a and any value of b, the values of the two sides are equal.

- Next we consider $(a - b)^2 = (a - b) (a - b) = a (a - b) - b (a - b)$

We have $= a^2 - ab - ba + b^2 = a^2 - 2ab + b^2$

or

$$\boxed{(a - b)^2 = a^2 - 2ab + b^2} \qquad \text{(II)}$$

- Finally, consider $(a + b) (a - b)$. We have $(a + b) (a - b) = a (a - b) + b (a - b)$

$$= a^2 - ab + ba - b^2 = a^2 - b^2 \text{(since } ab = ba\text{)}$$

or

$$\boxed{(a + b) (a - b) = a^2 - b^2} \qquad \text{(III)}$$

The identities (I), (II) and (III) are known as **standard identities**.

TRY THESE

1. Put $-b$ in place of b in Identity (I). Do you get Identity (II)?

- We shall now work out one more useful identity.

$$(x + a) (x + b) = x (x + b) + a (x + b)$$
$$= x^2 + bx + ax + ab$$

or

$$\boxed{(x + a) (x + b) = x^2 + (a + b) x + ab} \qquad \text{(IV)}$$

TRY THESE

1. Verify Identity (IV), for $a = 2, b = 3, x = 5$.
2. Consider, the special case of Identity (IV) with $a = b$, what do you get? Is it related to Identity (I)?
3. Consider, the special case of Identity (IV) with $a = -c$ and $b = -c$. What do you get? Is it related to Identity (II)?
4. Consider the special case of Identity (IV) with $b = -a$. What do you get? Is it related to Identity (III)?

We can see that Identity (IV) is the general form of the other three identities also.

9.12 Applying Identities

We shall now see how, for many problems on multiplication of binomial expressions and also of numbers, use of the identities gives a simple alternative method of solving them.

Example 11: Using the Identity (I), find   (i) $(2x + 3y)^2$ (ii) 103^2

Solution:

(i) $(2x + 3y)^2 = (2x)^2 + 2(2x)(3y) + (3y)^2$ [Using the Identity (I)]
$$= 4x^2 + 12xy + 9y^2$$

We may work out $(2x + 3y)^2$ directly.

$$(2x + 3y)^2 = (2x + 3y)(2x + 3y)$$
$$= (2x)(2x) + (2x)(3y) + (3y)(2x) + (3y)(3y)$$
$$= 4x^2 + 6xy + 6\,yx + 9y^2 \qquad (\text{as } xy = yx)$$
$$= 4x^2 + 12xy + 9y^2$$

Using Identity (I) gave us an alternative method of squaring $(2x + 3y)$. Do you notice that the Identity method required fewer steps than the above direct method? You will realise the simplicity of this method even more if you try to square more complicated binomial expressions than $(2x + 3y)$.

(ii) $(103)^2 = (100 + 3)^2$
$$= 100^2 + 2 \times 100 \times 3 + 3^2 \qquad (\text{Using Identity I})$$
$$= 10000 + 600 + 9 = 10609$$

We may also directly multiply 103 by 103 and get the answer. Do you see that Identity (I) has given us a less tedious method than the direct method of squaring 103? Try squaring 1013. You will find in this case, the method of using identities even more attractive than the direct multiplication method.

Example 12: Using Identity (II), find   (i) $(4p - 3q)^2$ (ii) $(4.9)^2$

Solution:

(i) $(4p - 3q)^2 = (4p)^2 - 2(4p)(3q) + (3q)^2$ [Using the Identity (II)]
$$= 16p^2 - 24pq + 9q^2$$

Do you agree that for squaring $(4p - 3q)^2$ the method of identities is quicker than the direct method?

(ii) $(4.9)^2 = (5.0 - 0.1)^2 = (5.0)^2 - 2(5.0)(0.1) + (0.1)^2$
$$= 25.00 - 1.00 + 0.01 = 24.01$$

Is it not that, squaring 4.9 using Identity (II) is much less tedious than squaring it by direct multiplication?

Example 13: Using Identity (III), find

(i) $\left(\dfrac{3}{2}m + \dfrac{2}{3}n\right)\left(\dfrac{3}{2}m - \dfrac{2}{3}n\right)$ (ii) $983^2 - 17^2$ (iii) 194×206

Solution:

(i) $\left(\dfrac{3}{2}m + \dfrac{2}{3}n\right)\left(\dfrac{3}{2}m - \dfrac{2}{3}n\right) = \left(\dfrac{3}{2}m\right)^2 - \left(\dfrac{2}{3}n\right)^2$

Try doing this directly. You will realise how easy our method of using Identity (III) is.

$$= \dfrac{9}{4}m^2 - \dfrac{4}{9}n^2$$

(ii) $983^2 - 17^2 = (983 + 17)(983 - 17)$
[Here $a = 983$, $b = 17$, $a^2 - b^2 = (a + b)(a - b)$]
Therefore, $983^2 - 17^2 = 1000 \times 966 = 966000$

(iii) $\qquad 194 \times 206 = (200 - 6) \times (200 + 6) = 200^2 - 6^2$
$$= 40000 - 36 = 39964$$

Example 14: Use the Identity $(x + a) (x + b) = x^2 + (a + b) x + ab$ to find the following:

(i) 501×502

(ii) 95×103

Solution:

(i) $\qquad 501 \times 502 = (500 + 1) \times (500 + 2) = 500^2 + (1 + 2) \times 500 + 1 \times 2$
$$= 250000 + 1500 + 2 = 251502$$

(ii) $\qquad 95 \times 103 = (100 - 5) \times (100 + 3) = 100^2 + (-5 + 3) \times 100 + (-5) \times 3$
$$= 10000 - 200 - 15 = 9785$$

EXERCISE 9.5

1. Use a suitable identity to get each of the following products.

(i) $(x + 3) (x + 3)$

(ii) $(2y + 5) (2y + 5)$

(iii) $(2a - 7) (2a - 7)$

(iv) $\left(3a - \dfrac{1}{2}\right)\left(3a - \dfrac{1}{2}\right)$

(v) $(1.1m - 0.4) (1.1m + 0.4)$

(vi) $(a^2 + b^2) (-a^2 + b^2)$

(vii) $(6x - 7) (6x + 7)$

(viii) $(-a + c) (-a + c)$

(ix) $\left(\dfrac{x}{2} + \dfrac{3y}{4}\right)\left(\dfrac{x}{2} + \dfrac{3y}{4}\right)$

(x) $(7a - 9b) (7a - 9b)$

2. Use the identity $(x + a) (x + b) = x^2 + (a + b) x + ab$ to find the following products.

(i) $(x + 3) (x + 7)$

(ii) $(4x + 5) (4x + 1)$

(iii) $(4x - 5) (4x - 1)$

(iv) $(4x + 5) (4x - 1)$

(v) $(2x + 5y) (2x + 3y)$

(vi) $(2a^2 + 9) (2a^2 + 5)$

(vii) $(xyz - 4) (xyz - 2)$

3. Find the following squares by using the identities.

(i) $(b - 7)^2$

(ii) $(xy + 3z)^2$

(iii) $(6x^2 - 5y)^2$

(iv) $\left(\dfrac{2}{3}m + \dfrac{3}{2}n\right)^2$

(v) $(0.4p - 0.5q)^2$

(vi) $(2xy + 5y)^2$

4. Simplify.

(i) $(a^2 - b^2)^2$

(ii) $(2x + 5)^2 - (2x - 5)^2$

(iii) $(7m - 8n)^2 + (7m + 8n)^2$

(iv) $(4m + 5n)^2 + (5m + 4n)^2$

(v) $(2.5p - 1.5q)^2 - (1.5p - 2.5q)^2$

(vi) $(ab + bc)^2 - 2ab^2c$

(vii) $(m^2 - n^2m)^2 + 2m^3n^2$

5. Show that.

(i) $(3x + 7)^2 - 84x = (3x - 7)^2$

(ii) $(9p - 5q)^2 + 180pq = (9p + 5q)^2$

(iii) $\left(\dfrac{4}{3}m - \dfrac{3}{4}n\right)^2 + 2mn = \dfrac{16}{9}m^2 + \dfrac{9}{16}n^2$

(iv) $(4pq + 3q)^2 - (4pq - 3q)^2 = 48pq^2$

(v) $(a - b) (a + b) + (b - c) (b + c) + (c - a) (c + a) = 0$

6. Using identities, evaluate.
   (i) 71^2 (ii) 99^2 (iii) 102^2 (iv) 998^2
   (v) 5.2^2 (vi) 297×303 (vii) 78×82 (viii) 8.9^2
   (ix) 10.5×9.5

7. Using $a^2 - b^2 = (a + b)(a - b)$, find
   (i) $51^2 - 49^2$ (ii) $(1.02)^2 - (0.98)^2$ (iii) $153^2 - 147^2$
   (iv) $12.1^2 - 7.9^2$

8. Using $(x + a)(x + b) = x^2 + (a + b)x + ab$, find
   (i) 103×104 (ii) 5.1×5.2 (iii) 103×98 (iv) 9.7×9.8

WHAT HAVE WE DISCUSSED?

1. Expressions are formed from **variables** and **constants**.

2. Terms are added to form **expressions**. Terms themselves are formed as product of **factors**.

3. Expressions that contain exactly one, two and three terms are called **monomials**, **binomials** and **trinomials** respectively. In general, any expression containing one or more terms with non-zero coefficients (and with variables having non-negative integers as exponents) is called a **polynomial**.

4. **Like** terms are formed from the same variables and the powers of these variables are the same, too. Coefficients of like terms need not be the same.

5. While adding (or subtracting) polynomials, first look for like terms and add (or subtract) them; then handle the unlike terms.

6. There are number of situations in which we need to multiply algebraic expressions: for example, in finding area of a rectangle, the sides of which are given as expressions.

7. A monomial multiplied by a monomial always gives a monomial.

8. While multiplying a polynomial by a monomial, we multiply every term in the polynomial by the monomial.

9. In carrying out the multiplication of a polynomial by a binomial (or trinomial), we multiply term by term, i.e., every term of the polynomial is multiplied by every term in the binomial (or trinomial). Note that in such multiplication, we may get terms in the product which are like and have to be combined.

10. An **identity** is an equality, which is true for all values of the variables in the equality.

    On the other hand, an equation is true only for certain values of its variables. An equation is not an identity.

11. The following are the standard identities:
    $(a + b)^2 = a^2 + 2ab + b^2$ (I)
    $(a - b)^2 = a^2 - 2ab + b^2$ (II)
    $(a + b)(a - b) = a^2 - b^2$ (III)

12. Another useful identity is $(x + a)(x + b) = x^2 + (a + b)x + ab$ (IV)

13. The above four identities are useful in carrying out squares and products of algebraic expressions. They also allow easy alternative methods to calculate products of numbers and so on.

Visualising Solid Shapes

0852CH10

10.1 Introduction

In Class VII, you have learnt about plane shapes and solid shapes. Plane shapes have two measurements like length and breadth and therefore they are called two-dimensional shapes whereas a solid object has three measurements like length, breadth, height or depth. Hence, they are called three-dimensional shapes. Also, a solid object occupies some space. Two-dimensional and three-dimensional figures can also be briefly named as 2-D and 3-D figures. You may recall that triangle, rectangle, circle etc., are 2-D figures while cubes, cylinders, cones, spheres etc. are three-dimensional figures.

DO THIS

Match the following: (First one is done for you)

Shape	Type of Shape	Name of the shape
□	3-dimensional	Sphere
△ (cone)	2-Dimensional	Cylinder
▯ (cylinder)	3-dimensional	Square
△ (triangle)	2-dimensional	Circle

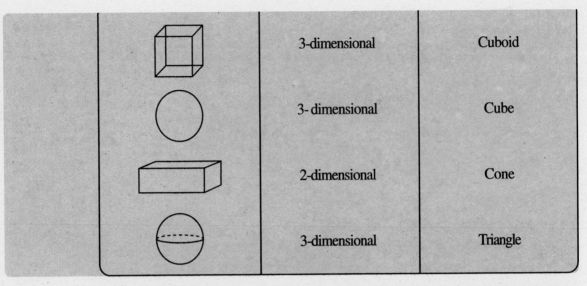

	3-dimensional	Cuboid
	3- dimensional	Cube
	2-dimensional	Cone
	3-dimensional	Triangle

Note that all the above shapes are single. However, in our practical life, many a times, we come across combinations of different shapes. For example, look at the following objects.

A tent
A cone surmounted
on a cylinder

A tin
A cylinderical shell

Softy (ice-cream)
A cone surmounted by a
hemisphere

A photoframe
A rectangular path

A bowl
A hemispherical shell

Tomb on a pillar
Cylinder surmounted
by a hemisphere

DO THIS
Match the following pictures (objects) with their shapes:

Picture (object)

(i) An agricultural field

Shape

Two rectangular cross paths inside a
rectangular park.

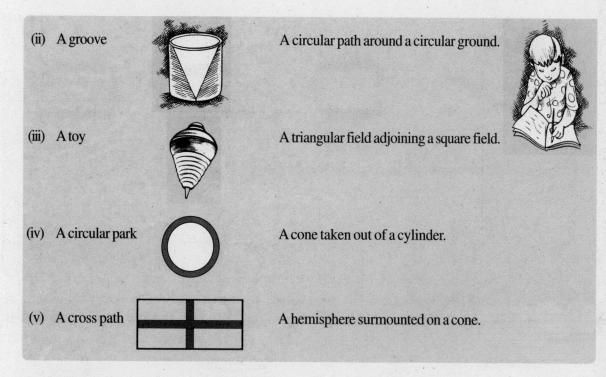

(ii)	A groove	A circular path around a circular ground.
(iii)	A toy	A triangular field adjoining a square field.
(iv)	A circular park	A cone taken out of a cylinder.
(v)	A cross path	A hemisphere surmounted on a cone.

10.2 Views of 3D-Shapes

You have learnt that a 3-dimensional object can look differently from different positions so they can be drawn from different perspectives. For example, a given hut can have the following views.

Front   A hut   Side   Front view   Side view   Top view

similarly, a glass can have the following views.

A glass   Side view   Top view

Why is the top view of the glass a pair of concentric circles? Will the side view appear different if taken from some other direction? Think about this! Now look at the different views of a brick.

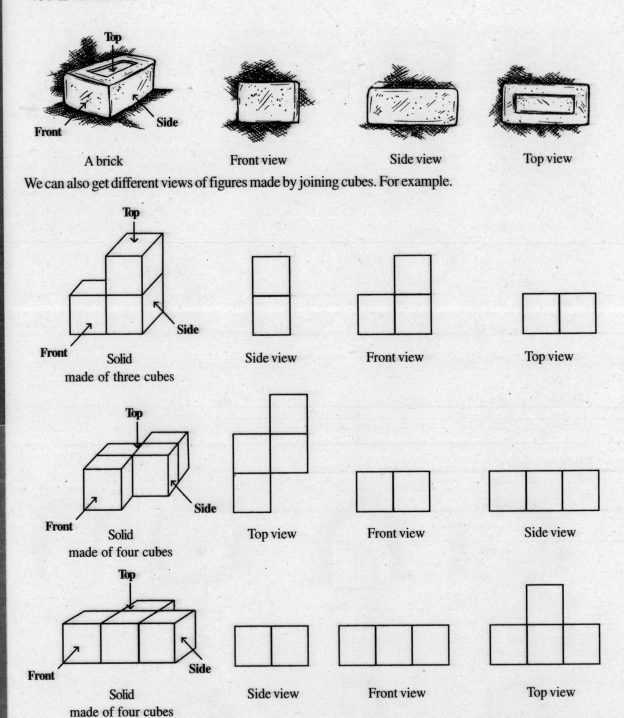

A brick   Front view   Side view   Top view

We can also get different views of figures made by joining cubes. For example.

Solid made of three cubes   Side view   Front view   Top view

Solid made of four cubes   Top view   Front view   Side view

Solid made of four cubes   Side view   Front view   Top view

DO THIS

Observe different things around you from different positions. Discuss with your friends their various views.

EXERCISE 10.1

1. For each of the given solid, the two views are given. Match for each solid the corresponding top and front views. The first one is done for you.

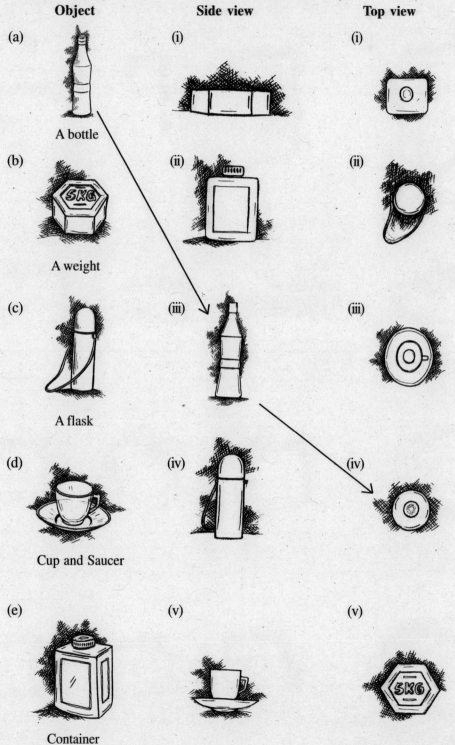

Object	Side view	Top view
(a) A bottle	(i)	(i)
(b) A weight	(ii)	(ii)
(c) A flask	(iii)	(iii)
(d) Cup and Saucer	(iv)	(iv)
(e) Container	(v)	(v)

2. For each of the given solid, the three views are given. Identify for each solid the corresponding top, front and side views.

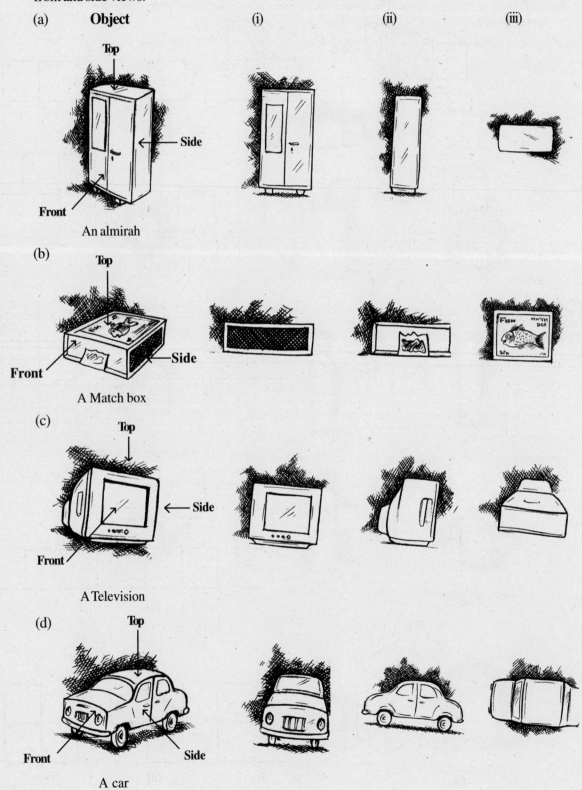

(a) **Object** (i) (ii) (iii)

An almirah

(b) A Match box

(c) A Television

(d) A car

3. For each given solid, identify the top view, front view and side view.

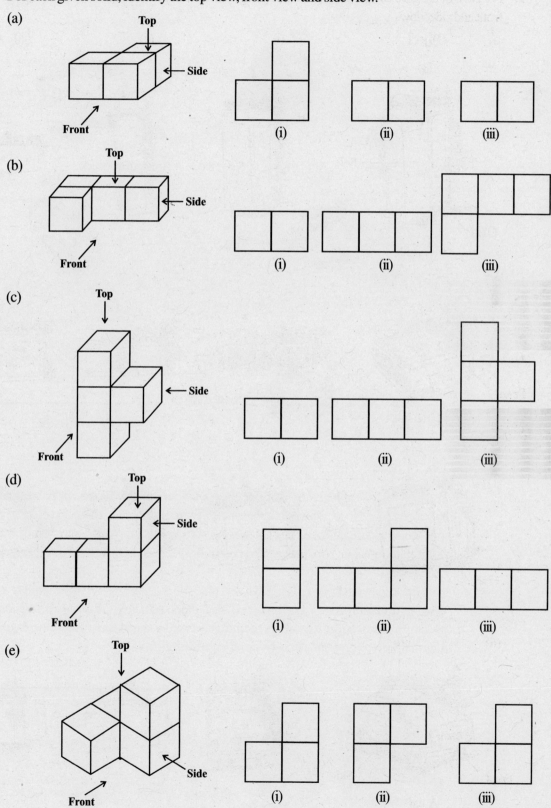

4. Draw the front view, side view and top view of the given objects.

    (a) A military tent   (b) A table

    (c) A nut   (d) A hexagonal block

    (e) A dice   (f) A solid

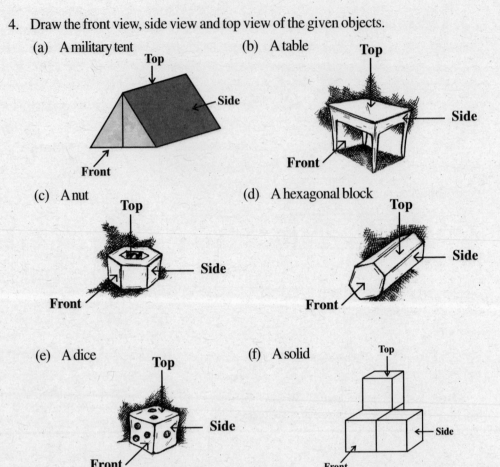

10.3 Mapping Space Around Us

You have been dealing with maps since you were in primary, classes. In Geography, you have been asked to locate a particular State, a particular river, a mountain etc., on a map. In History, you might have been asked to locate a particular place where some event had occured long back. You have traced routes of rivers, roads, railwaylines, traders and many others.

    How do we read maps? What can we conclude and understand while reading a map? What information does a map have and what it does not have? Is it any different from a picture? In this section, we will try to find answers to some of these questions. Look at the map of a house whose picture is given alongside (Fig 10.1).

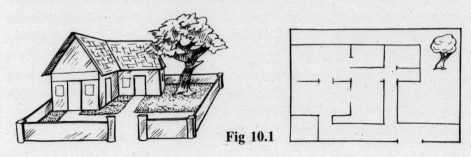

Fig 10.1

What can we conclude from the above illustration? When we draw a picture, we attempt to represent reality as it is seen with all its details, whereas, a map depicts only the location of an object, in relation to other objects. Secondly, different persons can give descriptions of pictures completely different from one another, depending upon the position from which they are looking at the house. But, this is not true in the case of a map. The map of the house remains the same irrespective of the position of the observer. In other words, **perspective is very important for drawing a picture but it is not relevant for a map.**

Now, look at the map (Fig 10.2), which has been drawn by seven year old Raghav, as the route from his house to his school:

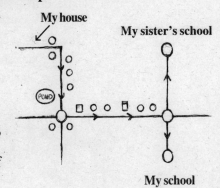

Fig 10.2

From this map, can you tell –

(i) how far is Raghav's school from his house?

(ii) would every circle in the map depict a round about?

(iii) whose school is nearer to the house, Raghav's or his sister's?

It is very difficult to answer the above questions on the basis of the given map. Can you tell why?

The reason is that we do not know if the distances have been drawn properly or whether the circles drawn are roundabouts or represent something else.

Now look at another map drawn by his sister, ten year old Meena, to show the route from her house to her school (Fig 10.3).

This map is different from the earlier maps. Here, Meena has used different symbols for different landmarks. Secondly, longer line segments have been drawn for longer distances and shorter line segments have been drawn for shorter distances, i.e., she has drawn the map to a scale.

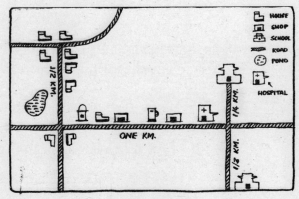

Fig 10.3

Now, you can answer the following questions:

● How far is Raghav's school from his residence?

● Whose school is nearer to the house, Raghav's or Meena's?

● Which are the important landmarks on the route?

Thus we realise that, use of certain symbols and mentioning of distances has helped us read the map easily. Observe that the distances shown on the map are proportional to the actual distances on the ground. This is done by considering a proper scale. While drawing (or reading) a map, one must know, to what scale it has to be drawn (or has been drawn), i.e., how much of actual distance is denoted by 1mm or 1cm in the map. This means, that if one draws a map, he/she has to decide that 1cm of space in that map shows a certain fixed distance of say 1 km or 10 km. This scale can vary from map to map but not within a map. For instance, look at the map of India alongside the map of Delhi.

You will find that when the maps are drawn of same size, scales and the distances in the two maps will vary. That is 1 cm of space in the map of Delhi will represent smaller distances as compared to the distances in the map of India.

The larger the place and smaller the size of the map drawn, the greater is the distance represented by 1 cm.

Thus, we can summarise that:

1. A map depicts the location of a particular object/place in relation to other objects/places.

2. Symbols are used to depict the different objects/places.

3. There is no reference or perspective in map, i.e., objects that are closer to the observer are shown to be of the same size as those that are farther away. For example, look at the following illustration (Fig 10.4).

 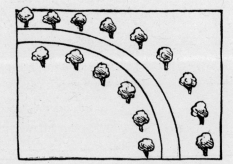

Fig 10.4

4. Maps use a scale which is fixed for a particular map. It reduces the real distances proportionately to distances on the paper.

DO THIS

1. Look at the following map of a city (Fig 10.5).

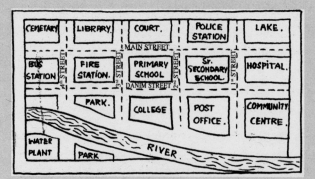

Fig 10.5

(a) Colour the map as follows: Blue-water, Red-fire station, Orange-Library, Yellow-schools, Green-Parks, Pink-Community Centre, Purple-Hospital, Brown-Cemetry.

(b) Mark a Green 'X' at the intersection of 2nd street and Danim street. A Black 'Y' where the river meets the third street. A red 'Z' at the intersection of main street and 1st street.

(c) In magenta colour, draw a short street route from the college to the lake.

2. Draw a map of the route from your house to your school showing important landmarks.

EXERCISE 10.2

1. Look at the given map of a city.

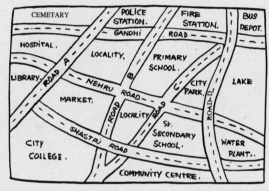

Answer the following.

(a) Colour the map as follows: Blue-water, red-fire station, orange-library, yellow - schools, Green - park, Pink - College, Purple - Hospital, Brown - Cemetery.

(b) Mark a green 'X' at the intersection of Road 'C' and Nehru Road, Green 'Y' at the intersection of Gandhi Road and Road A.

(c) In red, draw a short street route from Library to the bus depot.

(d) Which is further east, the city park or the market?

(e) Which is further south, the primary school or the Sr. Secondary School?

2. Draw a map of your class room using proper scale and symbols for different objects.

3. Draw a map of your school compound using proper scale and symbols for various features like play ground main building, garden etc.

4. Draw a map giving instructions to your friend so that she reaches your house without any difficulty.

10.4 Faces, Edges and Vertices

Look at the following solids!

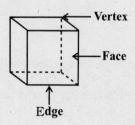

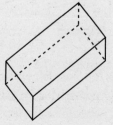

Riddle
I have no vertices.
I have no flat faces. Who am I?

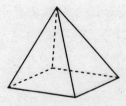
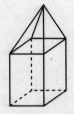

Each of these solids is made up of polygonal regions which are called its **faces**; these faces meet at **edges** which are line segments; and the edges meet at vertices which are **points**. Such solids are called **polyhedrons**.

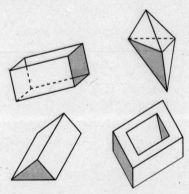
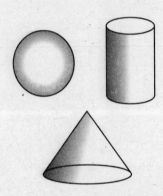

These are polyhedrons   **These are not polyhedrons**

How are the polyhedrons different from the non-polyhedrons? Study the figures carefully. You know three other types of common solids.

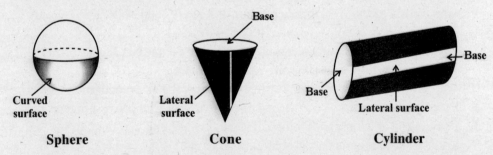

Sphere   **Cone**   **Cylinder**

Convex polyhedrons: You will recall the concept of convex polygons. The idea of convex polyhedron is similar.

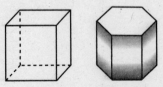
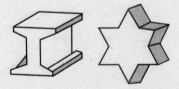

These are convex polyhedrons   **These are not convex polyhedrons**

Regular polyhedrons: A polyhedron is said to be **regular** if its faces are made up of regular polygons and the same number of faces meet at **each** vertex.

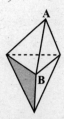

This polyhedron is regular. Its faces are congruent, regular polygons. Vertices are formed by the same number of faces

This polyhedon is not regular. All the sides are congruent; but the vertices are not formed by the same number of faces. 3 faces meet at A but 4 faces meet at B.

Two important members of polyhedron family around are prisms and pyramids.

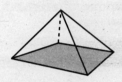

These are prisms   These are pyramids

We say that **a prism** is a polyhedron whose base and top are congruent polygons and whose other faces, i.e., lateral faces are parallelograms in shape.

On the other hand, **a pyramid** is a polyhedron whose base is a polygon (of any number of sides) and whose lateral faces are triangles with a common vertex. (If you join all the corners of a polygon to a point not in its plane, you get a model for pyramid).

A prism or a pyramid is named after its base. Thus a hexagonal prism has a hexagon as its base; and a triangular pyramid has a triangle as its base. What, then, is a rectangular prism? What is a square pyramid? Clearly their bases are rectangle and square respectively.

DO THIS

Tabulate the number of faces, edges and vertices for the following polyhedrons:
(Here 'V' stands for number of vertices, 'F' stands for number of faces and 'E' stands for number of edges).

Solid	F	V	E	F+V	E+2
Cuboid					
Triangular pyramid					
Triangular prism					
Pyramid with square base					
Prism with square base					

What do you infer from the last two columns? In each case, do you find
F + V = E + 2, i.e., F + V − E = 2? This relationship is called **Euler's formula.**
In fact this formula is true for any polyhedron.

THINK, DISCUSS AND WRITE

What happens to F, V and E if some parts are sliced off from a solid? (To start with,
you may take a plasticine cube, cut a corner off and investigate).

EXERCISE 10.3

1. Can a polyhedron have for its faces
   (i)   3 triangles?   (ii)   4 triangles?
   (iii) a square and four triangles?

2. Is it possible to have a polyhedron with any given number of faces? (**Hint:** Think of
   a pyramid).

3. Which are prisms among the following?

   (i)   (ii)

   A nail   **Unsharpened pencil**

   (iii)   (iv)

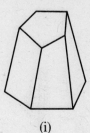   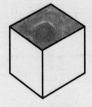

   A table weight   **A box**

4. (i)   How are prisms and cylinders alike?
   (ii) How are pyramids and cones alike?

5. Is a square prism same as a cube? Explain.

6. Verify Euler's formula for these solids.

   (i)   (ii)

7. Using Euler's formula find the unknown.

Faces	?	5	20
Vertices	6	?	12
Edges	12	9	?

8. Can a polyhedron have 10 faces, 20 edges and 15 vertices?

WHAT HAVE WE DISCUSSED?

1. Recognising 2D and 3D objects.

2. Recognising different shapes in nested objects.

3. 3D objects have different views from different positions.

4. A map is different from a picture.

5. A map depicts the location of a particular object/place in relation to other objects/places.

6. Symbols are used to depict the different objects/places.

7. There is no reference or perspective in a map.

8. Maps involve a scale which is fixed for a particular map.

9. For any polyhedron,

$$F + V - E = 2$$

where 'F' stands for number of faces, V stands for number of vertices and E stands for number of edges. This relationship is called **Euler's formula**.

NOTES

Mensuration

CHAPTER

11

0852CH11

11.1 Introduction

We have learnt that for a closed plane figure, the perimeter is the distance around its boundary and its area is the region covered by it. We found the area and perimeter of various plane figures such as triangles, rectangles, circles etc. We have also learnt to find the area of pathways or borders in rectangular shapes.

In this chapter, we will try to solve problems related to perimeter and area of other plane closed figures like quadrilaterals.

We will also learn about surface area and volume of solids such as cube, cuboid and cylinder.

11.2 Let us Recall

Let us take an example to review our previous knowledge.

This is a figure of a rectangular park (Fig 11.1) whose length is 30 m and width is 20 m.

(i) What is the total length of the fence surrounding it? To find the length of the fence we need to find the perimeter of this park, which is 100 m. (Check it)

(ii) How much land is occupied by the park? To find the land occupied by this park we need to find the area of this park which is 600 square meters (m^2) (How?).

(iii) There is a path of one metre width running inside along the perimeter of the park that has to be cemented. If 1 bag of cement is required to cement 4 m^2 area, how many bags of cement would be required to construct the cemented path?

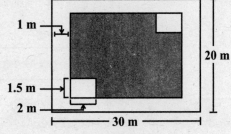

Fig 11.1

We can say that the number of cement bags used $= \dfrac{\text{area of the path}}{\text{area cemented by 1 bag}}$.

Area of cemented path = Area of park – Area of park not cemented.

Path is 1 m wide, so the rectangular area not cemented is $(30 - 2) \times (20 - 2)$ m^2.

That is 28×18 m^2.

Hence number of cement bags used = ------------------

(iv) There are two rectangular flower beds of size 1.5 m × 2 m each in the park as shown in the diagram (Fig 11.1) and the rest has grass on it. Find the area covered by grass.

Area of rectangular beds = ------------------

Area of park left after cementing the path = ------------------

Area covered by the grass = ------------------

We can find areas of geometrical shapes other than rectangles also if certain measurements are given to us . Try to recall and match the following:

Diagram	Shape	Area
	rectangle	$a \times a$
	square	$b \times h$
	triangle	πb^2
	parallelogram	$\dfrac{1}{2} b \times h$
	circle	$a \times b$

Can you write an expression for the perimeter of each of the above shapes?

TRY THESE

(a) Match the following figures with their respective areas in the box.

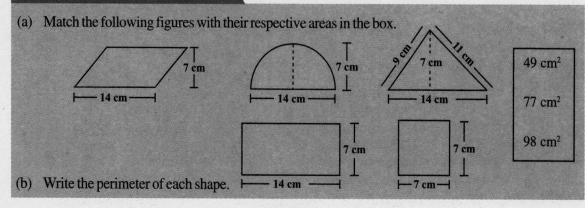

49 cm²

77 cm²

98 cm²

(b) Write the perimeter of each shape.

EXERCISE 11.1

1. A square and a rectangular field with measurements as given in the figure have the same perimeter. Which field has a larger area?

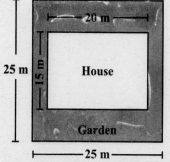

├─ 60 m ─┤   ├─── 80 m ───┤
(a)   (b)

2. Mrs. Kaushik has a square plot with the measurement as shown in the figure. She wants to construct a house in the middle of the plot. A garden is developed around the house. Find the total cost of developing a garden around the house at the rate of ₹ 55 per m².

3. The shape of a garden is rectangular in the middle and semi circular at the ends as shown in the diagram. Find the area and the perimeter of this garden [Length of rectangle is $20 - (3.5 + 3.5)$ metres].

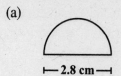

7 m

├─────── 20 m ───────┤

4. A flooring tile has the shape of a parallelogram whose base is 24 cm and the corresponding height is 10 cm. How many such tiles are required to cover a floor of area 1080 m²? (If required you can split the tiles in whatever way you want to fill up the corners).

5. An ant is moving around a few food pieces of different shapes scattered on the floor. For which food-piece would the ant have to take a longer round? Remember, circumference of a circle can be obtained by using the expression $c = 2\pi r$, where r is the radius of the circle.

(a)   (b)   (c)

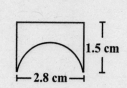

├─ 2.8 cm ─┤   1.5 cm   ├─ 2.8 cm ─┤

├─ 2.8 cm ─┤

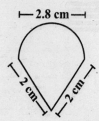

2 cm   2 cm

11.3 Area of Trapezium

Nazma owns a plot near a main road (Fig 11.2). Unlike some other rectangular plots in her neighbourhood, the plot has only one pair of parallel opposite sides. So, it is nearly a trapezium in shape. Can you find out its area?

Let us name the vertices of this plot as shown in Fig 11.3.

By drawing EC ∥ AB, we can divide it into two parts, one of rectangular shape and the other of triangular shape, (which is right angled at C), as shown in Fig 11.3.

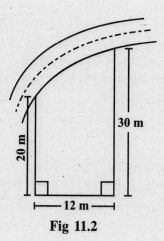

20 m   30 m   12 m

Fig 11.2

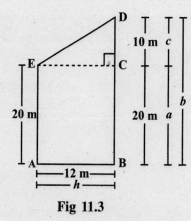

Fig 11.3

$(b = c + a = 30 \text{ m})$

[Figure 11.1 / house garden figure:]

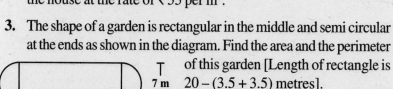

├─── 20 m ───┤

25 m   15 m   House

Garden

├─────── 25 m ───────┤

Area of $\triangle\,ECD = \dfrac{1}{2}h \times c = \dfrac{1}{2}\times 12\times 10 = 60$ m^2.

Area of rectangle ABCE $= h \times a = 12 \times 20 = 240$ m^2.

Area of trapezium ABDE $=$ area of $\triangle\,ECD +$ Area of rectangle ABCE $= 60 + 240 = 300$ m^2.

We can write the area by combining the two areas and write the area of trapezium as

$$\text{area of ABDE} = \dfrac{1}{2}h \times c + h \times a = h\left(\dfrac{c}{2} + a\right)$$

$$= h\left(\dfrac{c + 2a}{2}\right) = h\left(\dfrac{c + a + a}{2}\right)$$

$$= h\dfrac{(b+a)}{2} = \text{height}\ \dfrac{(\text{sum of parallel sides})}{2}$$

By substituting the values of h, b and a in this expression, we find $h\dfrac{(b+a)}{2} = 300$ m^2.

TRY THESE

1. Nazma's sister also has a trapezium shaped plot. Divide it into three parts as shown (Fig 11.4). Show that the area of trapezium WXYZ $= h\dfrac{(a+b)}{2}$.

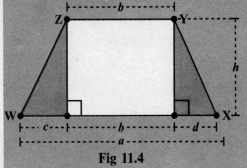

Fig 11.4

2. If $h = 10$ cm, $c = 6$ cm, $b = 12$ cm, $d = 4$ cm, find the values of each of its parts separetely and add to find the area WXYZ. Verify it by putting the values of h, a and b in the expression $\dfrac{h(a+b)}{2}$.

DO THIS

1. Draw any trapezium WXYZ on a piece of graph paper as shown in the figure and cut it out (Fig 11.5).

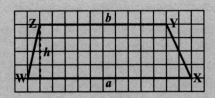

Fig 11.5

2. Find the mid point of XY by folding the side and name it A (Fig 11.6).

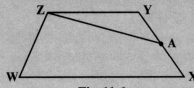

Fig 11.6

3. Cut trapezium WXYZ into two pieces by cutting along ZA. Place △ZYA as shown in Fig 11.7, where AY is placed on AX.

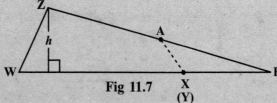

What is the length of the base of the larger triangle? Write an expression for the area of this triangle (Fig 11.7).

Fig 11.7

4. The area of this triangle and the area of the trapezium WXYZ are same (How?). Get the expression for the area of trapezium by using the expression for the area of triangle.

So to find the area of a trapezium we need to know the length of the parallel sides and the perpendicular distance between these two parallel sides. Half the product of the sum of the lengths of parallel sides and the perpendicular distance between them gives the area of trapezium.

TRY THESE

Find the area of the following trapeziums (Fig 11.8).

(i)

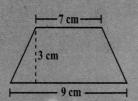

(ii)

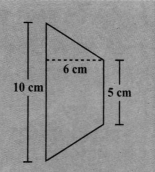

Fig 11.8

DO THIS

In Class VII we learnt to draw parallelograms of equal areas with different perimeters. Can it be done for trapezium? Check if the following trapeziums are of equal areas but have different perimeters (Fig 11.9).

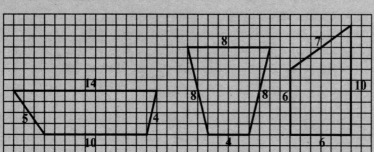

Fig 11.9

We know that all congruent figures are equal in area. Can we say figures equal in area need to be congruent too? Are these figures congruent?

Draw at least three trapeziums which have different areas but equal perimeters on a squared sheet.

11.4 Area of a General Quadrilateral

A general quadrilateral can be split into two triangles by drawing one of its diagonals. This "triangulation" helps us to find a formula for any general quadrilateral. Study the Fig 11.10.

Area of quadrilateral ABCD

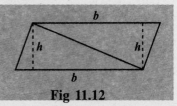

$$= \text{(area of } \Delta \text{ ABC)} + \text{(area of } \Delta \text{ ADC)}$$

$$= (\frac{1}{2} \text{ AC} \times h_1) + (\frac{1}{2} \text{ AC} \times h_2)$$

$$= \frac{1}{2} \text{ AC} \times (h_1 + h_2)$$

Fig 11.10

$$= \frac{1}{2} d (h_1 + h_2) \text{ where } d \text{ denotes the length of diagonal AC.}$$

Example 1: Find the area of quadrilateral PQRS shown in Fig 11.11.

Solution: In this case, $d = 5.5$ cm, $h_1 = 2.5$cm, $h_2 = 1.5$ cm,

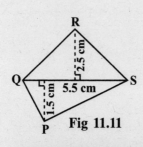

Fig 11.11

$$\text{Area} = \frac{1}{2} d (h_1 + h_2)$$

$$= \frac{1}{2} \times 5.5 \times (2.5 + 1.5) \text{ cm}^2$$

$$= \frac{1}{2} \times 5.5 \times 4 \text{ cm}^2 = 11 \text{ cm}^2$$

TRY THESE

We know that parallelogram is also a quadrilateral. Let us also split such a quadrilateral into two triangles, find their areas and hence that of the parallelogram. Does this agree with the formula that you know already? (Fig 11.12)

Fig 11.12

11.4.1 Area of special quadrilaterals

We can use the same method of splitting into triangles (which we called "triangulation") to find a formula for the area of a rhombus. In Fig 11.13 ABCD is a rhombus. Therefore, its diagonals are perpendicular bisectors of each other.

Area of rhombus ABCD = (area of Δ ACD) + (area of Δ ABC)

Fig 11.13

$$= (\frac{1}{2} \times AC \times OD) + (\frac{1}{2} \times AC \times OB) = \frac{1}{2} AC \times (OD + OB)$$

$$= \frac{1}{2} AC \times BD = \frac{1}{2} d_1 \times d_2 \quad \text{where } AC = d_1 \text{ and } BD = d_2$$

In other words, area of a rhombus is half the product of its diagonals.

Example 2: Find the area of a rhombus whose diagonals are of lengths 10 cm and 8.2 cm.

Solution: Area of the rhombus $= \frac{1}{2} d_1 d_2$ where d_1, d_2 are lengths of diagonals.

$$= \frac{1}{2} \times 10 \times 8.2 \text{ cm}^2 = 41 \text{ cm}^2.$$

THINK, DISCUSS AND WRITE

A parallelogram is divided into two congruent triangles by drawing a diagonal across it. Can we divide a trapezium into two congruent triangles?

TRY THESE

Find the area of these quadrilaterals (Fig 11.14).

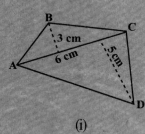

(i)

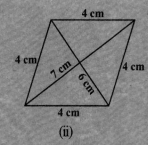

(ii)

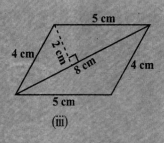

(iii)

Fig 11.14

11.5 Area of a Polygon

We split a quadrilateral into triangles and find its area. Similar methods can be used to find the area of a polygon. Observe the following for a pentagon: (Fig 11.15, 11.16)

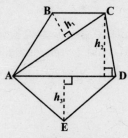

Fig 11.15

By constructing two diagonals AC and AD the pentagon ABCDE is divided into three parts. So, area ABCDE = area of $\triangle$ ABC + area of $\triangle$ ACD + area of $\triangle$ AED.

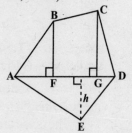

Fig 11.16

By constructing one diagonal AD and two perpendiculars BF and CG on it, pentagon ABCDE is divided into four parts. So, area of ABCDE = area of right angled $\triangle$ AFB + area of trapezium BFGC + area of right angled $\triangle$ CGD + area of $\triangle$ AED. (Identify the parallel sides of trapezium BFGC.)

TRY THESE

(i) Divide the following polygons (Fig 11.17) into parts (triangles and trapezium) to find out its area.

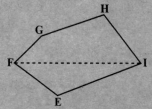
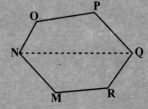

Fig 11.17

FI is a diagonal of polygon EFGHI   NQ is a diagonal of polygon MNOPQR

(ii) Polygon ABCDE is divided into parts as shown below (Fig 11.18). Find its area if AD = 8 cm, AH = 6 cm, AG = 4 cm, AF = 3 cm and perpendiculars BF = 2 cm, CH = 3 cm, EG = 2.5 cm.

Area of Polygon ABCDE = area of △ AFB + ...

Area of △ AFB = $\frac{1}{2}$ × AF × BF = $\frac{1}{2}$ × 3 × 2 = ...

Area of trapezium FBCH = FH × $\frac{(BF + CH)}{2}$

$= 3 \times \frac{(2+3)}{2}$ [FH = AH – AF]

Area of △CHD = $\frac{1}{2}$ × HD× CH = ...;   Area of △ADE = $\frac{1}{2}$ × AD × GE = ...

So, the area of polygon ABCDE = ...

Fig 11.18

(iii) Find the area of polygon MNOPQR (Fig 11.19) if
MP = 9 cm, MD = 7 cm, MC = 6 cm, MB = 4 cm, MA = 2 cm

NA, OC, QD and RB are perpendiculars to diagonal MP.

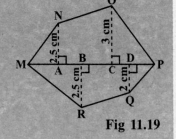

Fig 11.19

Example 1: The area of a trapezium shaped field is 480 m², the distance between two parallel sides is 15 m and one of the parallel side is 20 m. Find the other parallel side.

Solution: One of the parallel sides of the trapezium is a = 20 m, let another parallel side be b, height h = 15 m.

The given area of trapezium = 480 m².

Area of a trapezium = $\frac{1}{2}$ h ($a + b$)

So $480 = \frac{1}{2} \times 15 \times (20 + b)$ or $\frac{480 \times 2}{15} = 20 + b$

or $64 = 20 + b$ or $b = 44$ m

Hence the other parallel side of the trapezium is 44 m.

Example 2: The area of a rhombus is 240 cm² and one of the diagonals is 16 cm. Find the other diagonal.

Solution: Let length of one diagonal $d_1 = 16$ cm

and   length of the other diagonal $= d_2$

$$\text{Area of the rhombus} = \frac{1}{2}\, d_1 \cdot d_2 = 240$$

So, $\frac{1}{2} 16 \cdot d_2 = 240$

Therefore, $d_2 = 30$ cm

Hence the length of the second diagonal is 30 cm.

Example 3: There is a hexagon MNOPQR of side 5 cm (Fig 11.20). Aman and Ridhima divided it in two different ways (Fig 11.21).

Find the area of this hexagon using both ways.

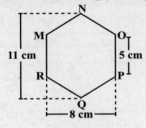

Fig 11.20

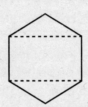

Ridhima's method

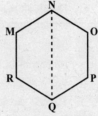

Aman's method

Fig 11.21

Solution: Aman's method:

Since it is a hexagon so NQ divides the hexagon into two congruent trapeziums. You can verify it by paper folding (Fig 11.22).

Now area of trapezium MNQR $= 4 \times \dfrac{(11+5)}{2} = 2 \times 16 = 32$ cm².

Fig 11.22

So the area of hexagon MNOPQR $= 2 \times 32 = 64$ cm².

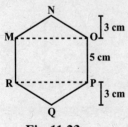

Fig 11.23

Ridhima's method:

Δ MNO and Δ RPQ are congruent triangles with altitude 3 cm (Fig 11.23).

You can verify this by cutting off these two triangles and placing them on one another.

Area of Δ MNO $= \dfrac{1}{2} \times 8 \times 3 = 12$ cm² = Area of Δ RPQ

Area of rectangle MOPR $= 8 \times 5 = 40$ cm².

Now, area of hexagon MNOPQR $= 40 + 12 + 12 = 64$ cm².

◢◣◤ EXERCISE 11.2

1. The shape of the top surface of a table is a trapezium. Find its area if its parallel sides are 1 m and 1.2 m and perpendicular distance between them is 0.8 m.

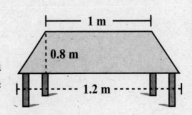

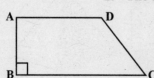

2. The area of a trapezium is 34 cm² and the length of one of the parallel sides is 10 cm and its height is 4 cm. Find the length of the other parallel side.

3. Length of the fence of a trapezium shaped field ABCD is 120 m. If BC = 48 m, CD = 17 m and AD = 40 m, find the area of this field. Side AB is perpendicular to the parallel sides AD and BC.

4. The diagonal of a quadrilateral shaped field is 24 m and the perpendiculars dropped on it from the remaining opposite vertices are 8 m and 13 m. Find the area of the field.

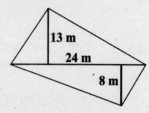

5. The diagonals of a rhombus are 7.5 cm and 12 cm. Find its area.

6. Find the area of a rhombus whose side is 5 cm and whose altitude is 4.8 cm. If one of its diagonals is 8 cm long, find the length of the other diagonal.

7. The floor of a building consists of 3000 tiles which are rhombus shaped and each of its diagonals are 45 cm and 30 cm in length. Find the total cost of polishing the floor, if the cost per m² is ₹ 4.

8. Mohan wants to buy a trapezium shaped field. Its side along the river is parallel to and twice the side along the road. If the area of this field is 10500 m² and the perpendicular distance between the two parallel sides is 100 m, find the length of the side along the river.

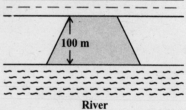

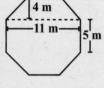

9. Top surface of a raised platform is in the shape of a regular octagon as shown in the figure. Find the area of the octagonal surface.

10. There is a pentagonal shaped park as shown in the figure.

For finding its area Jyoti and Kavita divided it in two different ways.

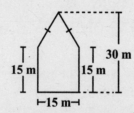

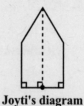

Joyti's diagram   **Kavita's diagram**

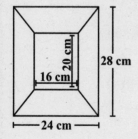

Find the area of this park using both ways. Can you suggest some other way of finding its area?

11. Diagram of the adjacent picture frame has outer dimensions = 24 cm × 28 cm and inner dimensions 16 cm × 20 cm. Find the area of each section of the frame, if the width of each section is same.

11.6 Solid Shapes

In your earlier classes you have studied that two dimensional figures can be identified as the faces of three dimensional shapes. Observe the solids which we have discussed so far (Fig 11.24).

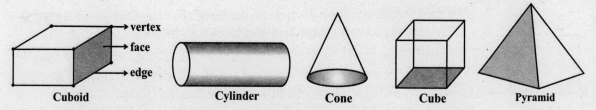

Fig 11.24

Observe that some shapes have two or more than two identical (congruent) faces. Name them. Which solid has all congruent faces?

DO THIS

Soaps, toys, pastes, snacks etc. often come in the packing of cuboidal, cubical or cylindrical boxes. Collect, such boxes (Fig 11.25).

Fig 11.25

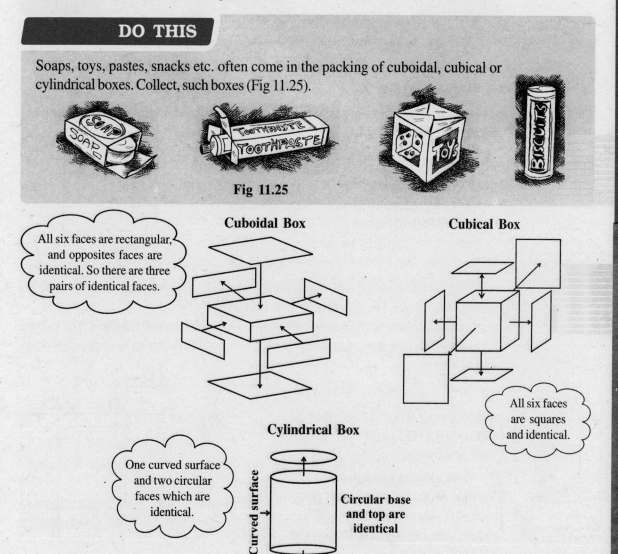

All six faces are rectangular, and opposites faces are identical. So there are three pairs of identical faces.

Cuboidal Box

Cubical Box

All six faces are squares and identical.

Cylindrical Box

One curved surface and two circular faces which are identical.

Curved surface

Circular base and top are identical

Now take one type of box at a time. Cut out all the faces it has. Observe the shape of each face and find the number of faces of the box that are identical by placing them on each other. Write down your observations.

Fig 11.26

(This is a right circular cylinder)

Did you notice the following:

The cylinder has congruent circular faces that are parallel to each other (Fig 11.26). Observe that the line segment joining the center of circular faces is perpendicular to the base. Such cylinders are known as **right circular cylinders**. We are only going to study this type of cylinders, though there are other types of cylinders as well (Fig 11.27).

Fig 11.27

(This is not a right circular cylinder)

THINK, DISCUSS AND WRITE

Why is it incorrect to call the solid shown here a cylinder?

11.7 Surface Area of Cube, Cuboid and Cylinder

Imran, Monica and Jaspal are painting a cuboidal, cubical and a cylindrical box respectively of same height (Fig 11.28).

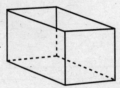

Fig 11.28

They try to determine who has painted more area. Hari suggested that finding the surface area of each box would help them find it out.

To find the total surface area, find the area of each face and then add. The surface area of a solid is the sum of the areas of its faces. To clarify further, we take each shape one by one.

11.7.1 Cuboid

Suppose you cut open a cuboidal box and lay it flat (Fig 11.29). We can see a net as shown below (Fig 11.30).

Write the dimension of each side. You know that a cuboid has three pairs of identical faces. What expression can you use to find the area of each face?

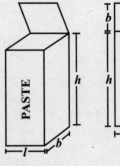

Fig 11.29

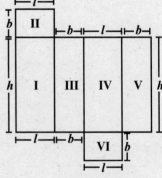

Fig 11.30

Find the total area of all the faces of the box. We see that the total surface area of a cuboid is area I + area II + area III + area IV +area V + area VI

$$= h \times l + b \times l + b \times h + l \times h + b \times h + l \times b$$

So total surface area $= 2 (h \times l + b \times h + b \times l) = 2(lb + bh + hl)$

where h, l and b are the height, length and width of the cuboid respectively.

Suppose the height, length and width of the box shown above are 20 cm, 15 cm and 10 cm respectively.

Then the total surface area $= 2 (20 \times 15 + 20 \times 10 + 10 \times 15)$

$= 2 (300 + 200 + 150) = 1300 \text{ m}^2$.

TRY THESE

Find the total surface area of the following cuboids (Fig 11.31):

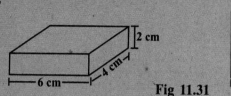
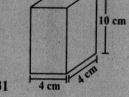

Fig 11.31

- The side walls (the faces excluding the top and bottom) make the lateral surface area of the cuboid. For example, the total area of all the four walls of the cuboidal room in which you are sitting is the lateral surface area of this room (Fig 11.32). Hence, the lateral surface area of a cuboid is given by $2(h \times l + b \times h)$ or $2h (l + b)$.

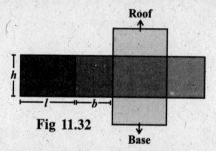

Fig 11.32

DO THIS

(i) Cover the lateral surface of a cuboidal duster (which your teacher uses in the class room) using a strip of brown sheet of paper, such that it just fits around the surface. Remove the paper. Measure the area of the paper. Is it the lateral surface area of the duster?

(ii) Measure length, width and height of your classroom and find
    (a) the total surface area of the room, ignoring the area of windows and doors.
    (b) the lateral surface area of this room.
    (c) the total area of the room which is to be white washed.

THINK, DISCUSS AND WRITE

1. Can we say that the total surface area of cuboid = lateral surface area + 2 × area of base?

2. If we interchange the lengths of the base and the height of a cuboid (Fig 11.33(i)) to get another cuboid (Fig 11.33(ii)), will its lateral surface area change?

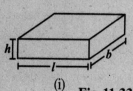
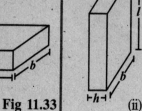

Fig 11.33

11.7.2 Cube

DO THIS

Draw the pattern shown on a squared paper and cut it out [Fig 11.34(i)]. (You know that this pattern is a net of a cube. Fold it along the lines [Fig 11.34(ii)] and tape the edges to form a cube [Fig 11.34(iii)].

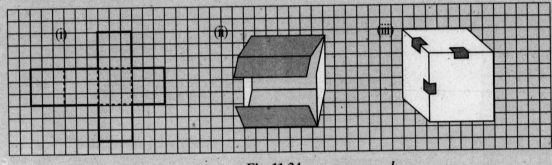

Fig 11.34

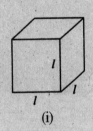

(i)

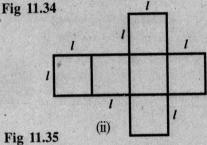

(ii)

Fig 11.35

(a) What is the length, width and height of the cube? Observe that all the faces of a cube are square in shape. This makes length, height and width of a cube equal (Fig 11.35(i)).

(b) Write the area of each of the faces. Are they equal?

(c) Write the total surface area of this cube.

(d) If each side of the cube is l, what will be the area of each face? (Fig 11.35(ii)).

Can we say that the total surface area of a cube of side l is $6l^2$?

TRY THESE

Find the surface area of cube A and lateral surface area of cube B (Fig 11.36).

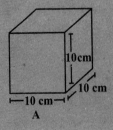

10 cm
10 cm
10 cm
A

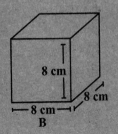

8 cm
8 cm
8 cm
B

Fig 11.36

THINK, DISCUSS AND WRITE

(i) Two cubes each with side b are joined to form a cuboid (Fig 11.37). What is the surface area of this cuboid? Is it $12b^2$? Is the surface area of cuboid formed by joining three such cubes, $18b^2$? Why?

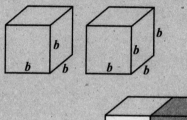
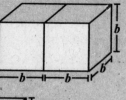

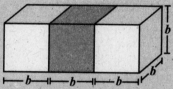

Fig 11.37

(ii) How will you arrange 12 cubes of equal length to form a cuboid of smallest surface area?

(iii) After the surface area of a cube is painted, the cube is cut into 64 smaller cubes of same dimensions (Fig 11.38). How many have no face painted? 1 face painted? 2 faces painted? 3 faces painted?

Fig 11.38

11.7.3 Cylinders

Most of the cylinders we observe are right circular cylinders. For example, a tin, round pillars, tube lights, water pipes etc.

DO THIS

(i) Take a cylindrical can or box and trace the base of the can on graph paper and cut it [Fig 11.39(i)]. Take another graph paper in such a way that its width is equal to the height of the can. Wrap the strip around the can such that it just fits around the can (remove the excess paper) [Fig 11.39(ii)].

Tape the pieces [Fig 11.39(iii)] together to form a cylinder [Fig 11.39(iv)]. What is the shape of the paper that goes around the can?

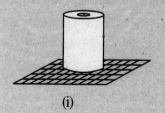
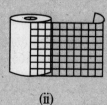
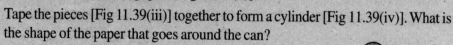

(i)　　　　(ii)　　　　(iii)　　　　(iv)

Fig 11.39

Of course it is rectangular in shape. When you tape the parts of this cylinder together, the length of the rectangular strip is equal to the circumference of the circle. Record the radius (r) of the circular base, length (l) and width (h) of the rectangular strip. Is $2\pi r$ = length of the strip. Check if the area of rectangular strip is $2\pi rh$. Count how many square units of the squared paper are used to form the cylinder. Check if this count is approximately equal to $2\pi r\,(r+h)$.

(ii) We can deduce the relation $2\pi r\,(r+h)$ as the surface area of a cylinder in another way. Imagine cutting up a cylinder as shown below (Fig 11.40).

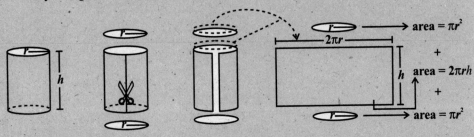

Fig 11.40

Note: We take π to be $\dfrac{22}{7}$ unless otherwise stated.

The lateral (or curved) surface area of a cylinder is $2\pi rh$.

The total surface area of a cylinder $= \pi r^2 + 2\pi rh + \pi r^2$

$$= 2\pi r^2 + 2\pi rh \text{ or } 2\pi r\,(r+h)$$

TRY THESE

Find total surface area of the following cylinders (Fig 11.41)

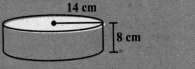

14 cm

8 cm

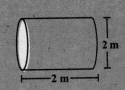

2 m

2 m

Fig 11.41

THINK, DISCUSS AND WRITE

Note that lateral surface area of a cylinder is the circumference of base × height of cylinder. Can we write lateral surface area of a cuboid as perimeter of base × height of cuboid?

Example 4: An aquarium is in the form of a cuboid whose external measures are 80 cm × 30 cm × 40 cm. The base, side faces and back face are to be covered with a coloured paper. Find the area of the paper needed?

Solution: The length of the aquarium $= l = 80$ cm

Width of the aquarium $= b = 30$ cm

Height of the aquarium = h = 40 cm

Area of the base = $l \times b$ = 80 × 30 = 2400 cm^2

Area of the side face = $b \times h$ = 30 × 40 = 1200 cm^2

Area of the back face = $l \times h$ = 80 × 40 = 3200 cm^2

Required area = Area of the base + area of the back face

+ (2 × area of a side face)

= 2400 + 3200 + (2 × 1200) = 8000 cm^2

Hence the area of the coloured paper required is 8000 cm^2.

Example 5: The internal measures of a cuboidal room are 12 m × 8 m × 4 m. Find the total cost of whitewashing all four walls of a room, if the cost of white washing is ₹ 5 per m^2. What will be the cost of white washing if the ceiling of the room is also whitewashed.

Solution: Let the length of the room = l = 12 m

Width of the room = b = 8 m

Height of the room = h = 4 m

Area of the four walls of the room = Perimeter of the base × Height of the room

= 2 $(l + b) \times h$ = 2 (12 + 8) × 4

= 2 × 20 × 4 = 160 m^2.

Cost of white washing per m^2 = ₹ 5

Hence the total cost of white washing four walls of the room = ₹ (160 × 5) = ₹ 800

Area of ceiling is 12 × 8 = 96 m^2

Cost of white washing the ceiling = ₹ (96 × 5) = ₹ 480

So the total cost of white washing = ₹ (800 + 480) = ₹ 1280

Example 6: In a building there are 24 cylindrical pillars. The radius of each pillar is 28 cm and height is 4 m. Find the total cost of painting the curved surface area of all pillars at the rate of ₹ 8 per m^2.

Solution: Radius of cylindrical pillar, r = 28 cm = 0.28 m

height, h = 4 m

curved surface area of a cylinder = $2\pi rh$

curved surface area of a pillar = $2 \times \dfrac{22}{7} \times 0.28 \times 4$ = 7.04 m^2

curved surface area of 24 such pillar = 7.04 × 24 = 168.96 m^2

cost of painting an area of 1 m^2 = ₹ 8

Therefore, cost of painting 1689.6 m^2 = 168.96 × 8 = ₹ 1351.68

Example 7: Find the height of a cylinder whose radius is 7 cm and the total surface area is 968 cm^2.

Solution: Let height of the cylinder = h, radius = r = 7cm

Total surface area = $2\pi r (h + r)$

i.e., $2 \times \dfrac{22}{7} \times 7 \times (7 + h) = 968$

$h = 15$ cm

Hence, the height of the cylinder is 15 cm.

EXERCISE 11.3

1. There are two cuboidal boxes as shown in the adjoining figure. Which box requires the lesser amount of material to make?

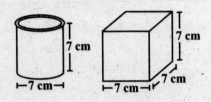

(a)   (b)

2. A suitcase with measures 80 cm × 48 cm × 24 cm is to be covered with a tarpaulin cloth. How many metres of tarpaulin of width 96 cm is required to cover 100 such suitcases?

3. Find the side of a cube whose surface area is 600 cm².

4. Rukhsar painted the outside of the cabinet of measure 1 m × 2 m × 1.5 m. How much surface area did she cover if she painted all except the bottom of the cabinet.

5. Daniel is painting the walls and ceiling of a cuboidal hall with length, breadth and height of 15 m, 10 m and 7 m respectively. From each can of paint 100 m² of area is painted.

   How many cans of paint will she need to paint the room?

6. Describe how the two figures at the right are alike and how they are different. Which box has larger lateral surface area?

7. A closed cylindrical tank of radius 7 m and height 3 m is made from a sheet of metal. How much sheet of metal is required?

8. The lateral surface area of a hollow cylinder is 4224 cm². It is cut along its height and formed a rectangular sheet of width 33 cm. Find the perimeter of rectangular sheet?

9. A road roller takes 750 complete revolutions to move once over to level a road. Find the area of the road if the diameter of a road roller is 84 cm and length is 1 m.

10. A company packages its milk powder in cylindrical container whose base has a diameter of 14 cm and height 20 cm. Company places a label around the surface of the container (as shown in the figure). If the label is placed 2 cm from top and bottom, what is the area of the label.

11.8 Volume of Cube, Cuboid and Cylinder

Amount of space occupied by a three dimensional object is called its **volume**. Try to compare the volume of objects surrounding you. For example, volume of a room is greater than the volume of an almirah kept inside it. Similarly, volume of your pencil box is greater than the volume of the pen and the eraser kept inside it.

Can you measure volume of either of these objects?

Remember, we use square units to find the area of a region. Here we will use cubic units to find the volume of a solid, as cube is the most convenient solid shape (just as square is the most convenient shape to measure area of a region).

For finding the area we divide the region into square units, similarly, to find the volume of a solid we need to divide it into cubical units.

Observe that the volume of each of the adjoining solids is 8 cubic units (Fig 11.42).

Fig 11.42

We can say that the volume of a solid is measured by counting the number of unit cubes it contains. Cubic units which we generally use to measure volume are

$$1 \text{ cubic cm} = 1 \text{ cm} \times 1 \text{ cm} \times 1 \text{ cm} = 1 \text{ cm}^3$$
$$= 10 \text{ mm} \times 10 \text{ mm} \times 10 \text{ mm} = \text{............... mm}^3$$
$$1 \text{ cubic m} = 1 \text{ m} \times 1 \text{ m} \times 1 \text{ m} = 1 \text{ m}^3$$
$$= \text{............................... cm}^3$$
$$1 \text{ cubic mm} = 1 \text{ mm} \times 1 \text{ mm} \times 1 \text{ mm} = 1 \text{ mm}^3$$
$$= 0.1 \text{ cm} \times 0.1 \text{ cm} \times 0.1 \text{ cm} = \text{...................... cm}^3$$

We now find some expressions to find volume of a cuboid, cube and cylinder. Let us take each solid one by one.

11.8.1 Cuboid

Take 36 cubes of equal size (i.e., length of each cube is same). Arrange them to form a cuboid. You can arrange them in many ways. Observe the following table and fill in the blanks.

cuboid	length	breadth	height	$l \times b \times h = V$
(i) 12 units, 3 units, 1	12	3	1	$12 \times 3 \times 1 = 36$
(ii) 6, 3, 2	...	...	...	...

		...	...	...	...
(iii)	9, 4, 1	...	...	...	...
(iv)	6, 6, 1	...	...	...	...

What do you observe?

Since we have used 36 cubes to form these cuboids, volume of each cuboid is 36 cubic units. Also volume of each cuboid is equal to the product of length, breadth and height of the cuboid. From the above example we can say volume of cuboid = $l \times b \times h$. Since $l \times b$ is the area of its base we can also say that,

Volume of cuboid = area of the base × height

DO THIS

Take a sheet of paper. Measure its area. Pile up such sheets of paper of same size to make a cuboid (Fig 11.43). Measure the height of this pile. Find the volume of the cuboid by finding the product of the area of the sheet and the height of this pile of sheets.

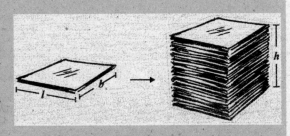

Fig 11.43

This activity illustrates the idea that volume of a solid can be deduced by this method also (if the base and top of the solid are congruent and parallel to each other and its edges are perpendicular to the base). Can you think of such objects whose volume can be found by using this method?

TRY THESE

Find the volume of the following cuboids (Fig 11.44).

(i) 8 cm × 3 cm × 2 cm   3 cm, 24m²

Fig 11.44

11.8.2 Cube

The cube is a special case of a cuboid, where $l = b = h$.
Hence, volume of cube $= l \times l \times l = l^3$

TRY THESE

Find the volume of the following cubes

(a) with a side 4 cm (b) with a side 1.5 m

DO THIS

Arrange 64 cubes of equal size in as many ways as you can to form a cuboid. Find the surface area of each arrangement. Can solid shapes of same volume have same surface area?

THINK, DISCUSS AND WRITE

A company sells biscuits. For packing purpose they are using cuboidal boxes: box A→3 cm × 8 cm × 20 cm, box B → 4 cm × 12 cm × 10 cm. What size of the box will be economical for the company? Why? Can you suggest any other size (dimensions) which has the same volume but is more economical than these?

11.8.3 Cylinder

We know that volume of a cuboid can be found by finding the product of area of base and its height. Can we find the volume of a cylinder in the same way?

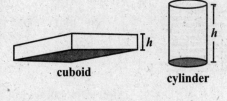

cuboid   cylinder

Just like cuboid, cylinder has got a top and a base which are congruent and parallel to each other. Its lateral surface is also perpendicular to the base, just like cuboid.

So   the Volume of a cuboid = area of base × height

$$= l \times b \times h = lbh$$

Volume of cylinder = area of base × height

$$= \pi r^2 \times h = \pi r^2 h$$

area of base
$(= \pi r^2)$

TRY THESE

Find the volume of the following cylinders.

(i) 7 cm   10 cm   (ii) 2 m   250 m²

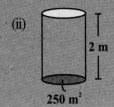

11.9 Volume and Capacity

There is not much difference between these two words.

(a) Volume refers to the amount of space occupied by an object.

(b) Capacity refers to the quantity that a container holds.

Note: If a water tin holds 100 cm³ of water then the capacity of the water tin is 100 cm³.

Capacity is also measured in terms of litres. The relation between litre and cm³ is, 1 mL = 1 cm³,1 L = 1000 cm³. Thus, 1 m³ = 1000000 cm³ = 1000 L.

Example 8: Find the height of a cuboid whose volume is 275 cm³ and base area is 25 cm².

Solution: Volume of a cuboid = Base area × Height

$$\text{Hence height of the cuboid} = \frac{\text{Volume of cuboid}}{\text{Base area}}$$

$$= \frac{275}{25} = 11 \text{ cm}$$

Height of the cuboid is 11 cm.

Example 9: A godown is in the form of a cuboid of measures 60 m × 40 m × 30 m. How many cuboidal boxes can be stored in it if the volume of one box is 0.8 m³ ?

Solution: Volume of one box = 0.8 m³

Volume of godown = 60 × 40 × 30 = 72000 m³

$$\text{Number of boxes that can be stored in the godown} = \frac{\text{Volume of the godown}}{\text{Volume of one box}}$$

$$= \frac{60 \times 40 \times 30}{0.8} = 90,000$$

Hence the number of cuboidal boxes that can be stored in the godown is 90,000.

Example 10: A rectangular paper of width 14 cm is rolled along its width and a cylinder of radius 20 cm is formed. Find the volume of the cylinder (Fig 11.45). (Take $\frac{22}{7}$ for π)

Solution: A cylinder is formed by rolling a rectangle about its width. Hence the width of the paper becomes height and radius of the cylinder is 20 cm.

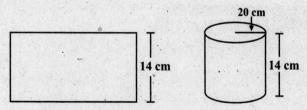

Fig 11.45

Height of the cylinder = h = 14 cm

Radius = r = 20 cm

Volume of the cylinder = V = $\pi\, r^2 h$

$$= \frac{22}{7} \times 20 \times 20 \times 14 = 17600 \text{ cm}^3$$

Hence, the volume of the cylinder is 17600 cm³.

Example 11: A rectangular piece of paper 11 cm × 4 cm is folded without overlapping to make a cylinder of height 4 cm. Find the volume of the cylinder.

Solution: Length of the paper becomes the perimeter of the base of the cylinder and width becomes height.

Let radius of the cylinder = r and height = h

Perimeter of the base of the cylinder = $2\pi r = 11$

or $$2 \times \frac{22}{7} \times r = 11$$

Therefore, $$r = \frac{7}{4} \text{ cm}$$

Volume of the cylinder = V = $\pi r^2 h$

$$= \frac{22}{7} \times \frac{7}{4} \times \frac{7}{4} \times 4 \text{ cm}^3 = 38.5 \text{ cm}^3.$$

Hence the volume of the cylinder is 38.5 cm³.

EXERCISE 11.4

1. Given a cylindrical tank, in which situation will you find surface area and in which situation volume.
   (a) To find how much it can hold.
   (b) Number of cement bags required to plaster it.
   (c) To find the number of smaller tanks that can be filled with water from it.

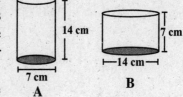

2. Diameter of cylinder A is 7 cm, and the height is 14 cm. Diameter of cylinder B is 14 cm and height is 7 cm. Without doing any calculations can you suggest whose volume is greater? Verify it by finding the volume of both the cylinders. Check whether the cylinder with greater volume also has greater surface area?

3. Find the height of a cuboid whose base area is 180 cm² and volume is 900 cm³?

4. A cuboid is of dimensions 60 cm × 54 cm × 30 cm. How many small cubes with side 6 cm can be placed in the given cuboid?

5. Find the height of the cylinder whose volume is 1.54 m³ and diameter of the base is 140 cm ?

6. A milk tank is in the form of cylinder whose radius is 1.5 m and length is 7 m. Find the quantity of milk in litres that can be stored in the tank?

7. If each edge of a cube is doubled,
   (i) how many times will its surface area increase?
   (ii) how many times will its volume increase?

8. Water is pouring into a cubiodal reservoir at the rate of 60 litres per minute. If the volume of reservoir is 108 m³, find the number of hours it will take to fill the reservoir.

WHAT HAVE WE DISCUSSED?

1. Area of
   (i) a trapezium = half of the sum of the lengths of parallel sides × perpendicular distance between them.
   (ii) a rhombus = half the product of its diagonals.

2. **Surface area** of a solid is the sum of the areas of its faces.

3. Surface area of
   a cuboid = $2(lb + bh + hl)$
   a cube = $6l^2$
   a cylinder = $2\pi r(r + h)$

4. Amount of region occupied by a solid is called its **volume**.

5. Volume of
   a cuboid = $l \times b \times h$
   a cube = l^3
   a cylinder = $\pi r^2 h$

6. (i) $1 \text{ cm}^3 = 1 \text{ mL}$
   (ii) $1 \text{ L} = 1000 \text{ cm}^3$
   (iii) $1 \text{ m}^3 = 1000000 \text{ cm}^3 = 1000 \text{ L}$

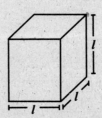

Exponents and Powers

CHAPTER 12

0852CH12

12.1 Introduction

Do you know?

Mass of earth is 5,970,000,000,000, 000, 000, 000, 000 kg. We have already learnt in earlier class how to write such large numbers more conveniently using exponents, as, 5.97×10^{24} kg.

We read 10^{24} as 10 raised to the power 24.

We know $2^5 = 2 \times 2 \times 2 \times 2 \times 2$

and $2^m = 2 \times 2 \times 2 \times 2 \times ... \times 2 \times 2 ...$ (m times)

Let us now find what is 2^{-2} is equal to?

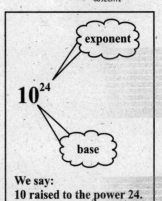

We say:
10 raised to the power 24.

Exponent is a negative integer.

12.2 Powers with Negative Exponents

You know that, $10^2 = 10 \times 10 = 100$

$$10^1 = 10 = \frac{100}{10}$$

$$10^0 = 1 = \frac{10}{10}$$

$$10^{-1} = ?$$

As the exponent decreases by 1, the value becomes one-tenth of the previous value.

Continuing the above pattern we get, $10^{-1} = \frac{1}{10}$

Similarly $10^{-2} = \frac{1}{10} \div 10 = \frac{1}{10} \times \frac{1}{10} = \frac{1}{100} = \frac{1}{10^2}$

$$10^{-3} = \frac{1}{100} \div 10 = \frac{1}{100} \times \frac{1}{10} = \frac{1}{1000} = \frac{1}{10^3}$$

What is 10^{-10} equal to?

Now consider the following.

$$3^3 = 3 \times 3 \times 3 = 27$$

$$3^2 = 3 \times 3 = 9 = \frac{27}{3}$$

$$3^1 = 3 = \frac{9}{3}$$

$$3^0 = 1 = \frac{3}{3}$$

The previous number is divided by the base 3.

So looking at the above pattern, we say

$$3^{-1} = 1 \div 3 = \frac{1}{3}$$

$$3^{-2} = \frac{1}{3} \div 3 = \frac{1}{3 \times 3} = \frac{1}{3^2}$$

$$3^{-3} = \frac{1}{3^2} \div 3 = \frac{1}{3^2} \times \frac{1}{3} = \frac{1}{3^3}$$

You can now find the value of 2^{-2} in a similar manner.

We have,

$$10^{-2} = \frac{1}{10^2} \qquad \text{or} \qquad 10^2 = \frac{1}{10^{-2}}$$

$$10^{-3} = \frac{1}{10^3} \qquad \text{or} \qquad 10^3 = \frac{1}{10^{-3}}$$

$$3^{-2} = \frac{1}{3^2} \qquad \text{or} \qquad 3^2 = \frac{1}{3^{-2}} \text{ etc.}$$

In general, we can say that for any non-zero integer a, $a^{-m} = \frac{1}{a^m}$, where m is a positive integer. a^{-m} is the multiplicative inverse of a^m.

TRY THESE

Find the multiplicative inverse of the following.

(i) 2^{-4} (ii) 10^{-5} (iii) 7^{-2} (iv) 5^{-3} (v) 10^{-100}

We learnt how to write numbers like 1425 in expanded form using exponents as $1 \times 10^3 + 4 \times 10^2 + 2 \times 10^1 + 5 \times 10^0$.

Let us see how to express 1425.36 in expanded form in a similar way.

We have $1425.36 = 1 \times 1000 + 4 \times 100 + 2 \times 10 + 5 \times 1 + \frac{3}{10} + \frac{6}{100}$

$$= 1 \times 10^3 + 4 \times 10^2 + 2 \times 10 + 5 \times 1 + 3 \times 10^{-1} + 6 \times 10^{-2}$$

$$10^{-1} = \frac{1}{10}, \quad 10^{-2} = \frac{1}{10^2} = \frac{1}{100}$$

TRY THESE

Expand the following numbers using exponents.

(i) 1025.63   (ii) 1256.249

12.3 Laws of Exponents

We have learnt that for any non-zero integer a, $a^m \times a^n = a^{m+n}$, where m and n are natural numbers. Does this law also hold if the exponents are negative? Let us explore.

(i) We know that $2^{-3} = \dfrac{1}{2^3}$ and $2^{-2} = \dfrac{1}{2^2}$

> $a^{-m} = \dfrac{1}{a^m}$ for any non-zero integer a.

Therefore, $2^{-3} \times 2^{-2} = \dfrac{1}{2^3} \times \dfrac{1}{2^2} = \dfrac{1}{2^3 \times 2^2} = \dfrac{1}{2^{3+2}} = 2^{-5}$

> -5 is the sum of two exponents -3 and -2

(ii) Take $(-3)^{-4} \times (-3)^{-3}$

$(-3)^{-4} \times (-3)^{-3} = \dfrac{1}{(-3)^4} \times \dfrac{1}{(-3)^3}$

$= \dfrac{1}{(-3)^4 \times (-3)^3} = \dfrac{1}{(-3)^{4+3}} = (-3)^{-7}$

> $(-4) + (-3) = -7$

(iii) Now consider $5^{-2} \times 5^4$

> $(-2) + 4 = 2$

> In Class VII, you have learnt that for any non-zero integer a, $\dfrac{a^m}{a^n} = a^{m-n}$, where m and n are natural numbers and $m > n$.

$5^{-2} \times 5^4 = \dfrac{1}{5^2} \times 5^4 = \dfrac{5^4}{5^2} = 5^{4-2} = 5^{(2)}$

(iv) Now consider $(-5)^{-4} \times (-5)^2$

$(-5)^{-4} \times (-5)^2 = \dfrac{1}{(-5)^4} \times (-5)^2 = \dfrac{(-5)^2}{(-5)^4} = \dfrac{1}{(-5)^4 \times (-5)^{-2}}$

$= \dfrac{1}{(-5)^{4-2}} = (-5)^{-(2)}$

> $(-4) + 2 = -2$

In general, we can say that for any non-zero integer a,
$a^m \times a^n = a^{m+n}$, where m and n are integers.

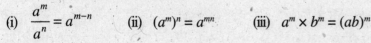

TRY THESE

Simplify and write in exponential form.
(i) $(-2)^{-3} \times (-2)^{-4}$ (ii) $p^3 \times p^{-10}$ (iii) $3^2 \times 3^{-5} \times 3^6$

On the same lines you can verify the following laws of exponents, where a and b are non zero integers and m, n are any integers.

(i) $\dfrac{a^m}{a^n} = a^{m-n}$ (ii) $(a^m)^n = a^{mn}$ (iii) $a^m \times b^m = (ab)^m$

> These laws you have studied in Class VII for positive exponents only.

(iv) $\dfrac{a^m}{b^m} = \left(\dfrac{a}{b}\right)^m$ (v) $a^0 = 1$

Let us solve some examples using the above Laws of Exponents.

Example 1: Find the value of

(i) 2^{-3} (ii) $\dfrac{1}{3^{-2}}$

Solution:

(i) $2^{-3} = \dfrac{1}{2^3} = \dfrac{1}{8}$ (ii) $\dfrac{1}{3^{-2}} = 3^2 = 3 \times 3 = 9$

Example 2: Simplify

(i) $(-4)^5 \times (-4)^{-10}$ (ii) $2^5 \div 2^{-6}$

Solution:

(i) $(-4)^5 \times (-4)^{-10} = (-4)^{(5-10)} = (-4)^{-5} = \dfrac{1}{(-4)^5}$ $\left(a^m \times a^n = a^{m+n},\ a^{-m} = \dfrac{1}{a^m}\right)$

(ii) $2^5 \div 2^{-6} = 2^{5-(-6)} = 2^{11}$ $(a^m \div a^n = a^{m-n})$

Example 3: Express 4^{-3} as a power with the base 2.

Solution: We have, $4 = 2 \times 2 = 2^2$

Therefore, $(4)^{-3} = (2 \times 2)^{-3} = (2^2)^{-3} = 2^{2 \times (-3)} = 2^{-6}$ $[(a^m)^n = a^{mn}]$

Example 4: Simplify and write the answer in the exponential form.

(i) $(2^5 \div 2^8)^5 \times 2^{-5}$

(ii) $(-4)^{-3} \times (5)^{-3} \times (-5)^{-3}$

(iii) $\dfrac{1}{8} \times (3)^{-3}$

(iv) $(-3)^4 \times \left(\dfrac{5}{3}\right)^4$

Solution:

(i) $(2^5 \div 2^8)^5 \times 2^{-5} = (2^{5-8})^5 \times 2^{-5} = (2^{-3})^5 \times 2^{-5} = 2^{-15-5} = 2^{-20} = \dfrac{1}{2^{20}}$

(ii) $(-4)^{-3} \times (5)^{-3} \times (-5)^{-3} = [(-4) \times 5 \times (-5)]^{-3} = [100]^{-3} = \dfrac{1}{100^3}$

$\left[\text{using the law } a^m \times b^m = (ab)^m,\ a^{-m} = \dfrac{1}{a^m}\right]$

(iii) $\dfrac{1}{8} \times (3)^{-3} = \dfrac{1}{2^3} \times (3)^{-3} = 2^{-3} \times 3^{-3} = (2 \times 3)^{-3} = 6^{-3} = \dfrac{1}{6^3}$

(iv) $(-3)^4 \times \left(\dfrac{5}{3}\right)^4 = (-1 \times 3)^4 \times \dfrac{5^4}{3^4} = (-1)^4 \times 3^4 \times \dfrac{5^4}{3^4}$

$= (-1)^4 \times 5^4 = 5^4$ $[(-1)^4 = 1]$

Example 5: Find m so that $(-3)^{m+1} \times (-3)^5 = (-3)^7$

Solution: $(-3)^{m+1} \times (-3)^5 = (-3)^7$

$(-3)^{m+1+5} = (-3)^7$

$(-3)^{m+6} = (-3)^7$

On both the sides powers have the same base different from 1 and – 1, so their exponents must be equal.

Therefore, $m + 6 = 7$
or $m = 7 - 6 = 1$

$a^n = 1$ only if $n = 0$. This will work for any a.
For $a = 1$, $1^1 = 1^2 = 1^3 = 1^{-2} = ... = 1$ or $(1)^n = 1$ for infinitely many n.
For $a = -1$,
$(-1)^0 = (-1)^2 = (-1)^4 = (-1)^{-2} = ... = 1$ or $(-1)^p = 1$ for any even integer p.

Example 6: Find the value of $\left(\dfrac{2}{3}\right)^{-2}$.

Solution: $\left(\dfrac{2}{3}\right)^{-2} = \dfrac{2^{-2}}{3^{-2}} = \dfrac{3^2}{2^2} = \dfrac{9}{4}$

Example 7: Simplify (i) $\left\{\left(\dfrac{1}{3}\right)^{-2} - \left(\dfrac{1}{2}\right)^{-3}\right\} \div \left(\dfrac{1}{4}\right)^{-2}$

(ii) $\left(\dfrac{5}{8}\right)^{-7} \times \left(\dfrac{8}{5}\right)^{-5}$

$\left(\dfrac{2}{3}\right)^{-2} = \dfrac{2^{-2}}{3^{-2}} = \dfrac{3^2}{2^2} = \left(\dfrac{3}{2}\right)^2$

In general, $\left(\dfrac{a}{b}\right)^{-m} = \left(\dfrac{b}{a}\right)^m$

Solution:

(i) $\left\{\left(\dfrac{1}{3}\right)^{-2} - \left(\dfrac{1}{2}\right)^{-3}\right\} \div \left(\dfrac{1}{4}\right)^{-2} = \left\{\dfrac{1^{-2}}{3^{-2}} - \dfrac{1^{-3}}{2^{-3}}\right\} \div \dfrac{1^{-2}}{4^{-2}}$

$= \left\{\dfrac{3^2}{1^2} - \dfrac{2^3}{1^3}\right\} \div \dfrac{4^2}{1^2} = \{9 - 8\} \div 16 = \dfrac{1}{16}$

(ii) $\left(\dfrac{5}{8}\right)^{-7} \times \left(\dfrac{8}{5}\right)^{-5} = \dfrac{5^{-7}}{8^{-7}} \times \dfrac{8^{-5}}{5^{-5}} = \dfrac{5^{-7}}{5^{-5}} \times \dfrac{8^{-5}}{8^{-7}} = 5^{(-7)-(-5)} \times 8^{(-5)-(-7)}$

$= 5^{-2} \times 8^2 = \dfrac{8^2}{5^2} = \dfrac{64}{25}$

EXERCISE 12.1

1. Evaluate.

   (i) 3^{-2} (ii) $(-4)^{-2}$ (iii) $\left(\dfrac{1}{2}\right)^{-5}$

2. Simplify and express the result in power notation with positive exponent.

   (i) $(-4)^5 \div (-4)^8$ (ii) $\left(\dfrac{1}{2^3}\right)^2$

   (iii) $(-3)^4 \times \left(\dfrac{5}{3}\right)^4$ (iv) $(3^{-7} \div 3^{-10}) \times 3^{-5}$ (v) $2^{-3} \times (-7)^{-3}$

3. Find the value of.

   (i) $(3^0 + 4^{-1}) \times 2^2$ (ii) $(2^{-1} \times 4^{-1}) \div 2^{-2}$ (iii) $\left(\dfrac{1}{2}\right)^{-2} + \left(\dfrac{1}{3}\right)^{-2} + \left(\dfrac{1}{4}\right)^{-2}$

(iv) $(3^{-1} + 4^{-1} + 5^{-1})^0$ (v) $\left\{\left(\dfrac{-2}{3}\right)^{-2}\right\}^2$

4. Evaluate (i) $\dfrac{8^{-1} \times 5^3}{2^{-4}}$ (ii) $(5^{-1} \times 2^{-1}) \times 6^{-1}$

5. Find the value of m for which $5^m \div 5^{-3} = 5^5$.

6. Evaluate (i) $\left\{\left(\dfrac{1}{3}\right)^{-1} - \left(\dfrac{1}{4}\right)^{-1}\right\}^{-1}$ (ii) $\left(\dfrac{5}{8}\right)^{-7} \times \left(\dfrac{8}{5}\right)^{-4}$

7. Simplify.

   (i) $\dfrac{25 \times t^{-4}}{5^{-3} \times 10 \times t^{-8}}$ $(t \neq 0)$ (ii) $\dfrac{3^{-5} \times 10^{-5} \times 125}{5^{-7} \times 6^{-5}}$

12.4 Use of Exponents to Express Small Numbers in Standard Form

Observe the following facts.

1. The distance from the Earth to the Sun is 149,600,000,000 m.
2. The speed of light is 300,000,000 m/sec.
3. Thickness of Class VII Mathematics book is 20 mm.
4. The average diameter of a Red Blood Cell is 0.000007 mm.
5. The thickness of human hair is in the range of 0.005 cm to 0.01 cm.
6. The distance of moon from the Earth is 384, 467, 000 m (approx).
7. The size of a plant cell is 0.00001275 m.
8. Average radius of the Sun is 695000 km.
9. Mass of propellant in a space shuttle solid rocket booster is 503600 kg.
10. Thickness of a piece of paper is 0.0016 cm.
11. Diameter of a wire on a computer chip is 0.000003 m.
12. The height of Mount Everest is 8848 m.

Observe that there are few numbers which we can read like 2 cm, 8848 m, 6,95,000 km. There are some large numbers like 150,000,000,000 m and some very small numbers like 0.000007 m.

Identify very large and very small numbers from the above facts and write them in the adjacent table:

Very large numbers	Very small numbers
150,000,000,000 m	0.000007 m
-------------	-------------
-------------	-------------
-------------	-------------
-------------	-------------

We have learnt how to express very large numbers in standard form in the previous class.

For example: $150,000,000,000 = 1.5 \times 10^{11}$

Now, let us try to express 0.000007 m in standard form.

$$0.000007 = \frac{7}{1000000} = \frac{7}{10^6} = 7 \times 10^{-6}$$

$$0.000007 \text{ m} = 7 \times 10^{-6} \text{ m}$$

Similarly, consider the thickness of a piece of paper which is 0.0016 cm.

$$0.0016 = \frac{16}{10000} = \frac{1.6 \times 10}{10^4} = 1.6 \times 10 \times 10^{-4}$$
$$= 1.6 \times 10^{-3}$$

Therefore, we can say thickness of paper is 1.6×10^{-3} cm.

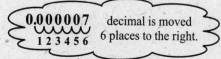

Again notice
0.0016   decimal is moved
1 2 3   3 places to the right.

TRY THESE

1. Write the following numbers in standard form.
   (i) 0.000000564   (ii) 0.0000021   (iii) 21600000   (iv) 15240000
2. Write all the facts given in the standard form.

12.4.1 Comparing very large and very small numbers

The diameter of the Sun is 1.4×10^9 m and the diameter of the Earth is 1.2756×10^7 m. Suppose you want to compare the diameter of the Earth, with the diameter of the Sun.

Diameter of the Sun = 1.4×10^9 m
Diameter of the earth = 1.2756×10^7 m

Therefore $\dfrac{1.4 \times 10^9}{1.2756 \times 10^7} = \dfrac{1.4 \times 10^{9-7}}{1.2756} = \dfrac{1.4 \times 100}{1.2756}$ which is approximately 100

So, the diameter of the Sun is about 100 times the diameter of the earth.

Let us compare the size of a Red Blood cell which is 0.000007 m to that of a plant cell which is 0.00001275 m.

Size of Red Blood cell = 0.000007 m = 7×10^{-6} m
Size of plant cell = 0.00001275 = 1.275×10^{-5} m

Therefore, $\dfrac{7 \times 10^{-6}}{1.275 \times 10^{-5}} = \dfrac{7 \times 10^{-6-(-5)}}{1.275} = \dfrac{7 \times 10^{-1}}{1.275} = \dfrac{0.7}{1.275} = \dfrac{0.7}{1.3} = \dfrac{1}{2}$ (approx.)

So a red blood cell is half of plant cell in size.

Mass of earth is 5.97×10^{24} kg and mass of moon is 7.35×10^{22} kg. What is the total mass?

Total mass = 5.97×10^{24} kg + 7.35×10^{22} kg.
= $5.97 \times 100 \times 10^{22} + 7.35 \times 10^{22}$
= $597 \times 10^{22} + 7.35 \times 10^{22}$
= $(597 + 7.35) \times 10^{22}$
= 604.35×10^{22} kg.

When we have to add numbers in standard form, we convert them into numbers with the same exponents.

The distance between Sun and Earth is 1.496×10^{11} m and the distance between Earth and Moon is 3.84×10^8 m.

During solar eclipse moon comes in between Earth and Sun.

At that time what is the distance between Moon and Sun.

Distance between Sun and Earth = 1.496×10^{11} m
Distance between Earth and Moon = 3.84×10^{8} m
Distance between Sun and Moon = $1.496 \times 10^{11} - 3.84 \times 10^{8}$
$$= 1.496 \times 1000 \times 10^{8} - 3.84 \times 10^{8}$$
$$= (1496 - 3.84) \times 10^{8} \text{ m} = 1492.16 \times 10^{8} \text{ m}$$

Example 8: Express the following numbers in standard form.

(i) 0.000035   (ii) 4050000

Solution: (i) $0.000035 = 3.5 \times 10^{-5}$ (ii) $4050000 = 4.05 \times 10^{6}$

Example 9: Express the following numbers in usual form.

(i) 3.52×10^{5} (ii) 7.54×10^{-4} (iii) 3×10^{-5}

Solution:

(i) $3.52 \times 10^{5} = 3.52 \times 100000 = 352000$

(ii) $7.54 \times 10^{-4} = \dfrac{7.54}{10^{4}} = \dfrac{7.54}{10000} = 0.000754$

(iii) $3 \times 10^{-5} = \dfrac{3}{10^{5}} = \dfrac{3}{100000} = 0.00003$

> Again we need to convert numbers in standard form into a numbers with the same exponents.

EXERCISE 12.2

1. Express the following numbers in standard form.
   (i) 0.0000000000085   (ii) 0.00000000000942
   (iii) 6020000000000000   (iv) 0.00000000837
   (v) 31860000000

2. Express the following numbers in usual form.
   (i) 3.02×10^{-6} (ii) 4.5×10^{4} (iii) 3×10^{-8}
   (iv) 1.0001×10^{9} (v) 5.8×10^{12} (vi) 3.61492×10^{6}

3. Express the number appearing in the following statements in standard form.

   (i) 1 micron is equal to $\dfrac{1}{1000000}$ m.

   (ii) Charge of an electron is 0.000,000,000,000,000,000,16 coulomb.

   (iii) Size of a bacteria is 0.0000005 m

   (iv) Size of a plant cell is 0.00001275 m

   (v) Thickness of a thick paper is 0.07 mm

4. In a stack there are 5 books each of thickness 20mm and 5 paper sheets each of thickness 0.016 mm. What is the total thickness of the stack.

WHAT HAVE WE DISCUSSED?

1. Numbers with negative exponents obey the following laws of exponents.
   (a) $a^{m} \times a^{n} = a^{m+n}$ (b) $a^{m} \div a^{n} = a^{m-n}$ (c) $(a^{m})^{n} = a^{mn}$

   (d) $a^{m} \times b^{m} = (ab)^{m}$ (e) $a^{0} = 1$ (f) $\dfrac{a^{m}}{b^{m}} = \left(\dfrac{a}{b}\right)^{m}$

2. Very small numbers can be expressed in standard form using negative exponents.

Direct and Inverse Proportions

0852CH13

13.1 Introduction

Mohan prepares tea for himself and his sister. He uses 300 mL of water, 2 spoons of sugar, 1 spoon of tea leaves and 50 mL of milk. How much quantity of each item will he need, if he has to make tea for five persons?

If two students take 20 minutes to arrange chairs for an assembly, then how much time would five students take to do the same job?

We come across many such situations in our day-to-day life, where we need to see variation in one quantity bringing in variation in the other quantity.

For example:

(i) If the number of articles purchased increases, the total cost also increases.

(ii) More the money deposited in a bank, more is the interest earned.

(iii) As the speed of a vehicle increases, the time taken to cover the same distance decreases.

(iv) For a given job, more the number of workers, less will be the time taken to complete the work.

Observe that change in one quantity leads to change in the other quantity.

Write five more such situations where change in one quantity leads to change in another quantity.

How do we find out the quantity of each item needed by Mohan? Or, the time five students take to complete the job?

To answer such questions, we now study some concepts of variation.

13.2 Direct Proportion

If the cost of 1 kg of sugar is ₹ 36, then what would be the cost of 3 kg sugar? It is ₹ 108.

Similarly, we can find the cost of 5 kg or 8 kg of sugar. Study the following table.

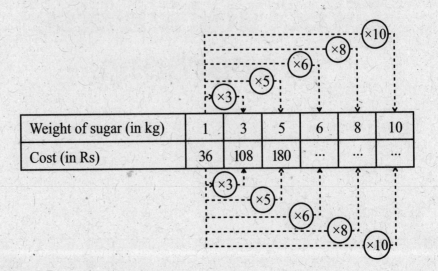

Weight of sugar (in kg)	1	3	5	6	8	10
Cost (in Rs)	36	108	180	...	...	...

Observe that as weight of sugar increases, cost also increases in such a manner that their ratio remains constant.

Take one more example. Suppose a car uses 4 litres of petrol to travel a distance of 60 km. How far will it travel using 12 litres? The answer is 180 km. How did we calculate it? Since petrol consumed in the second instance is 12 litres, i.e., three times of 4 litres, the distance travelled will also be three times of 60 km. In other words, when the petrol consumption becomes three-fold, the distance travelled is also three fold the previous one. Let the consumption of petrol be x litres and the corresponding distance travelled be y km . Now, complete the following table:

Petrol in litres (x)	4	8	12	15	20	25
Distance in km (y)	60	...	180	...	...	...

We find that as the value of x increases, value of y also increases in such a way that the ratio $\dfrac{x}{y}$ does not change; it remains constant (say k). In this case, it is $\dfrac{1}{15}$ (check it!).

We say that x and y are in direct proportion, if $\dfrac{x}{y} = k$ or $x = ky$.

In this example, $\dfrac{4}{60} = \dfrac{12}{180}$, where 4 and 12 are the quantities of petrol consumed in litres (x) and 60 and 180 are the distances (y) in km. So when x and y are in **direct proportion**, we can write $\dfrac{x_1}{y_1} = \dfrac{x_2}{y_2}$. [y_1, y_2 are values of y corresponding to the values x_1, x_2 of x respectively]

The consumption of petrol and the distance travelled by a car is a case of direct proportion. Similarly, the total amount spent and the number of articles purchased is also an example of direct proportion.

Think of a few more examples for direct proportion. Check whether Mohan [in the initial example] will take 750 mL of water, 5 spoons of sugar, $2\frac{1}{2}$ spoons of tea leaves and 125 mL of milk to prepare tea for five persons! Let us try to understand further the concept of direct proportion through the following activities.

DO THIS

(i) • Take a clock and fix its minute hand at 12.

   • Record the angle turned through by the minute hand from its original position and the time that has passed, in the following table:

Time Passed (T) (in minutes)	(T_1) 15	(T_2) 30	(T_3) 45	(T_4) 60
Angle turned (A) (in degree)	(A_1) 90	(A_2) ...	(A_3) ...	(A_4) ...
$\dfrac{T}{A}$	...	...	...	...

What do you observe about T and A? Do they increase together? Is $\dfrac{T}{A}$ same every time?

Is the angle turned through by the minute hand directly proportional to the time that has passed? Yes!

From the above table, you can also see

$$T_1 : T_2 = A_1 : A_2 \text{, because}$$
$$T_1 : T_2 = 15 : 30 \quad = 1:2$$
$$A_1 : A_2 = 90 : 180 \quad = 1:2$$

Check if $\quad T_2 : T_3 = A_2 : A_3 \text{ and } T_3 : T_4 = A_3 : A_4$

You can repeat this activity by choosing your own time interval.

(ii) Ask your friend to fill the following table and find the ratio of his age to the corresponding age of his mother.

	Age five years ago	Present age	Age after five years
Friend's age (F)			
Mother's age (M)			
$\dfrac{F}{M}$			

What do you observe?

Do F and M increase (or decrease) together? Is $\dfrac{F}{M}$ same every time? No!

You can repeat this activity with other friends and write down your observations.

Thus, variables increasing (or decreasing) together need not always be in direct proportion. For example:

(i) physical changes in human beings occur with time but not necessarily in a predetermined ratio.

(ii) changes in weight and height among individuals are not in any known proportion and

(iii) there is no direct relationship or ratio between the height of a tree and the number of leaves growing on its branches. Think of some more similar examples.

TRY THESE

1. Observe the following tables and find if x and y are directly proportional.

(i)

x	20	17	14	11	8	5	2
y	40	34	28	22	16	10	4

(ii)

x	6	10	14	18	22	26	30
y	4	8	12	16	20	24	28

(iii)

x	5	8	12	15	18	20
y	15	24	36	60	72	100

2. Principal = ₹ 1000, Rate = 8% per annum. Fill in the following table and find which type of interest (simple or compound) changes in direct proportion with time period.

$$\frac{P \times r \times t}{100}$$

$$P\left(1 + \frac{r}{100}\right)^t - P$$

Time period	1 year	2 years	3 years
Simple Interest (in ₹)			
Compound Interest (in ₹)			

THINK, DISCUSS AND WRITE

If we fix time period and the rate of interest, simple interest changes proportionally with principal. Would there be a similar relationship for compound interest? Why?

Let us consider some solved examples where we would use the concept of direct proportion.

Example 1: The cost of 5 metres of a particular quality of cloth is ₹ 210. Tabulate the cost of 2, 4, 10 and 13 metres of cloth of the same type.

Solution: Suppose the length of cloth is x metres and its cost, in ₹, is y.

x	2	4	5	10	13
y	y_2	y_3	210	y_4	y_5

As the length of cloth increases, cost of the cloth also increases in the same ratio. It is a case of direct proportion.

We make use of the relation of type $\dfrac{x_1}{y_1} = \dfrac{x_2}{y_2}$

(i) Here $x_1 = 5$, $y_1 = 210$ and $x_2 = 2$

Therefore, $\dfrac{x_1}{y_1} = \dfrac{x_2}{y_2}$ gives $\dfrac{5}{210} = \dfrac{2}{y_2}$ or $5y_2 = 2 \times 210$ or $y_2 = \dfrac{2 \times 210}{5} = 84$

(ii) If $x_3 = 4$, then $\dfrac{5}{210} = \dfrac{4}{y_3}$ or $5y_3 = 4 \times 210$ or $y_3 = \dfrac{4 \times 210}{5} = 168$

[Can we use $\dfrac{x_2}{y_2} = \dfrac{x_3}{y_3}$ here? Try!]

(iii) If $x_4 = 10$, then $\dfrac{5}{210} = \dfrac{10}{y_4}$ or $y_4 = \dfrac{10 \times 210}{5} = 420$

(iv) If $x_5 = 13$, then $\dfrac{5}{210} = \dfrac{13}{y_5}$ or $y_5 = \dfrac{13 \times 210}{5} = 546$

$$\left[\text{Note that here we can also use } \dfrac{2}{84} \text{ or } \dfrac{4}{168} \text{ or } \dfrac{10}{420} \text{ in the place of } \dfrac{5}{210} \right]$$

Example 2: An electric pole, 14 metres high, casts a shadow of 10 metres. Find the height of a tree that casts a shadow of 15 metres under similar conditions.

Solution: Let the height of the tree be x metres. We form a table as shown below:

height of the object (in metres)	14	x
length of the shadow (in metres)	10	15

Note that more the height of an object, the more would be the length of its shadow.

Hence, this is a case of direct proportion. That is, $\dfrac{x_1}{y_1} = \dfrac{x_2}{y_2}$

We have $\quad \dfrac{14}{10} = \dfrac{x}{15}$ (Why?)

or $\quad \dfrac{14}{10} \times 15 = x$

or $\quad \dfrac{14 \times 3}{2} = x$

So $\quad 21 = x$

Thus, height of the tree is 21 metres.

Alternately, we can write $\dfrac{x_1}{y_1} = \dfrac{x_2}{y_2}$ as $\dfrac{x_1}{x_2} = \dfrac{y_1}{y_2}$

so $\qquad x_1 : x_2 = y_1 : y_2$

or $\qquad 14 : x = 10 : 15$

Therefore, $\qquad 10 \times x = 15 \times 14$

or $\qquad x = \dfrac{15 \times 14}{10} = 21$

Example 3: If the weight of 12 sheets of thick paper is 40 grams, how many sheets of the same paper would weigh $2\dfrac{1}{2}$ kilograms?

Solution:

Let the number of sheets which weigh $2\dfrac{1}{2}$ kg be x. We put the above information in the form of a table as shown below:

Number of sheets	12	x
Weight of sheets (in grams)	40	2500

More the number of sheets, the more would their weight be. So, the number of sheets and their weights are directly proportional to each other.

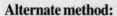

1 kilogram = 1000 grams

$2\dfrac{1}{2}$ kilograms = 2500 grams

So, $\qquad \dfrac{12}{40} = \dfrac{x}{2500}$

or $\qquad \dfrac{12 \times 2500}{40} = x$

or $\qquad 750 = x$

Thus, the required number of sheets of paper = 750.

Alternate method:

Two quantities x and y which vary in direct proportion have the relation $x = ky$ or $\dfrac{x}{y} = k$

Here, $\qquad k = \dfrac{\text{number of sheets}}{\text{weight of sheets in grams}} = \dfrac{12}{40} = \dfrac{3}{10}$

Now x is the number of sheets of the paper which weigh $2\dfrac{1}{2}$ kg [2500 g].

Using the relation $x = ky$, $\ x = \dfrac{3}{10} \times 2500 = 750$

Thus, 750 sheets of paper would weigh $2\dfrac{1}{2}$ kg.

Example 4: A train is moving at a uniform speed of 75 km/hour.

(i) How far will it travel in 20 minutes?

(ii) Find the time required to cover a distance of 250 km.

Solution: Let the distance travelled (in km) in 20 minutes be x and time taken (in minutes) to cover 250 km be y.

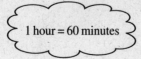

1 hour = 60 minutes

Distance travelled (in km)	75	x	250
Time taken (in minutes)	60	20	y

Since the speed is uniform, therefore, the distance covered would be directly proportional to time.

(i) We have $\dfrac{75}{60} = \dfrac{x}{20}$

or $\quad \dfrac{75}{60} \times 20 = x$

or $\quad x = 25$

So, the train will cover a distance of 25 km in 20 minutes.

(ii) Also, $\dfrac{75}{60} = \dfrac{250}{y}$

or $\quad y = \dfrac{250 \times 60}{75} = 200$ minutes or 3 hours 20 minutes.

Therefore, 3 hours 20 minutes will be required to cover a distance of 250 kilometres.

Alternatively, when x is known, then one can determine y from the relation $\dfrac{x}{20} = \dfrac{250}{y}$.

You know that a map is a miniature representation of a very large region. A scale is usually given at the bottom of the map. The scale shows a relationship between actual length and the length represented on the map. The scale of the map is thus the ratio of the distance between two points on the map to the actual distance between two points on the large region.

For example, if 1 cm on the map represents 8 km of actual distance [i.e., the scale is 1 cm : 8 km or 1 : 800,000] then 2 cm on the same map will represent 16 km. Hence, we can say that scale of a map is based on the concept of direct proportion.

Example 5: The scale of a map is given as 1:30000000. Two cities are 4 cm apart on the map. Find the actual distance between them.

Solution: Let the map distance be x cm and actual distance be y cm, then

$$1:30000000 = x : y$$

or $\quad \dfrac{1}{3 \times 10^7} = \dfrac{x}{y}$

Since $\quad x = 4 \quad$ so, $\quad \dfrac{1}{3 \times 10^7} = \dfrac{4}{y}$

or $\quad y = 4 \times 3 \times 10^7 = 12 \times 10^7$ cm $= 1200$ km.

Thus, two cities, which are 4 cm apart on the map, are actually 1200 km away from each other.

DO THIS

Take a map of your State. Note the scale used there. Using a ruler, measure the "map distance" between any two cities. Calculate the actual distance between them.

EXERCISE 13.1

1. Following are the car parking charges near a railway station upto

4 hours	₹ 60
8 hours	₹ 100
12 hours	₹ 140
24 hours	₹ 180

Check if the parking charges are in direct proportion to the parking time.

2. A mixture of paint is prepared by mixing 1 part of red pigments with 8 parts of base. In the following table, find the parts of base that need to be added.

Parts of red pigment	1	4	7	12	20
Parts of base	8	...	...	...	...

3. In Question 2 above, if 1 part of a red pigment requires 75 mL of base, how much red pigment should we mix with 1800 mL of base?

4. A machine in a soft drink factory fills 840 bottles in six hours. How many bottles will it fill in five hours?

5. A photograph of a bacteria enlarged 50,000 times attains a length of 5 cm as shown in the diagram. What is the *actual* length of the bacteria? If the photograph is enlarged 20,000 times only, what would be its enlarged length?

6. In a model of a ship, the mast is 9 cm high, while the mast of the actual ship is 12 m high. If the length of the ship is 28 m, how long is the model ship?

7. Suppose 2 kg of sugar contains 9×10^6 crystals. How many sugar crystals are there in (i) 5 kg of sugar? (ii) 1.2 kg of sugar?

8. Rashmi has a road map with a scale of 1 cm representing 18 km. She drives on a road for 72 km. What would be her distance covered in the map?

9. A 5 m 60 cm high vertical pole casts a shadow 3 m 20 cm long. Find at the same time (i) the length of the shadow cast by another pole 10 m 50 cm high (ii) the height of a pole which casts a shadow 5m long.

10. A loaded truck travels 14 km in 25 minutes. If the speed remains the same, how far can it travel in 5 hours?

DO THIS	

1. On a squared paper, draw five squares of different sides. Write the following information in a tabular form.

	Square-1	Square-2	Square-3	Square-4	Square-5
Length of a side (L)					
Perimeter (P)					
$\dfrac{L}{P}$					

Area (A)					
$\dfrac{L}{A}$					

Find whether the length of a side is in direct proportion to:

(a) the perimeter of the square.

(b) the area of the square.

2. The following ingredients are required to make halwa for 5 persons:

Suji/Rawa = 250 g, Sugar = 300 g, Ghee = 200 g, Water = 500 mL.

Using the concept of proportion, estimate the changes in the quantity of ingredients, to prepare halwa for your class.

3. Choose a scale and make a map of your classroom, showing windows, doors, blackboard etc. (An example is given here).

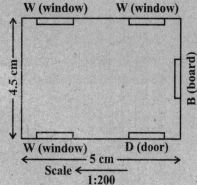

THINK, DISCUSS AND WRITE

Take a few problems discussed so far under 'direct variation'. Do you think that they can be solved by 'unitary method'?

13.3 Inverse Proportion

Two quantities may change in such a manner that if one quantity increases, the other quantity decreases and vice versa. For example, as the number of workers increases, time taken to finish the job decreases. Similarly, if we increase the speed, the time taken to cover a given distance decreases.

To understand this, let us look into the following situation.

Zaheeda can go to her school in four different ways. She can walk, run, cycle or go by car. Study the following table.

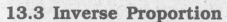

	Walking	Running	Cycling	By Car
Speed in km/hour	3	6	9	45
Time taken (in minutes)	30	15	10	2

Observe that as the speed increases, time taken to cover the same distance decreases.

As Zaheeda doubles her speed by running, time reduces to half. As she increases her speed to three times by cycling, time decreases to one third. Similarly, as she increases her speed to 15 times, time decreases to one fifteenth. (Or, in other words the ratio by which time decreases is inverse of the ratio by which the corresponding speed increases). Can we say that speed and time change inversely in proportion?

> Multiplicative inverse of a number is its reciprocal. Thus, $\frac{1}{2}$ is the inverse of 2 and vice versa. (Note that $2 \times \frac{1}{2} = \frac{1}{2} \times 2 = 1$).

Let us consider another example. A school wants to spend ₹ 6000 on mathematics textbooks. How many books could be bought at ₹ 40 each? Clearly 150 books can be bought. If the price of a textbook is more than ₹ 40, then the number of books which could be purchased with the same amount of money would be less than 150. Observe the following table.

Price of each book (in ₹)	40	50	60	75	80	100
Number of books that can be bought	150	120	100	80	75	60

What do you observe? You will appreciate that as the price of the books increases, the number of books that can be bought, keeping the fund constant, will decrease.

Ratio by which the price of books increases when going from 40 to 50 is 4 : 5, and the ratio by which the corresponding number of books decreases from 150 to 120 is 5 : 4. This means that the two ratios are inverses of each other.

Notice that the product of the corresponding values of the two quantities is constant; that is, $40 \times 150 = 50 \times 120 = 6000$.

If we represent the price of one book as x and the number of books bought as y, then as x increases y decreases and vice-versa. It is important to note that the product xy remains constant. We say that x varies inversely with y and y varies inversely with x. *Thus two quantities x and y are said to vary in inverse proportion, if there exists a relation of the type $xy = k$ between them, k being a constant. If y_1, y_2 are the values of y corresponding to the values x_1, x_2 of x respectively then $x_1 y_1 = x_2 y_2 (= k)$, or $\frac{x_1}{x_2} = \frac{y_2}{y_1}$.*

We say that x and y are in **inverse proportion**.

Hence, in this example, cost of a book and number of books purchased in a fixed amount are inversely proportional. Similarly, speed of a vehicle and the time taken to cover a fixed distance changes in inverse proportion.

Think of more such examples of pairs of quantities that vary in inverse proportion. You may now have a look at the furniture – arranging problem, stated in the introductory part of this chapter.

Here is an activity for better understanding of the inverse proportion.

DO THIS

Take a squared paper and arrange 48 counters on it in different number of rows as shown below.

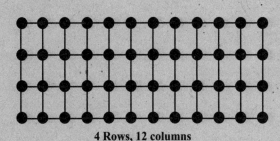

4 Rows, 12 columns

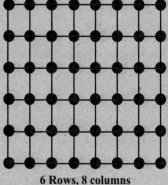

6 Rows, 8 columns

Number of Rows (R)	(R_1) 2	(R_2) 3	(R_3) 4	(R_4) 6	(R_5) 8
Number of Columns (C)	(C_1) ...	(C_2) ...	(C_3) 12	(C_4) 8	(C_5) ...

What do you observe? As R increases, C decreases.

  (i)   Is $R_1 : R_2 = C_2 : C_1$?   (ii)   Is $R_3 : R_4 = C_4 : C_3$?

 (iii)   Are R and C inversely proportional to each other?

Try this activity with 36 counters.

TRY THESE

Observe the following tables and find which pair of variables (here x and y) are in inverse proportion.

(i)

x	50	40	30	20
y	5	6	7	8

(ii)

x	100	200	300	400
y	60	30	20	15

(iii)

x	90	60	45	30	20	5
y	10	15	20	25	30	35

Let us consider some examples where we use the concept of inverse proportion.

When two quantities x and y are in direct proportion (or vary directly) they are also written as $x \propto y$.

When two quantities x and y are in inverse proportion (or vary inversely) they are also written as $x \propto \dfrac{1}{y}$.

Example 7: 6 pipes are required to fill a tank in 1 hour 20 minutes. How long will it take if only 5 pipes of the same type are used?

Solution:

Let the desired time to fill the tank be x minutes. Thus, we have the following table.

Number of pipes	6	5
Time (in minutes)	80	x

Lesser the number of pipes, more will be the time required by it to fill the tank. So, this is a case of inverse proportion.

Hence, $\quad 80 \times 6 = x \times 5 \qquad [x_1 y_1 = x_2 y_2]$

or $\qquad \dfrac{80 \times 6}{5} = x$

or $\qquad x = 96$

Thus, time taken to fill the tank by 5 pipes is 96 minutes or 1 hour 36 minutes.

Example 8: There are 100 students in a hostel. Food provision for them is for 20 days. How long will these provisions last, if 25 more students join the group?

Solution: Suppose the provisions last for y days when the number of students is 125. We have the following table.

Number of students	100	125
Number of days	20	y

Note that more the number of students, the sooner would the provisions exhaust. Therefore, this is a case of inverse proportion.

So, $\qquad 100 \times 20 = 125 \times y$

or $\qquad \dfrac{100 \times 20}{125} = y \quad$ or $\quad 16 = y$

Thus, the provisions will last for 16 days, if 25 more students join the hostel.

Alternately, we can write $x_1 y_1 = x_2 y_2 \quad$ as $\quad \dfrac{x_1}{x_2} = \dfrac{y_2}{y_1}$.

That is, $\qquad x_1 : x_2 = y_2 : y_1$

or $\qquad 100 : 125 = y : 20$

or $\qquad y = \dfrac{100 \times 20}{125} = 16$

Example 9: If 15 workers can build a wall in 48 hours, how many workers will be required to do the same work in 30 hours?

Solution:

Let the number of workers employed to build the wall in 30 hours be y.

We have the following table.

Number of hours	48	30
Number of workers	15	y

Obviously more the number of workers, faster will they build the wall.
So, the number of hours and number of workers vary in inverse proportion.

So $48 \times 15 = 30 \times y$

Therefore, $\dfrac{48 \times 15}{30} = y$ or $y = 24$

i.e., to finish the work in 30 hours, 24 workers are required.

EXERCISE 13.2

1. Which of the following are in inverse proportion?

   (i) The number of workers on a job and the time to complete the job.

   (ii) The time taken for a journey and the distance travelled in a uniform speed.

   (iii) Area of cultivated land and the crop harvested.

   (iv) The time taken for a fixed journey and the speed of the vehicle.

   (v) The population of a country and the area of land per person.

2. In a Television game show, the prize money of ₹ 1,00,000 is to be divided equally amongst the winners. Complete the following table and find whether the prize money given to an individual winner is directly or inversely proportional to the number of winners?

Number of winners	1	2	4	5	8	10	20
Prize for each winner (in ₹)	1,00,000	50,000	...	...	...	...	...

3. Rehman is making a wheel using spokes. He wants to fix equal spokes in such a way that the angles between any pair of consecutive spokes are equal. Help him by completing the following table.

Number of spokes	4	6	8	10	12
Angle between a pair of consecutive spokes	90°	60°	...	...	...

    (i) Are the number of spokes and the angles formed between the pairs of consecutive spokes in inverse proportion?

    (ii) Calculate the angle between a pair of consecutive spokes on a wheel with 15 spokes.

    (iii) How many spokes would be needed, if the angle between a pair of consecutive spokes is 40°?

4. If a box of sweets is divided among 24 children, they will get 5 sweets each. How many would each get, if the number of the children is reduced by 4?

5. A farmer has enough food to feed 20 animals in his cattle for 6 days. How long would the food last if there were 10 more animals in his cattle?

6. A contractor estimates that 3 persons could rewire Jasminder's house in 4 days. If, he uses 4 persons instead of three, how long should they take to complete the job?

7. A batch of bottles were packed in 25 boxes with 12 bottles in each box. If the same batch is packed using 20 bottles in each box, how many boxes would be filled?

8. A factory requires 42 machines to produce a given number of articles in 63 days. How many machines would be required to produce the same number of articles in 54 days?

9. A car takes 2 hours to reach a destination by travelling at the speed of 60 km/h. How long will it take when the car travels at the speed of 80 km/h?

10. Two persons could fit new windows in a house in 3 days.

    (i) One of the persons fell ill before the work started. How long would the job take now?

    (ii) How many persons would be needed to fit the windows in one day?

11. A school has 8 periods a day each of 45 minutes duration. How long would each period be, if the school has 9 periods a day, assuming the number of school hours to be the same?

DO THIS

1. Take a sheet of paper. Fold it as shown in the figure. Count the number of parts and the area of a part in each case.

Tabulate your observations and discuss with your friends. Is it a case of inverse proportion? Why?

Number of parts	1	2	4	8	16
Area of each part	area of the paper	$\frac{1}{2}$ the area of the paper	...	...	...

2. Take a few containers of different sizes with circular bases. Fill the same amount of water in each container. Note the diameter of each container and the respective height at which the water level stands. Tabulate your observations. Is it a case of inverse proportion?

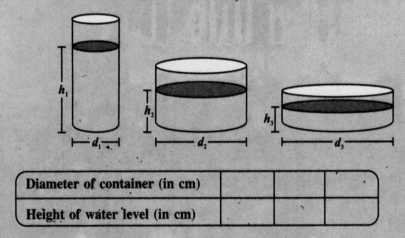

Diameter of container (in cm)			
Height of water level (in cm)			

WHAT HAVE WE DISCUSSED?

1. Two quantities x and y are said to be in **direct proportion** if they increase (decrease) together in such a manner that the ratio of their corresponding values remains constant. That is if $\frac{x}{y} = k$ [k is a positive number], then x and y are said to vary directly. In such a case if y_1, y_2 are the values of y corresponding to the values x_1, x_2 of x respectively then $\frac{x_1}{y_1} = \frac{x_2}{y_2}$.

2. Two quantities x and y are said to be in **inverse proportion** if an increase in x causes a proportional decrease in y (and vice-versa) in such a manner that the product of their corresponding values remains constant. That is, if $xy = k$, then x and y are said to vary inversely. In this case if y_1, y_2 are the values of y corresponding to the values x_1, x_2 of x respectively then $x_1 y_1 = x_2 y_2$ or $\dfrac{x_1}{x_2} = \dfrac{y_2}{y_1}$.

Factorisation

14.1 Introduction

14.1.1 Factors of natural numbers

You will remember what you learnt about factors in Class VI. Let us take a natural number, say 30, and write it as a product of other natural numbers, say

$$30 = 2 \times 15$$
$$= 3 \times 10 = 5 \times 6$$

Thus, 1, 2, 3, 5, 6, 10, 15 and 30 are the factors of 30. Of these, 2, 3 and 5 are the prime factors of 30 (Why?)

A number written as a product of prime factors is said to be in the prime factor form; for example, 30 written as $2 \times 3 \times 5$ is in the prime factor form.

The prime factor form of 70 is $2 \times 5 \times 7$.

The prime factor form of 90 is $2 \times 3 \times 3 \times 5$, and so on.

> We know that 30 can also be written as
> $$30 = 1 \times 30$$
> Thus, 1 and 30 are also factors of 30. You will notice that 1 is a factor of any number. For example, $101 = 1 \times 101$. However, when we write a number as a product of factors, we shall not write 1 as a factor, unless it is specially required.

Similarly, we can express algebraic expressions as products of their factors. This is what we shall learn to do in this chapter.

14.1.2 Factors of algebraic expressions

We have seen in Class VII that in algebraic expressions, terms are formed as products of factors. For example, in the algebraic expression $5xy + 3x$ the term $5xy$ has been formed by the factors 5, x and y, i.e.,

$$5xy = 5 \times x \times y$$

Observe that the factors 5, x and y of $5xy$ cannot further be expressed as a product of factors. We may say that 5, x and y are 'prime' factors of $5xy$. In algebraic expressions, we use the word 'irreducible' in place of 'prime'. We say that $5 \times x \times y$ is the irreducible form of $5xy$. Note $5 \times (xy)$ is not an irreducible form of $5xy$, since the factor xy can be further expressed as a product of x and y, i.e., $xy = x \times y$.

> Note 1 is a factor of $5xy$, since
> $$5xy = 1 \times 5 \times x \times y$$
> In fact, 1 is a factor of every term. As in the case of natural numbers, unless it is specially required, we do not show 1 as a separate factor of any term.

Next consider the expression $3x(x+2)$. It can be written as a product of factors. $3, x$ and $(x+2)$

$$3x(x+2) = 3 \times x \times (x+2)$$

The factors $3, x$ and $(x+2)$ are irreducible factors of $3x(x+2)$.

Similarly, the expression $10x(x+2)(y+3)$ is expressed in its irreducible factor form as $10x(x+2)(y+3) = 2 \times 5 \times x \times (x+2) \times (y+3)$.

14.2 What is Factorisation?

When we factorise an algebraic expression, we write it as a product of factors. These factors may be numbers, algebraic variables or algebraic expressions.

Expressions like $3xy$, $5x^2y$, $2x(y+2)$, $5(y+1)(x+2)$ are already in factor form. Their factors can be just read off from them, as we already know.

On the other hand consider expressions like $2x+4$, $3x+3y$, x^2+5x, x^2+5x+6. It is not obvious what their factors are. We need to develop systematic methods to factorise these expressions, i.e., to find their factors. This is what we shall do now.

14.2.1 Method of common factors

- We begin with a simple example: Factorise $2x+4$.

  We shall write each term as a product of irreducible factors;
  $$2x = 2 \times x$$
  $$4 = 2 \times 2$$
  Hence $\qquad\qquad 2x + 4 = (2 \times x) + (2 \times 2)$
  Notice that factor 2 is common to both the terms.
  Observe, by distributive law
  $$2 \times (x+2) = (2 \times x) + (2 \times 2)$$
  Therefore, we can write
  $$2x + 4 = 2 \times (x+2) = 2(x+2)$$

  Thus, the expression $2x+4$ is the same as $2(x+2)$. Now we can read off its factors: they are 2 and $(x+2)$. These factors are irreducible.

Next, factorise $5xy + 10x$.

The irreducible factor forms of $5xy$ and $10x$ are respectively,
$$5xy = 5 \times x \times y$$
$$10x = 2 \times 5 \times x$$

Observe that the two terms have 5 and x as common factors. Now,
$$5xy + 10x = (5 \times x \times y) + (5 \times x \times 2)$$
$$= (5x \times y) + (5x \times 2)$$

We combine the two terms using the distributive law,
$$(5x \times y) + (5x \times 2) = 5x \times (y+2)$$

Therefore, $5xy + 10x = 5x(y+2)$. (This is the desired factor form.)

Example 1: Factorise $12a^2b + 15ab^2$

Solution: We have $12a^2b = 2 \times 2 \times 3 \times a \times a \times b$

$$15ab^2 = 3 \times 5 \times a \times b \times b$$

The two terms have 3, a and b as common factors.

Therefore, $12a^2b + 15ab^2 = (3 \times a \times b \times 2 \times 2 \times a) + (3 \times a \times b \times 5 \times b)$

$$= 3 \times a \times b \times [(2 \times 2 \times a) + (5 \times b)] \qquad \text{(combining the terms)}$$

$$= 3ab \times (4a + 5b)$$

$$= 3ab\,(4a + 5b) \qquad \text{(required factor form)}$$

Example 2: Factorise $10x^2 - 18x^3 + 14x^4$

Solution: $10x^2 = 2 \times 5 \times x \times x$

$$18x^3 = 2 \times 3 \times 3 \times x \times x \times x$$

$$14x^4 = 2 \times 7 \times x \times x \times x \times x$$

The common factors of the three terms are 2, x and x.

Therefore, $10x^2 - 18x^3 + 14x^4 = (2 \times x \times x \times 5) - (2 \times x \times x \times 3 \times 3 \times x)$

$$+ (2 \times x \times x \times 7 \times x \times x)$$

$$= 2 \times x \times x \times [(5 - (3 \times 3 \times x) + (7 \times x \times x)] \quad \text{(combining the three terms)}$$

$$= 2x^2 \times (5 - 9x + 7x^2) = \underline{2x^2(7x^2 - 9x + 5)}$$

TRY THESE

Factorise: (i) $12x + 36$ (ii) $22y - 33z$ (iii) $14pq + 35pqr$

Do you notice that the factor form of an expression has only one term?

14.2.2 Factorisation by regrouping terms

Look at the expression $2xy + 2y + 3x + 3$. You will notice that the first two terms have common factors 2 and y and the last two terms have a common factor 3. But there is no single factor common to all the terms. How shall we proceed?

Let us write $(2xy + 2y)$ in the factor form:

$$2xy + 2y = (2 \times x \times y) + (2 \times y)$$

$$= (2 \times y \times x) + (2 \times y \times 1)$$

$$= (2y \times x) + (2y \times 1) = 2y\,(x + 1)$$

Note, we need to show 1 as a factor here. Why?

Similarly, $3x + 3 = (3 \times x) + (3 \times 1)$

$$= 3 \times (x + 1) = 3\,(x + 1)$$

Hence, $2xy + 2y + 3x + 3 = 2y\,(x + 1) + 3\,(x + 1)$

Observe, now we have a common factor $(x + 1)$ in both the terms on the right hand side. Combining the two terms,

$$2xy + 2y + 3x + 3 = 2y\,(x + 1) + 3\,(x + 1) = (x + 1)\,(2y + 3)$$

The expression $2xy + 2y + 3x + 3$ is now in the form of a product of factors. Its factors are $(x + 1)$ and $(2y + 3)$. Note, these factors are irreducible.

What is regrouping?

Suppose, the above expression was given as $2xy + 3 + 2y + 3x$; then it will not be easy to see the factorisation. Rearranging the expression, as $2xy + 2y + 3x + 3$, allows us to form groups $(2xy + 2y)$ and $(3x + 3)$ leading to factorisation. This is regrouping.

Regrouping may be possible in more than one ways. Suppose, we regroup the expression as: $2xy + 3x + 2y + 3$. This will also lead to factors. Let us try:

$$2xy + 3x + 2y + 3 = 2 \times x \times y + 3 \times x + 2 \times y + 3$$
$$= x \times (2y + 3) + 1 \times (2y + 3)$$
$$= (2y + 3)(x + 1)$$

The factors are the same (as they have to be), although they appear in different order.

Example 3: Factorise $6xy - 4y + 6 - 9x$.

Solution:

Step 1   Check if there is a common factor among all terms. There is none.

Step 2   Think of grouping. Notice that first two terms have a common factor $2y$;

$$6xy - 4y = 2y (3x - 2) \tag{a}$$

What about the last two terms? Observe them. If you change their order to $-9x + 6$, the factor $(3x - 2)$ will come out;

$$-9x + 6 = -3 (3x) + 3 (2)$$
$$= -3 (3x - 2) \tag{b}$$

Step 3   Putting (a) and (b) together,

$$6xy - 4y + 6 - 9x = 6xy - 4y - 9x + 6$$
$$= 2y (3x - 2) - 3 (3x - 2)$$
$$= (3x - 2)(2y - 3)$$

The factors of $(6xy - 4y + 6 - 9x)$ are $(3x - 2)$ and $(2y - 3)$.

◣ EXERCISE 14.1

1. Find the common factors of the given terms.

    (i) $12x$, 36 (ii) $2y$, $22xy$ (iii) $14\ pq$, $28p^2q^2$
    (iv) $2x$, $3x^2$, 4 (v) $6\ abc$, $24ab^2$, $12\ a^2b$
    (vi) $16\ x^3$, $-4x^2$, $32x$ (vii) $10\ pq$, $20qr$, $30rp$
    (viii) $3x^2\ y^3$, $10x^3\ y^2$, $6\ x^2\ y^2z$

2. Factorise the following expressions.

    (i) $7x - 42$ (ii) $6p - 12q$ (iii) $7a^2 + 14a$
    (iv) $-16\ z + 20\ z^3$ (v) $20\ l^2\ m + 30\ a\ l\ m$
    (vi) $5\ x^2\ y - 15\ xy^2$ (vii) $10\ a^2 - 15\ b^2 + 20\ c^2$
    (viii) $-4\ a^2 + 4\ ab - 4\ ca$ (ix) $x^2\ y\ z + x\ y^2z + x\ y\ z^2$
    (x) $a\ x^2\ y + b\ x\ y^2 + c\ x\ y\ z$

3. Factorise.

    (i) $x^2 + x\ y + 8x + 8y$
                                         (ii) $15\ xy - 6x + 5y - 2$

(iii) $ax + bx - ay - by$ (iv) $15\,pq + 15 + 9q + 25p$

(v) $z - 7 + 7\,x\,y - x\,y\,z$

14.2.3 Factorisation using identities

We know that

$$(a + b)^2 = a^2 + 2ab + b^2 \qquad\qquad \text{(I)}$$

$$(a - b)^2 = a^2 - 2ab + b^2 \qquad\qquad \text{(II)}$$

$$(a + b)\,(a - b) = a^2 - b^2 \qquad\qquad \text{(III)}$$

The following solved examples illustrate how to use these identities for factorisation. What we do is to observe the given expression. If it has a form that fits the right hand side of one of the identities, then the expression corresponding to the left hand side of the identity gives the desired factorisation.

Example 4: Factorise $x^2 + 8x + 16$

Solution: Observe the expression; it has three terms. Therefore, it does not fit Identity III. Also, it's first and third terms are perfect squares with a positive sign before the middle term. So, it is of the form $a^2 + 2ab + b^2$ where $a = x$ and $b = 4$

such that $a^2 + 2ab + b^2 = x^2 + 2\,(x)\,(4) + 4^2$

$$= x^2 + 8x + 16$$

Since $a^2 + 2ab + b^2 = (a + b)^2$,

by comparison $x^2 + 8x + 16 = (x + 4)^2$ (the required factorisation)

> Observe here the given expression is of the form $a^2 - 2ab + b^2$. Where $a = 2y$, and $b = 3$ with $2ab = 2 \times 2y \times 3 = 12y$.

Example 5: Factorise $4y^2 - 12y + 9$

Solution: Observe $4y^2 = (2y)^2$, $9 = 3^2$ and $12y = 2 \times 3 \times (2y)$

Therefore, $4y^2 - 12y + 9 = (2y)^2 - 2 \times 3 \times (2y) + (3)^2$

$$= (2y - 3)^2 \qquad \text{(required factorisation)}$$

Example 6: Factorise $49p^2 - 36$

Solution: There are two terms; both are squares and the second is negative. The expression is of the form $(a^2 - b^2)$. Identity III is applicable here;

$$49p^2 - 36 = (7p)^2 - (6)^2$$

$$= (7p - 6)\,(7p + 6) \text{ (required factorisation)}$$

Example 7: Factorise $a^2 - 2ab + b^2 - c^2$

Solution: The first three terms of the given expression form $(a - b)^2$. The fourth term is a square. So the expression can be reduced to a difference of two squares.

Thus, $a^2 - 2ab + b^2 - c^2 = (a - b)^2 - c^2$ (Applying Identity II)

$$= [(a - b) - c)\,((a - b) + c)] \qquad \text{(Applying Identity III)}$$

$$= (a - b - c)\,(a - b + c) \qquad \text{(required factorisation)}$$

Notice, how we applied two identities one after the other to obtain the required factorisation.

Example 8: Factorise $m^4 - 256$

Solution: We note $m^4 = (m^2)^2$ and $256 = (16)^2$

Thus, the given expression fits Identity III.

Therefore, $m^4 - 256 = (m^2)^2 - (16)^2$

$= (m^2 - 16)(m^2 + 16)$ [(using Identity (III)]

Now, $(m^2 + 16)$ cannot be factorised further, but $(m^2 - 16)$ is factorisable again as per Identity III.

$$m^2 - 16 = m^2 - 4^2$$
$$= (m - 4)(m + 4)$$

Therefore, $m^4 - 256 = (m - 4)(m + 4)(m^2 + 16)$

14.2.4 Factors of the form $(x + a)(x + b)$

Let us now discuss how we can factorise expressions in one variable, like $x^2 + 5x + 6$, $y^2 - 7y + 12$, $z^2 - 4z - 12$, $3m^2 + 9m + 6$, etc. Observe that these expressions are not of the type $(a + b)^2$ or $(a - b)^2$, i.e., they are not perfect squares. For example, in $x^2 + 5x + 6$, the term 6 is not a perfect square. These expressions obviously also do not fit the type $(a^2 - b^2)$ either.

They, however, seem to be of the type $x^2 + (a + b)x + ab$. We may therefore, try to use Identity IV studied in the last chapter to factorise these expressions:

$$(x + a)(x + b) = x^2 + (a + b)x + ab \tag{IV}$$

For that we have to look at the coefficients of x and the constant term. Let us see how it is done in the following example.

Example 9: Factorise $x^2 + 5x + 6$

Solution: If we compare the R.H.S. of Identity (IV) with $x^2 + 5x + 6$, we find $ab = 6$, and $a + b = 5$. From this, we must obtain a and b. The factors then will be $(x + a)$ and $(x + b)$.

If $ab = 6$, it means that a and b are factors of 6. Let us try $a = 6$, $b = 1$. For these values $a + b = 7$, and not 5, So this choice is not right.

Let us try $a = 2$, $b = 3$. For this $a + b = 5$ exactly as required.

The factorised form of this given expression is then $(x + 2)(x + 3)$.

In general, for factorising an algebraic expression of the type $x^2 + px + q$, we find two factors a and b of q (i.e., the constant term) such that

$$ab = q \quad \text{and} \quad a + b = p$$

Then, the expression becomes $x^2 + (a + b)x + ab$

or $x^2 + ax + bx + ab$

or $x(x + a) + b(x + a)$

or $(x + a)(x + b)$ which are the required factors.

Example 10: Find the factors of $y^2 - 7y + 12$.

Solution: We note $12 = 3 \times 4$ and $3 + 4 = 7$. Therefore,

$$y^2 - 7y + 12 = y^2 - 3y - 4y + 12$$
$$= y(y - 3) - 4(y - 3) = (y - 3)(y - 4)$$

Note, this time we did not compare the expression with that in Identity (IV) to identify a and b. After sufficient practice you may not need to compare the given expressions for their factorisation with the expressions in the identities; instead you can proceed directly as we did above.

Example 11: Obtain the factors of $z^2 - 4z - 12$.

Solution: Here $ab = -12$; this means one of a and b is negative. Further, $a + b = -4$, this means the one with larger numerical value is negative. We try $a = -4$, $b = 3$; but this will not work, since $a + b = -1$. Next possible values are $a = -6$, $b = 2$, so that $a + b = -4$ as required.

Hence,
$$z^2 - 4z - 12 = z^2 - 6z + 2z - 12$$
$$= z(z - 6) + 2(z - 6)$$
$$= (z - 6)(z + 2)$$

Example 12: Find the factors of $3m^2 + 9m + 6$.

Solution: We notice that 3 is a common factor of all the terms.

Therefore,
$$3m^2 + 9m + 6 = 3(m^2 + 3m + 2)$$

Now,
$$m^2 + 3m + 2 = m^2 + m + 2m + 2 \qquad \text{(as } 2 = 1 \times 2\text{)}$$
$$= m(m + 1) + 2(m + 1)$$
$$= (m + 1)(m + 2)$$

Therefore,
$$3m^2 + 9m + 6 = 3(m + 1)(m + 2)$$

◤ EXERCISE 14.2

1. Factorise the following expressions.
   - (i) $a^2 + 8a + 16$
   - (ii) $p^2 - 10p + 25$
   - (iii) $25m^2 + 30m + 9$
   - (iv) $49y^2 + 84yz + 36z^2$
   - (v) $4x^2 - 8x + 4$
   - (vi) $121b^2 - 88bc + 16c^2$
   - (vii) $(l + m)^2 - 4lm$ (Hint: Expand $(l + m)^2$ first)
   - (viii) $a^4 + 2a^2b^2 + b^4$

2. Factorise.
   - (i) $4p^2 - 9q^2$
   - (ii) $63a^2 - 112b^2$
   - (iii) $49x^2 - 36$
   - (iv) $16x^5 - 144x^3$
   - (v) $(l + m)^2 - (l - m)^2$
   - (vi) $9x^2 y^2 - 16$
   - (vii) $(x^2 - 2xy + y^2) - z^2$
   - (viii) $25a^2 - 4b^2 + 28bc - 49c^2$

3. Factorise the expressions.
   - (i) $ax^2 + bx$
   - (ii) $7p^2 + 21q^2$
   - (iii) $2x^3 + 2xy^2 + 2xz^2$
   - (iv) $am^2 + bm^2 + bn^2 + an^2$
   - (v) $(lm + l) + m + 1$
   - (vi) $y(y + z) + 9(y + z)$
   - (vii) $5y^2 - 20y - 8z + 2yz$
   - (viii) $10ab + 4a + 5b + 2$
   - (ix) $6xy - 4y + 6 - 9x$

4. Factorise.

  (i) $a^4 - b^4$ (ii) $p^4 - 81$ (iii) $x^4 - (y + z)^4$

  (iv) $x^4 - (x - z)^4$ (v) $a^4 - 2a^2b^2 + b^4$

5. Factorise the following expressions.

  (i) $p^2 + 6p + 8$ (ii) $q^2 - 10q + 21$ (iii) $p^2 + 6p - 16$

14.3 Division of Algebraic Expressions

We have learnt how to add and subtract algebraic expressions. We also know how to multiply two expressions. We have not however, looked at division of one algebraic expression by another. This is what we wish to do in this section.

We recall that division is the inverse operation of multiplication. Thus, $7 \times 8 = 56$ gives $56 \div 8 = 7$ or $56 \div 7 = 8$.

We may similarly follow the division of algebraic expressions. For example,

(i) $$2x \times 3x^2 = 6x^3$$

  Therefore, $$6x^3 \div 2x = 3x^2$$

  and also, $$6x^3 \div 3x^2 = 2x.$$

(ii) $$5x (x + 4) = 5x^2 + 20x$$

  Therefore, $$(5x^2 + 20x) \div 5x = x + 4$$

  and also $$(5x^2 + 20x) \div (x + 4) = 5x.$$

We shall now look closely at how the division of one expression by another can be carried out. To begin with we shall consider the division of a monomial by another monomial.

14.3.1 Division of a monomial by another monomial

Consider $6x^3 \div 2x$

We may write $2x$ and $6x^3$ in irreducible factor forms,

$$2x = 2 \times x$$

$$6x^3 = 2 \times 3 \times x \times x \times x$$

Now we group factors of $6x^3$ to separate $2x$,

$$6x^3 = 2 \times x \times (3 \times x \times x) = (2x) \times (3x^2)$$

Therefore, $$6x^3 \div 2x = 3x^2.$$

A shorter way to depict cancellation of common factors is as we do in division of numbers:

$$77 \div 7 = \frac{77}{7} = \frac{7 \times 11}{7} = 11$$

Similarly, $$6x^3 \div 2x = \frac{6x^3}{2x}$$

$$= \frac{2 \times 3 \times x \times x \times x}{2 \times x} = 3 \times x \times x = 3x^2$$

Example 13: Do the following divisions.

  (i) $-20x^4 \div 10x^2$ (ii) $7x^2y^2z^2 \div 14xyz$

Solution:

  (i) $-20x^4 = -2 \times 2 \times 5 \times x \times x \times x \times x$

  $10x^2 = 2 \times 5 \times x \times x$

Therefore, $(-20x^4) \div 10x^2 = \dfrac{-2 \times 2 \times 5 \times x \times x \times x \times x \times x}{2 \times 5 \times x \times x} = -2 \times x \times x = -2x^2$

(ii) $7x^2y^2z^2 \div 14xyz$
$= \dfrac{7 \times x \times x \times y \times y \times z \times z}{2 \times 7 \times x \times y \times z}$

$= \dfrac{x \times y \times z}{2} = \dfrac{1}{2}xyz$

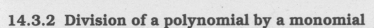

TRY THESE

Divide.

(i) $24xy^2z^3$ by $6yz^2$ (ii) $63a^2b^4c^6$ by $7a^2b^2c^3$

14.3.2 Division of a polynomial by a monomial

Let us consider the division of the trinomial $4y^3 + 5y^2 + 6y$ by the monomial $2y$.

$4y^3 + 5y^2 + 6y = (2 \times 2 \times y \times y \times y) + (5 \times y \times y) + (2 \times 3 \times y)$

(Here, we expressed each term of the polynomial in factor form) we find that $2 \times y$ is common in each term. Therefore, separating $2 \times y$ from each term. We get

$4y^3 + 5y^2 + 6y = 2 \times y \times (2 \times y \times y) + 2 \times y \times \left(\dfrac{5}{2} \times y\right) + 2 \times y \times 3$

$= 2y\,(2y^2) + 2y\left(\dfrac{5}{2}y\right) + 2y\,(3)$

$= 2y\left(2y^2 + \dfrac{5}{2}y + 3\right)$ (The common factor $2y$ is shown separately.)

Therefore, $(4y^3 + 5y^2 + 6y) \div 2y$

$= \dfrac{4y^3 + 5y^2 + 6y}{2y} = \dfrac{2y\left(2y^2 + \dfrac{5}{2}y + 3\right)}{2y} = 2y^2 + \dfrac{5}{2}y + 3$

> Here, we divide each term of the polynomial in the numerator by the monomial in the denominator.

Alternatively, we could divide each term of the trinomial by the monomial using the cancellation method.

$(4y^3 + 5y^2 + 6y) \div 2y = \dfrac{4y^3 + 5y^2 + 6y}{2y}$

$= \dfrac{4y^3}{2y} + \dfrac{5y^2}{2y} + \dfrac{6y}{2y} = 2y^2 + \dfrac{5}{2}y + 3$

Example 14: Divide $24(x^2yz + xy^2z + xyz^2)$ by $8xyz$ using both the methods.

Solution: $24\,(x^2yz + xy^2z + xyz^2)$

$= 2 \times 2 \times 2 \times 3 \times [(x \times x \times y \times z) + (x \times y \times y \times z) + (x \times y \times z \times z)]$

$= 2 \times 2 \times 2 \times 3 \times x \times y \times z \times (x + y + z) = 8 \times 3 \times xyz \times (x + y + z)$ (By taking out the common factor)

Therefore, $24\,(x^2yz + xy^2z + xyz^2) \div 8xyz$

$= \dfrac{8 \times 3 \times xyz \times (x + y + z)}{8 \times xyz} = 3 \times (x + y + z) = 3\,(x + y + z)$

Alternately, $24(x^2yz + xy^2z + xyz^2) \div 8xyz = \dfrac{24x^2yz}{8xyz} + \dfrac{24xy^2z}{8xyz} + \dfrac{24xyz^2}{8xyz}$

$$= 3x + 3y + 3z = 3(x + y + z)$$

14.4 Division of Algebraic Expressions Continued (Polynomial ÷ Polynomial)

- Consider $(7x^2 + 14x) \div (x + 2)$

  We shall factorise $(7x^2 + 14x)$ first to check and match factors with the denominator:

  $$7x^2 + 14x = (7 \times x \times x) + (2 \times 7 \times x)$$

  $$= 7 \times x \times (x + 2) = 7x(x + 2)$$

Will it help here to divide each term of the numerator by the binomial in the denominator?

  Now $(7x^2 + 14x) \div (x + 2) = \dfrac{7x^2 + 14x}{x + 2}$

  $$= \dfrac{7x(x + 2)}{x + 2} = 7x \quad \text{(Cancelling the factor } (x + 2))$$

Example 15: Divide $44(x^4 - 5x^3 - 24x^2)$ by $11x\,(x - 8)$

Solution: Factorising $44(x^4 - 5x^3 - 24x^2)$, we get

$$44(x^4 - 5x^3 - 24x^2) = 2 \times 2 \times 11 \times x^2(x^2 - 5x - 24)$$

(taking the common factor x^2 out of the bracket)

$$= 2 \times 2 \times 11 \times x^2(x^2 - 8x + 3x - 24)$$

$$= 2 \times 2 \times 11 \times x^2\,[x\,(x - 8) + 3(x - 8)]$$

$$= 2 \times 2 \times 11 \times x^2\,(x + 3)\,(x - 8)$$

Therefore, $44(x^4 - 5x^3 - 24x^2) \div 11x(x - 8)$

$$= \dfrac{2 \times 2 \times 11 \times x \times x \times x \times (x + 3) \times (x - 8)}{11 \times x \times x \times (x - 8)}$$

$$= 2 \times 2 \times x\,(x + 3) = 4x(x + 3)$$

We cancel the factors 11, x and $(x - 8)$ common to both the numerator and denominator.

Example 16: Divide $z(5z^2 - 80)$ by $5z(z + 4)$

Solution: Dividend $= z(5z^2 - 80)$

$$= z[(5 \times z^2) - (5 \times 16)]$$

$$= z \times 5 \times (z^2 - 16)$$

$$= 5z \times (z + 4)\,(z - 4) \qquad \text{[using the identity}$$

$$a^2 - b^2 = (a + b)\,(a - b)]$$

Thus, $\qquad z(5z^2 - 80) \div 5z(z + 4) = \dfrac{5z(z - 4)\,(z + 4)}{5z(z + 4)} = (z - 4)$

EXERCISE 14.3

1. Carry out the following divisions.
   (i) $28x^4 \div 56x$ (ii) $-36y^3 \div 9y^2$ (iii) $66pq^2r^3 \div 11qr^2$
   (iv) $34x^3y^3z^3 \div 51xy^2z^3$ (v) $12a^8b^8 \div (-6a^6b^4)$

2. Divide the given polynomial by the given monomial.
   (i) $(5x^2 - 6x) \div 3x$ (ii) $(3y^8 - 4y^6 + 5y^4) \div y^4$
   (iii) $8(x^3y^2z^2 + x^2y^3z^2 + x^2y^2z^3) \div 4x^2y^2z^2$ (iv) $(x^3 + 2x^2 + 3x) \div 2x$
   (v) $(p^3q^6 - p^6q^3) \div p^3q^3$

3. Work out the following divisions.
   (i) $(10x - 25) \div 5$ (ii) $(10x - 25) \div (2x - 5)$
   (iii) $10y(6y + 21) \div 5(2y + 7)$ (iv) $9x^2y^2(3z - 24) \div 27xy(z - 8)$
   (v) $96abc(3a - 12)(5b - 30) \div 144(a - 4)(b - 6)$

4. Divide as directed.
   (i) $5(2x + 1)(3x + 5) \div (2x + 1)$ (ii) $26xy(x + 5)(y - 4) \div 13x(y - 4)$
   (iii) $52pqr(p + q)(q + r)(r + p) \div 104pq(q + r)(r + p)$
   (iv) $20(y + 4)(y^2 + 5y + 3) \div 5(y + 4)$ (v) $x(x + 1)(x + 2)(x + 3) \div x(x + 1)$

5. Factorise the expressions and divide them as directed.
   (i) $(y^2 + 7y + 10) \div (y + 5)$ (ii) $(m^2 - 14m - 32) \div (m + 2)$
   (iii) $(5p^2 - 25p + 20) \div (p - 1)$ (iv) $4yz(z^2 + 6z - 16) \div 2y(z + 8)$
   (v) $5pq(p^2 - q^2) \div 2p(p + q)$
   (vi) $12xy(9x^2 - 16y^2) \div 4xy(3x + 4y)$ (vii) $39y^3(50y^2 - 98) \div 26y^2(5y + 7)$

14.5 Can you Find the Error?

Task 1   While solving an equation, Sarita does the following.

$$3x + x + 5x = 72$$

Therefore $8x = 72$

and so, $x = \dfrac{72}{8} = 9$

Where has she gone wrong? Find the correct answer.

> Coefficient 1 of a term is usually not shown. But while adding like terms, we include it in the sum.

Task 2   Appu did the following:

For $x = -3$, $5x = 5 - 3 = 2$

Is his procedure correct? If not, correct it.

> Remember to make use of brackets, while substituting a negative value.

Task 3   Namrata and Salma have done the multiplication of algebraic expressions in the following manner.

> Remember, when you multiply the expression enclosed in a bracket by a constant (or a variable) outside, each term of the expression has to be multiplied by the constant (or the variable).

Namrata	**Salma**
(a) $3(x - 4) = 3x - 4$	$3(x - 4) = 3x - 12$

(b) $(2x)^2 = 2x^2$

(b) $(2x)^2 = 4x^2$

> Remember, when you square a monomial, the numerical coefficient and each factor has to be squared.

> Make sure, before applying any formula, whether the formula is really applicable.

(c) $(2a - 3)(a + 2)$
$= 2a^2 - 6$

(c) $(2a - 3)(a + 2)$
$= 2a^2 + a - 6$

(d) $(x + 8)^2 = x^2 + 64$

(d) $(x + 8)^2$
$= x^2 + 16x + 64$

(e) $(x - 5)^2 = x^2 - 25$

(e) $(x - 5)^2 = x^2 - 10x + 25$

Is the multiplication done by both Namrata and Salma correct? Give reasons for your answer.

Task 4 Joseph does a division as : $\dfrac{a+5}{5} = a + 1$

> While dividing a polynomial by a monomial, we divide each term of the polynomial in the numerator by the monomial in the denominator.

His friend Sirish has done the same division as: $\dfrac{a+5}{5} = a$

And his other friend Suman does it this way: $\dfrac{a+5}{5} = \dfrac{a}{5} + 1$

Who has done the division correctly? Who has done incorrectly? Why?

Some fun!

Atul always thinks differently. He asks Sumathi teacher, "If what you say is true, then why do I get the right answer for $\dfrac{64}{16} = \dfrac{4}{1} = 4$?" The teacher explains, " This is so because 64 happens to be 16×4; $\dfrac{64}{16} = \dfrac{16 \times 4}{16 \times 1} = \dfrac{4}{1}$. In reality, we cancel a factor of 16 and not 6, as you can see. In fact, 6 is not a factor of either 64 or of 16." The teacher adds further, "Also, $\dfrac{664}{166} = \dfrac{4}{1}, \dfrac{6664}{1666} = \dfrac{4}{1}$, and so on". Isn't that interesting? Can you help Atul to find some other examples like $\dfrac{64}{16}$?

EXERCISE 14.4

Find and correct the errors in the following mathematical statements.

1. $4(x - 5) = 4x - 5$ 2. $x(3x + 2) = 3x^2 + 2$ 3. $2x + 3y = 5xy$

4. $x + 2x + 3x = 5x$ 5. $5y + 2y + y - 7y = 0$ 6. $3x + 2x = 5x^2$

7. $(2x)^2 + 4(2x) + 7 = 2x^2 + 8x + 7$ 8. $(2x)^2 + 5x = 4x + 5x = 9x$

9. $(3x + 2)^2 = 3x^2 + 6x + 4$

10. Substituting $x = -3$ in

   (a) $x^2 + 5x + 4$ gives $(-3)^2 + 5(-3) + 4 = 9 + 2 + 4 = 15$

   (b) $x^2 - 5x + 4$ gives $(-3)^2 - 5(-3) + 4 = 9 - 15 + 4 = -2$

   (c) $x^2 + 5x$ gives $(-3)^2 + 5(-3) = -9 - 15 = -24$

11. $(y - 3)^2 = y^2 - 9$ 12. $(z + 5)^2 = z^2 + 25$

13. $(2a + 3b)(a - b) = 2a^2 - 3b^2$ 14. $(a + 4)(a + 2) = a^2 + 8$

15. $(a - 4)(a - 2) = a^2 - 8$ 16. $\dfrac{3x^2}{3x^2} = 0$

17. $\dfrac{3x^2 + 1}{3x^2} = 1 + 1 = 2$ 18. $\dfrac{3x}{3x + 2} = \dfrac{1}{2}$ 19. $\dfrac{3}{4x + 3} = \dfrac{1}{4x}$

20. $\dfrac{4x + 5}{4x} = 5$ 21. $\dfrac{7x + 5}{5} = 7x$

WHAT HAVE WE DISCUSSED?

1. When we factorise an expression, we write it as a product of factors. These factors may be numbers, algebraic variables or algebraic expressions.

2. An irreducible factor is a factor which cannot be expressed further as a product of factors.

3. A systematic way of factorising an expression is the common factor method. It consists of three steps: (i) Write each term of the expression as a product of irreducible factors (ii) Look for and separate the common factors and (iii) Combine the remaining factors in each term in accordance with the distributive law.

4. Sometimes, all the terms in a given expression do not have a common factor; but the terms can be grouped in such a way that all the terms in each group have a common factor. When we do this, there emerges a common factor across all the groups leading to the required factorisation of the expression. This is the method of regrouping.

5. In factorisation by regrouping, we should remember that any regrouping (i.e., rearrangement) of the terms in the given expression may not lead to factorisation. We must observe the expression and come out with the desired regrouping by trial and error.

6. A number of expressions to be factorised are of the form or can be put into the form : $a^2 + 2\,ab + b^2$, $a^2 - 2ab + b^2$, $a^2 - b^2$ and $x^2 + (a + b) + ab$. These expressions can be easily factorised using Identities I, II, III and IV, given in Chapter 9,

$$a^2 + 2\,ab + b^2 = (a + b)^2$$
$$a^2 - 2ab + b^2 = (a - b)^2$$
$$a^2 - b^2 = (a + b)(a - b)$$
$$x^2 + (a + b)\,x + ab = (x + a)(x + b)$$

7. In expressions which have factors of the type $(x + a)(x + b)$, remember the numerical term gives ab. Its factors, a and b, should be so chosen that their sum, with signs taken care of, is the coefficient of x.

8. We know that in the case of numbers, division is the inverse of multiplication. This idea is applicable also to the division of algebraic expressions.

9. In the case of division of a polynomial by a monomial, we may carry out the division either by dividing each term of the polynomial by the monomial or by the common factor method.

10. In the case of division of a polynomial by a polynomial, we cannot proceed by dividing each term in the dividend polynomial by the divisor polynomial. Instead, we factorise both the polynomials and cancel their common factors.

11. In the case of divisions of algebraic expressions that we studied in this chapter, we have

Dividend = Divisor × Quotient.

In general, however, the relation is

Dividend = Divisor × Quotient + Remainder

Thus, we have considered in the present chapter only those divisions in which the remainder is zero.

12. There are many errors students commonly make when solving algebra exercises. You should avoid making such errors.

Introduction to Graphs

0852CH15

15.1 Introduction

Have you seen graphs in the newspapers, television, magazines, books etc.? The purpose of the graph is to show numerical facts in visual form so that they can be understood quickly, easily and clearly. Thus graphs are visual representations of data collected. Data can also be presented in the form of a table; however a graphical presentation is easier to understand. This is true in particular when there is **a trend** or **comparison** to be shown. We have already seen some types of graphs. Let us quickly recall them here.

15.1.1 A Bar graph

A bar graph is used to show comparison among categories. It may consist of two or more parallel vertical (or horizontal) bars (rectangles).

The bar graph in Fig 15.1 shows Anu's mathematics marks in the three terminal examinations. It helps you to compare her performance easily. She has shown good progress.

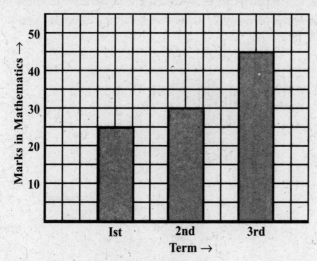

Fig 15.1

Bar graphs can also have double bars as in Fig 15.2. This graph gives a comparative account of sales (in ₹) of various fruits over a two-day period. How is Fig 15.2 different from Fig 15.1? Discuss with your friends.

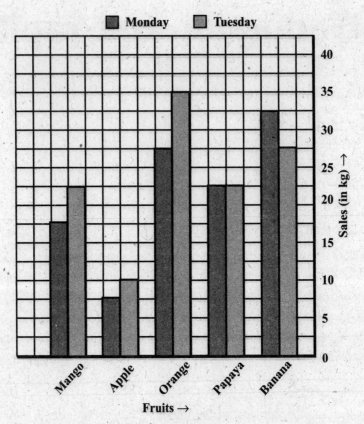

Fig 15.2

15.1.2 A Pie graph (or a circle-graph)

A pie-graph is used to compare parts of a whole. The circle represents the whole. Fig 15.3 is a pie-graph. It shows the percentage of viewers watching different types of TV channels.

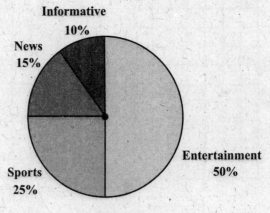

Fig 15.3

15.1.3 A histogram

A Histogram is a bar graph that shows data in intervals. It has adjacent bars over the intervals.

The histogram in Fig 15.4 illustrates the distribution of weights (in kg) of 40 persons of a locality.

Weights (kg)	40-45	45-50	50-55	55-60	60-65
No. of persons	4	12	13	6	5

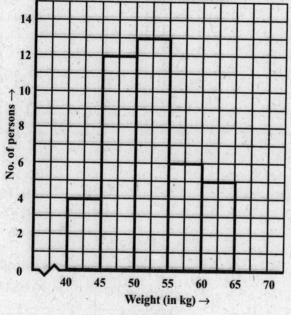

In Fig 15.4 a jagged line (∿) has been used along horizontal line to indicate that we are not showing numbers between 0 and 40.

Fig 15.4

There are no gaps between bars, because there are no gaps between the intervals. What is the information that you gather from this histogram? Try to list them out.

15.1.4 A line graph

A **line graph** displays data that changes continuously over periods of time.

When Renu fell sick, her doctor maintained a record of her body temperature, taken every four hours. It was in the form of a graph (shown in Fig 15.5 and Fig 15.6).

We may call this a "time-temperature graph".

It is a pictorial representation of the following data, given in tabular form.

Time	6 a.m.	10 a.m.	2 p.m.	6 p.m.
Temperature(°C)	37	40	38	35

The horizontal line (usually called the x-axis) shows the timings at which the temperatures were recorded. What are labelled on the vertical line (usually called the y-axis)?

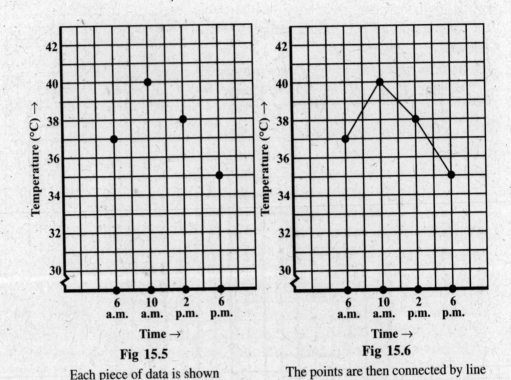

Fig 15.5	**Fig 15.6**
Each piece of data is shown by a point on the square grid.	The points are then connected by line segments. The result is the **line graph**.

What all does this graph tell you? For example you can see the pattern of temperature; more at 10 a.m. (see Fig 15.5) and then decreasing till 6 p.m. Notice that the temperature increased by 3° C(= 40° C – 37° C) during the period 6 a.m. to 10 a.m.

There was no recording of temperature at 8 a.m., however the graph *suggests* that it was more than 37 °C (How?).

Example 1: (A graph on "performance")

The given graph (Fig 15.7) represents the total runs scored by two batsmen A and B, during each of the ten different matches in the year 2007. Study the graph and answer the following questions.

  (i)   What information is given on the two axes?

  (ii) Which line shows the runs scored by batsman A?

  (iii) Were the run scored by them same in any match in 2007? If so, in which match?

  (iii) Among the two batsmen, who is steadier? How do you judge it?

Solution:

  (i)   The horizontal axis (or the *x*-axis) indicates the matches played during the year 2007. The vertical axis (or the *y*-axis) shows the total runs scored in each match.

  (ii) The dotted line shows the runs scored by Batsman A. (This is already indicated at the top of the graph).

(iii) During the 4th match, both have scored the same number of 60 runs. (This is indicated by the point at which both graphs meet).

(iv) Batsman A has one great "peak" but many deep "valleys". He does not appear to be consistent. B, on the other hand has never scored below a total of 40 runs, even though his highest score is only 100 in comparison to 115 of A. Also A has scored a zero in two matches and in a total of 5 matches he has scored less than 40 runs. Since A has a lot of ups and downs, B is a more consistent and reliable batsman.

Example 2: The given graph (Fig 15.8) describes the distances of a car from a city P at different times when it is travelling from City P to City Q, which are 350 km apart. Study the graph and answer the following:

(i) What information is given on the two axes?

(ii) From where and when did the car begin its journey?

(iii) How far did the car go in the first hour?

(iv) How far did the car go during (i) the 2nd hour? (ii) the 3rd hour?

(v) Was the speed same during the first three hours? How do you know it?

(vi) Did the car stop for some duration at any place? Justify your answer.

(vii) When did the car reach City Q?

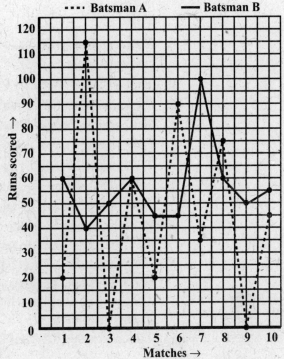

Fig 15.7

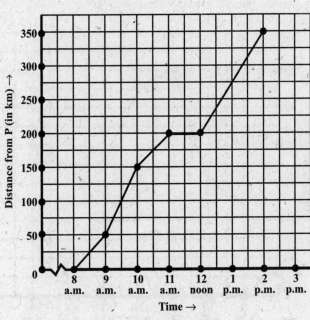

Fig 15.8

Solution:

(i) The horizontal (*x*) axis shows the time. The vertical (*y*) axis shows the distance of the car from City P.

(ii) The car started from City P at 8 a.m.

(iii) The car travelled 50 km during the first hour. [This can be seen as follows. At 8 a.m. it just started from City P. At 9 a.m. it was at the 50th km (seen from graph). Hence during the one-hour time between 8 a.m. and 9 a.m. the car travelled 50 km].

(iv) The distance covered by the car during

    (a) the 2nd hour (i.e., from 9 am to 10 am) is 100 km, (150 – 50).

    (b) the 3rd hour (i.e., from 10 am to 11 am) is 50 km (200 – 150).

(v) From the answers to questions (iii) and (iv), we find that the speed of the car was not the same all the time. (In fact the graph illustrates how the speed varied).

(vi) We find that the car was 200 km away from city P when the time was 11 a.m. and also at 12 noon. This shows that the car did not travel during the interval 11 a.m. to 12 noon. The horizontal line segment representing "travel" during this period is illustrative of this fact.

(vii) The car reached City Q at 2 p.m.

EXERCISE 15.1

1. The following graph shows the temperature of a patient in a hospital, recorded every hour.

    (a) What was the patient's temperature at 1 p.m. ?

    (b) When was the patient's temperature 38.5° C?

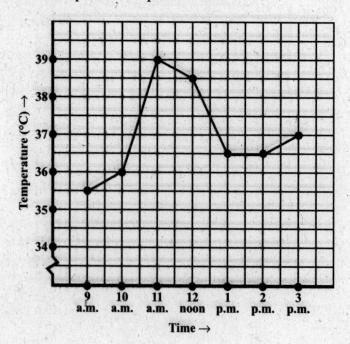

(c) The patient's temperature was the same two times during the period given. What were these two times?

(d) What was the temperature at 1.30 p.m.? How did you arrive at your answer?

(e) During which periods did the patients' temperature showed an upward trend?

2. The following line graph shows the yearly sales figures for a manufacturing company.
   (a) What were the sales in (i) 2002   (ii) 2006?
   (b) What were the sales in (i) 2003   (ii) 2005?
   (c) Compute the difference between the sales in 2002 and 2006.
   (d) In which year was there the greatest difference between the sales as compared to its previous year?

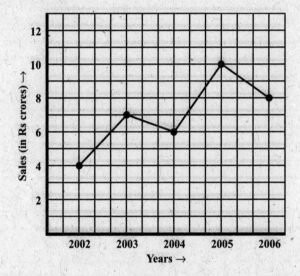

3. For an experiment in Botany, two different plants, plant A and plant B were grown under similar laboratory conditions. Their heights were measured at the end of each week for 3 weeks. The results are shown by the following graph.

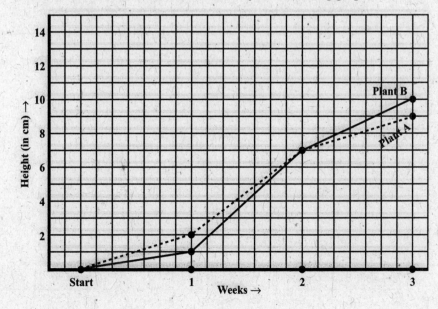

(a) How high was Plant A after (i) 2 weeks (ii) 3 weeks?

(b) How high was Plant B after (i) 2 weeks (ii) 3 weeks?

(c) How much did Plant A grow during the 3rd week?

(d) How much did Plant B grow from the end of the 2nd week to the end of the 3rd week?

(e) During which week did Plant A grow most?

(f) During which week did Plant B grow least?

(g) Were the two plants of the same height during any week shown here? Specify.

4. The following graph shows the temperature forecast and the actual temperature for each day of a week.

(a) On which days was the forecast temperature the same as the actual temperature?

(b) What was the maximum forecast temperature during the week?

(c) What was the minimum actual temperature during the week?

(d) On which day did the actual temperature differ the most from the forecast temperature?

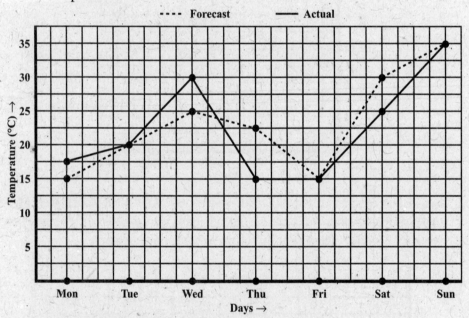

5. Use the tables below to draw linear graphs.

(a) The number of days a hill side city received snow in different years.

Year	2003	2004	2005	2006
Days	8	10	5	12

(b) Population (in thousands) of men and women in a village in different years.

Year	2003	2004	2005	2006	2007
Number of Men	12	12.5	13	13.2	13.5
Number of Women	11.3	11.9	13	13.6	12.8

6. A courier-person cycles from a town to a neighbouring suburban area to deliver a parcel to a merchant. His distance from the town at different times is shown by the following graph.

   (a) What is the scale taken for the time axis?

   (b) How much time did the person take for the travel?

   (c) How far is the place of the merchant from the town?

   (d) Did the person stop on his way? Explain.

   (e) During which period did he ride fastest?

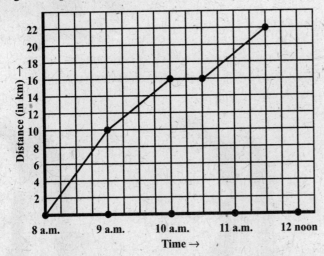

7. Can there be a time-temperature graph as follows? Justify your answer.

(i)

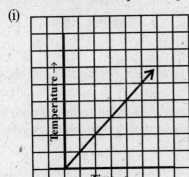

(ii)

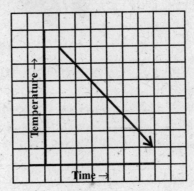

(iii)

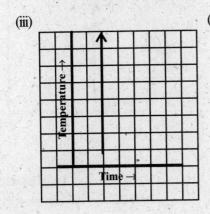

(iv)

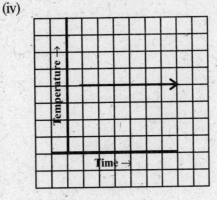

15.2 Linear Graphs

A line graph consists of bits of line segments joined consecutively. Sometimes the graph may be a whole unbroken line. Such a graph is called a **linear graph**. To draw such a line we need to locate some points on the graph sheet. We will now learn how to locate points conveniently on a graph sheet.

15.2.1 Location of a point

The teacher put a dot on the black-board. She asked the students how they would describe its location. There were several responses (Fig 15. 9).

The dot is in the upper half of the board

The dot is near the left edge of the board

The dot is very close to the left upper corner of board

Fig 15.9

Can any one of these statements help fix the position of the dot? No! Why not? Think about it.

John then gave a suggestion. He measured the distance of the dot from the left edge of the board and said, "The dot is 90 cm from the left edge of the board". Do you think John's suggestion is really helpful? (Fig 15.10)

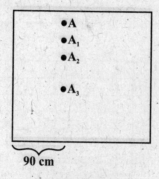

Fig 15.10

A, A$_1$, A$_2$, A$_3$ are all 90 cm away from the left edge.

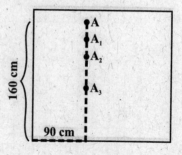

Fig 15.11

A is 90 cm from left edge and 160 cm from the bottom edge.

Rekha then came up with a modified statement : "The dot is 90 cm from the left edge and 160 cm from the bottom edge". That solved the problem completely! (Fig 15.11) The teacher said, "We describe the position of this dot by writing it as (90, 160)". Will the point (160, 90) be different from (90, 160)? Think about it.

*The 17th century mathematician **Rene Descartes**, it is said, noticed the movement of an insect near a corner of the ceiling and began to think of determining the position of a given point in a plane. His system of fixing a point with the help of two measurements, vertical and horizontal, came to be known as Cartesian system, in his honour.*

Rene Descartes
(1596-1650)

15.2.2 Coordinates

Suppose you go to an auditorium and search for your reserved seat. You need to know two numbers, the row number and the seat number. This is the basic method for fixing a point in a plane.

Observe in Fig 15.12 how the point (3, 4) which is 3 units from left edge and 4 units from bottom edge is plotted on a graph sheet. The graph sheet itself is a square grid. We draw the *x* and *y* axes conveniently and then fix the required point. 3 is called the **x-coordinate** of the point; 4 is the **y-coordinate** of the point. We say that the **coordinates** of the point are (3, 4).

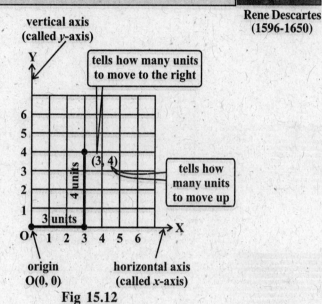

Fig 15.12

Example 3: Plot the point (4, 3) on a graph sheet. Is it the same as the point (3, 4)?

Solution: Locate the *x*, *y* axes, (they are actually number lines!). Start at O (0, 0). Move 4 units to the right; then move 3 units up, you reach the point (4, 3). From Fig 15.13, you can see that the points (3, 4) and (4, 3) are two different points.

Example 4: From Fig 15.14, choose the letter(s) that indicate the location of the points given below:

(i)   (2, 1)

(ii) (0, 5)

(iii) (2, 0)

Also write

(iv) The coordinates of A.

(v)   The coordinates of F.

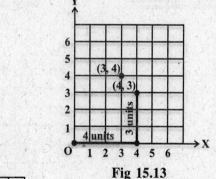

Fig 15.13

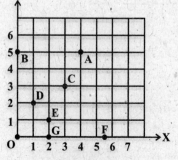

Fig 15.14

Solution:

  (i)   (2, 1) is the point E (It is not D!).

  (ii) (0, 5) is the point B (why? Discuss with your friends!). (iii) (2, 0) is the point G.

  (iv) Point A is (4, 5)   (v) F is (5.5, 0)

Example 5: Plot the following points and verify if they lie on a line. If they lie on a line, name it.

  (i)   (0, 2), (0, 5), (0, 6), (0, 3.5)   (ii) A (1, 1), B (1, 2), C (1, 3), D (1, 4)

  (iii) K (1, 3), L (2, 3), M (3, 3), N (4, 3)   (iv) W (2, 6), X (3, 5), Y (5, 3), Z (6, 2)

Solution:

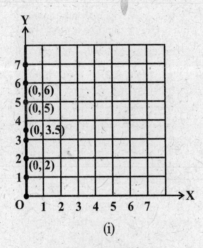

(i)

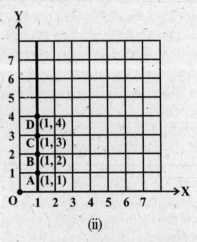

(ii)

These lie on a line.
The line is y-axis.

These lie on a line. The line is AD.
(You may also use other ways
of naming it). It is parallel to the y-axis

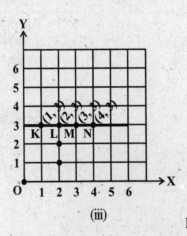

(iii)

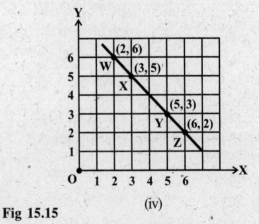

Fig 15.15

(iv)

These lie on a line. We can name it as KL
or KM or MN etc. It is parallel to x-axis

These lie on a line. We can name
it as XY or WY or YZ etc.

Note that in each of the above cases, graph obtained by joining the plotted points is a line. Such graphs are called **linear graphs**.

EXERCISE 15.2

1. Plot the following points on a graph sheet. Verify if they lie on a line
   (a) A(4, 0), B(4, 2), C(4, 6), D(4, 2.5)
   (b) P(1, 1), Q(2, 2), R(3, 3), S(4, 4)
   (c) K(2, 3), L(5, 3), M(5, 5), N(2, 5)

2. Draw the line passing through (2, 3) and (3, 2). Find the coordinates of the points at which this line meets the x-axis and y-axis.

3. Write the coordinates of the vertices of each of these adjoining figures.

4. State whether True or False. Correct that are false.

   (i) A point whose x coordinate is zero and y-coordinate is non-zero will lie on the y-axis.

   (ii) A point whose y coordinate is zero and x-coordinate is 5 will lie on y-axis.

   (iii) The coordinates of the origin are (0, 0).

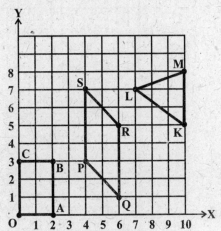

15.3 Some Applications

In everyday life, you might have observed that the more you use a facility, the more you pay for it. If more electricity is consumed, the bill is bound to be high. If less electricity is used, then the bill will be easily manageable. This is an instance where one quantity affects another. Amount of electric bill depends on the quantity of electricity used. We say that the quantity of electricity is an **independent variable** (or sometimes **control variable**) and the amount of electric bill is **the dependent variable**. The relation between such variables can be shown through a graph.

THINK, DISCUSS AND WRITE

The number of litres of petrol you buy to fill a car's petrol tank will decide the amount you have to pay. Which is the independent variable here? Think about it.

Example 6: (Quantity and Cost)

The following table gives the quantity of petrol and its cost.

No. of Litres of petrol	10	15	20	25
Cost of petrol in ₹	500	750	1000	1250

Plot a graph to show the data.

Solution: (i) Let us take a suitable scale on both the axes (Fig 15.16).

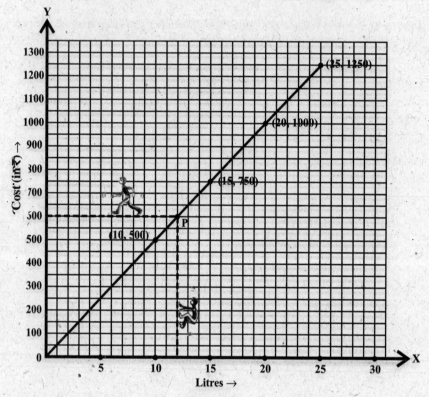

Fig 15.16

(ii) Mark number of litres along the horizontal axis.

(iii) Mark cost of petrol along the vertical axis.

(iv) Plot the points: (10,500), (15,750), (20,1000), (25,1250).

(v) Join the points.

We find that the graph is a line. (It is a linear graph). Why does this graph pass through the origin? Think about it.

This graph can help us to estimate a few things. Suppose we want to find the amount needed to buy 12 litres of petrol. Locate 12 on the horizontal axis.

Follow the vertical line through 12 till you meet the graph at P (say).

From P you take a horizontal line to meet the vertical axis. This meeting point provides the answer.

This is the graph of a situation in which two quantities, are in direct variation. (How ?).

In such situations, the graphs will always be linear.

TRY THESE

In the above example, use the graph to find how much petrol can be purchased for ₹ 800.

Example 7: (Principal and Simple Interest)

A bank gives 10% Simple Interest (S.I.) on deposits by senior citizens. Draw a graph to illustrate the relation between the sum deposited and simple interest earned. Find from your graph

(a) the annual interest obtainable for an investment of ₹ 250.

(b) the investment one has to make to get an annual simple interest of ₹ 70.

Solution:

Sum deposited	Simple interest for a year
₹ 100	$₹ \dfrac{100 \times 1 \times 10}{100} = ₹ 10$
₹ 200	$₹ \dfrac{200 \times 1 \times 10}{100} = ₹ 20$
₹ 300	$₹ \dfrac{300 \times 1 \times 10}{100} = ₹ 30$
₹ 500	$₹ \dfrac{500 \times 1 \times 10}{100} = ₹ 50$
₹ 1000	₹ 100

Steps to follow:
1. Find the quantities to be plotted as Deposit and SI.
2. Decide the quantities to be taken on x-axis and on y-axis.
3. Choose a scale.
4. Plot points.
5. Join the points.

We get a table of values.

Deposit (in ₹)	100	200	300	500	1000
Annual S.I. (in ₹)	10	20	30	50	100

(i) Scale : 1 unit = ₹ 100 on horizontal axis; 1 unit = ₹ 10 on vertical axis.

(ii) Mark Deposits along horizontal axis.

(iii) Mark Simple Interest along vertical axis.

(iv) Plot the points : (100,10), (200, 20), (300, 30), (500,50) etc.

(v) Join the points. We get a graph that is a line (Fig 15.17).

  (a) Corresponding to ₹ 250 on horizontal axis, we get the interest to be ₹ 25 on vertical axis.

  (b) Corresponding to ₹ 70 on the vertical axis, we get the sum to be ₹ 700 on the horizontal axis.

TRY THESE

Is Example 7, a case of direct variation?

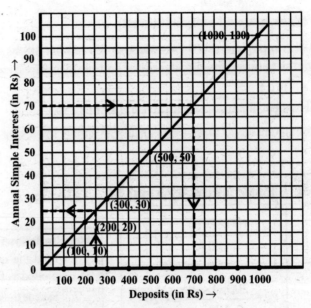

Fig 15.17

Example 8: (Time and Distance)

Ajit can ride a scooter constantly at a speed of 30 kms/hour. Draw a time-distance graph for this situation. Use it to find

(i) the time taken by Ajit to ride 75 km.   (ii) the distance covered by Ajit in $3\frac{1}{2}$ hours.

Solution:

Hours of ride	Distance covered
1 hour	30 km
2 hours	2 × 30 km = 60 km
3 hours	3 × 30 km = 90 km
4 hours	4 × 30 km = 120 km and so on.

We get a table of values.

Time (in hours)	1	2	3	4
Distance covered (in km)	30	60	90	120

(i) Scale: (Fig 15.18)

Horizontal: 2 units = 1 hour

Vertical: 1 unit = 10 km

(ii) Mark time on horizontal axis.

(iii) Mark distance on vertical axis.

(iv) Plot the points: (1, 30), (2, 60), (3, 90), (4, 120).

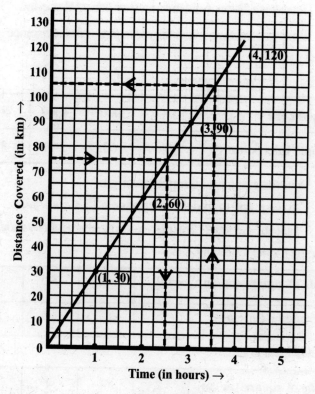

Fig 15.18

(v) Join the points. We get a linear graph.

(a) Corresponding to 75 km on the vertical axis, we get the time to be 2.5 hours on the horizontal axis. Thus 2.5 hours are needed to cover 75 km.

(b) Corresponding to $3\frac{1}{2}$ hours on the horizontal axis, the distance covered is 105 km on the vertical axis.

EXERCISE 15.3

1. Draw the graphs for the following tables of values, with suitable scales on the axes.

   (a) Cost of apples

Number of apples	1	2	3	4	5
Cost (in ₹)	5	10	15	20	25

   (b) Distance travelled by a car

Time (in hours)	6 a.m.	7 a.m.	8 a.m.	9 a.m.
Distances (in km)	40	80	120	160

(i) How much distance did the car cover during the period 7.30 a.m. to 8 a.m?

(ii) What was the time when the car had covered a distance of 100 km since it's start?

(c) Interest on deposits for a year.

Deposit (in ₹)	1000	2000	3000	4000	5000
Simple Interest (in ₹)	80	160	240	320	400

(i) Does the graph pass through the origin?

(ii) Use the graph to find the interest on ₹ 2500 for a year.

(iii) To get an interest of ₹ 280 per year, how much money should be deposited?

2. Draw a graph for the following.

(i)

Side of square (in cm)	2	3	3.5	5	6
Perimeter (in cm)	8	12	14	20	24

Is it a linear graph?

(ii)

Side of square (in cm)	2	3	4	5	6
Area (in cm²)	4	9	16	25	36

Is it a linear graph?

WHAT HAVE WE DISCUSSED?

1. Graphical presentation of data is easier to understand.

2. (i) A **bar graph** is used to show comparison among categories.

   (ii) A **pie graph** is used to compare parts of a whole.

   (iii) A **Histogram** is a bar graph that shows data in intervals.

3. A **line graph** displays data that changes continuously over periods of time.

4. A line graph which is a whole unbroken line is called a **linear graph**.

5. For fixing a point on the graph sheet we need, *x*-coordinate and *y*-coordinate.

6. The relation between **dependent variable** and **independent variable** is shown through a graph.

Playing with Numbers

0852CH16

16.1 Introduction

You have studied various types of numbers such as natural numbers, whole numbers, integers and rational numbers. You have also studied a number of interesting properties about them. In Class VI, we explored finding factors and multiples and the relationships among them.

In this chapter, we will explore numbers in more detail. These ideas help in justifying tests of divisibility.

16.2 Numbers in General Form

Let us take the number 52 and write it as

$$52 = 50 + 2 = 10 \times 5 + 2$$

Similarly, the number 37 can be written as

$$37 = 10 \times 3 + 7$$

In general, any two digit number ab made of digits a and b can be written as

$$ab = 10 \times a + b = 10a + b$$

What about ba? $ba = 10 \times b + a = 10b + a$

Here ab does not mean $a \times b$!

Let us now take number 351. This is a three digit number. It can also be written as

$$351 = 300 + 50 + 1 = 100 \times 3 + 10 \times 5 + 1 \times 1$$

Similarly $497 = 100 \times 4 + 10 \times 9 + 1 \times 7$

In general, a 3-digit number abc made up of digits a, b and c is written as

$$abc = 100 \times a + 10 \times b + 1 \times c$$
$$= 100a + 10b + c$$

In the same way,

$$cab = 100c + 10a + b$$
$$bca = 100b + 10c + a \qquad \text{and so on.}$$

TRY THESE

1. Write the following numbers in generalised form.

    (i) 25   (ii) 73   (iii) 129   (iv) 302

2. Write the following in the usual form.

    (i) $10 \times 5 + 6$ (ii) $100 \times 7 + 10 \times 1 + 8$ (iii) $100 \times a + 10 \times c + b$

16.3 Games with Numbers

(i) Reversing the digits – two digit number

Minakshi asks Sundaram to think of a 2-digit number, and then to do whatever she asks him to do, to that number. Their conversation is shown in the following figure. **Study the figure carefully before reading on**.

Conversations between Minakshi and Sundaram: First Round ...

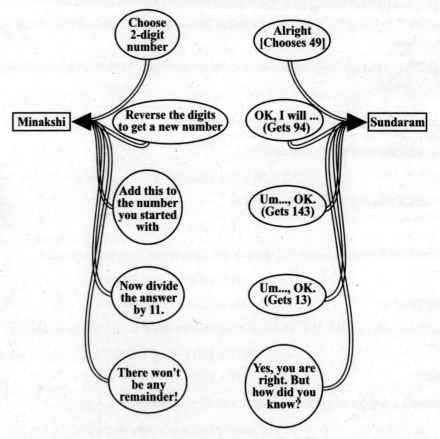

It so happens that Sundaram chose the number 49. So, he got the reversed number 94; then he added these two numbers and got $49 + 94 = 143$. Finally he divided this number by 11 and got $143 \div 11 = 13$, with no remainder. This is just what Minakshi had predicted.

TRY THESE

Check what the result would have been if Sundaram had chosen the numbers shown below.

1. 27   2. 39   3. 64   4. 17

Now, let us see if we can **explain** Minakshi's "trick".

Suppose Sundaram chooses the number ab, which is a short form for the 2-digit number $10a + b$. On reversing the digits, he gets the number $ba = 10b + a$. When he adds the two numbers he gets:

$$(10a + b) + (10b + a) = 11a + 11b$$
$$= 11\,(a + b).$$

So, the sum is always a multiple of 11, just as Minakshi had claimed.

Observe here that if we divide the sum by 11, the quotient is $a + b$, which is exactly the sum of the digits of chosen number ab.

You may check the same by taking any other two digit number.

The game between Minakshi and Sundaram continues!

Minakshi: Think of another 2-digit number, but don't tell me what it is.

Sundaram: Alright.

Minakshi: Now reverse the digits of the number, and *subtract* the smaller number from the larger one.

Sundaram: I have done the subtraction. What next?

Minakshi: Now divide your answer by 9. I claim that there will be no remainder!

Sundaram: Yes, you are right. There is indeed no remainder! But this time I think I know how you are so sure of this!

In fact, Sundaram had thought of 29. So his calculations were: first he got the number 92; then he got $92 - 29 = 63$; and finally he did $(63 \div 9)$ and got 7 as quotient, with no remainder.

TRY THESE

Check what the result would have been if Sundaram had chosen the numbers shown below.

1. 17   2. 21   3. 96   4. 37

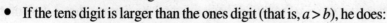

Let us see how Sundaram explains Minakshi's second "trick". (Now he feels confident of doing so!)

Suppose he chooses the 2-digit number $ab = 10a + b$. After reversing the digits, he gets the number $ba = 10b + a$. Now Minakshi tells him to do a subtraction, the smaller number from the larger one.

- If the tens digit is larger than the ones digit (that is, $a > b$), he does:
$$(10a + b) - (10b + a) = 10a + b - 10b - a$$
$$= 9a - 9b = 9(a - b).$$

- If the ones digit is larger than the tens digit (that is, $b > a$), he does:
$$(10b + a) - (10a + b) = 9(b - a).$$
- And, of course, if $a = b$, he gets 0.

In each case, the resulting number is divisible by 9. So, the remainder is 0. Observe here that if we divide the resulting number (obtained by subtraction), the quotient is $a - b$ or $b - a$ according as $a > b$ or $a < b$. You may check the same by taking any other two digit numbers.

(ii) **Reversing the digits – three digit number**.

Now it is Sundaram's turn to play some tricks!

Sundaram: Think of a 3-digit number, but don't tell me what it is.

Minakshi: Alright.

Sundaram: Now make a new number by putting the digits in reverse order, and subtract the smaller number from the larger one.

Minakshi: Alright, I have done the subtraction. What next?

Sundaram: Divide your answer by 99. I am sure that there will be no remainder!

In fact, Minakshi chose the 3-digit number 349. So she got:

- Reversed number: 943;
- Difference: $943 - 349 = 594$;
- Division: $594 \div 99 = 6$, with no remainder.

TRY THESE

Check what the result would have been if Minakshi had chosen the numbers shown below. In each case keep a record of the quotient obtained at the end.

1. 132   2. 469   3. 737   4. 901

Let us see how this trick works.

Let the 3-digit number chosen by Minakshi be $abc = 100a + 10b + c$.

After reversing the order of the digits, she gets the number $cba = 100c + 10b + a$. On subtraction:

- If $a > c$, then the difference between the numbers is
$$(100a + 10b + c) - (100c + 10b + a) = 100a + 10b + c - 100c - 10b - a$$
$$= 99a - 99c = 99(a - c).$$
- If $c > a$, then the difference between the numbers is
$$(100c + 10b + a) - (100a + 10b + c) = 99c - 99a = 99(c - a).$$
- And, of course, if $a = c$, the difference is 0.

In each case, the resulting number is divisible by 99. So the remainder is 0. Observe that quotient is $a - c$ or $c - a$. You may check the same by taking other 3-digit numbers.

(iii) **Forming three-digit numbers with given three-digits**.

Now it is Minakshi's turn once more.

Minakshi: Think of any 3-digit number.

Sundaram: Alright, I have done so.

Minakshi: Now use this number to form two more 3-digit numbers, like this: if the number you chose is *abc*, then

- 'the first number is *cab* (i.e., with the ones digit shifted to the "left end" of the number);
- the other number is *bca* (i.e., with the hundreds digit shifted to the "right end" of the number).

Now add them up. Divide the resulting number by 37. I claim that there will be no remainder.

Sundaram: Yes. You are right!

In fact, Sundaram had thought of the 3-digit number 237. After doing what Minakshi had asked, he got the numbers 723 and 372. So he did:

$$
\begin{array}{r}
2\ 3\ 7 \\
+\ \ 7\ 2\ 3 \\
+\ \ 3\ 7\ 2 \\
\hline
1\ 3\ 3\ 2
\end{array}
$$

> Form all possible 3-digit numbers using all the digits 2, 3 and 7 and find their sum. Check whether the sum is divisible by 37! Is it true for the sum of all the numbers formed by the digits *a*, *b* and *c* of the number *abc*?

Then he divided the resulting number 1332 by 37:

$$1332 \div 37 = 36, \quad \text{with no remainder.}$$

TRY THESE

Check what the result would have been if Sundaram had chosen the numbers shown below.

1. 417   2. 632   3. 117   4. 937

Will this trick always work?

Let us see.

$$abc = 100a + 10b + c$$
$$cab = 100c + 10a + b$$
$$bca = 100b + 10c + a$$
$$abc + cab + bca = 111(a + b + c)$$
$$= 37 \times 3(a + b + c), \text{ which is divisible by 37}$$

16.4 Letters for Digits

Here we have puzzles in which letters take the place of digits in an arithmetic 'sum', and the problem is to find out which letter represents which digit; so it is like cracking a code. Here we stick to problems of addition and multiplication.

Here are two rules we follow while doing such puzzles.

1. *Each letter in the puzzle must stand for just one digit. Each digit must be represented by just one letter.*

2. *The first digit of a number cannot be zero.* Thus, we write the number "sixty three" as 63, and not as 063, or 0063.

A rule that we would *like* to follow is that the puzzle must have just one answer.

Example 1: Find Q in the addition.

$$\begin{array}{r} 3\ 1\ Q \\ +\ 1\ Q\ 3 \\ \hline 5\ 0\ 1 \end{array}$$

Solution:

There is just one letter Q whose value we have to find.

Study the addition in the ones column: from Q + 3, we get '1', that is, a number whose ones digit is 1.

For this to happen, the digit Q should be 8. So the puzzle can be solved as shown below.

$$\begin{array}{r} 3\ 1\ 8 \\ +\ 1\ 8\ 3 \\ \hline 5\ 0\ 1 \end{array}$$

That is, Q = 8

Example 2: Find A and B in the addition.

$$\begin{array}{r} A \\ +\ \ A \\ +\ \ A \\ \hline B\ \ A \end{array}$$

Solution: This has *two* letters A and B whose values are to be found.

Study the addition in the ones column: the sum of *three* A's is a number whose ones digit is A. Therefore, the sum of *two* A's must be a number whose ones digit is 0. This happens only for A = 0 and A = 5.

If A = 0, then the sum is 0 + 0 + 0 = 0, which makes B = 0 too. We do not want this (as it makes A = B, and then the tens digit of BA too becomes 0), so we reject this possibility. So, A = 5.

Therefore, the puzzle is solved as shown below.

$$\begin{array}{r} 5 \\ +\ \ 5 \\ +\ \ 5 \\ \hline 1\ \ 5 \end{array}$$

That is, A = 5 and B = 1.

Example 3: Find the digits A and B.

$$
\begin{array}{r}
\text{B A} \\
\times\ \text{B 3} \\
\hline
\text{5 7 A}
\end{array}
$$

Solution:

This also has two letters A and B whose values are to be found.
Since the ones digit of 3 × A is A, it must be that A = 0 or A = 5.

Now look at B. If B = 1, then BA × B3 would *at most* be equal to 19 × 19; that is, it would at most be equal to 361. But the product here is 57A, which is more than 500. So we cannot have B = 1.

If B = 3, then BA × B3 would be more than 30 × 30; that is, more than 900. But 57A is less than 600. So, B can not be equal to 3.

Putting these two facts together, we see that B = 2 only. So the multiplication is either 20 × 23, or 25 × 23.

The first possibility fails, since 20 × 23 = 460. But, the second one works out correctly, since 25 × 23 = 575.
So the answer is A = 5, B = 2.

$$
\begin{array}{r}
\text{2 5} \\
\times\ \text{2 3} \\
\hline
\text{5 7 5}
\end{array}
$$

DO THIS

Write a 2-digit number *ab* and the number obtained by reversing its digits i.e., *ba*. Find their sum. Let the sum be a 3-digit number *dad*

i.e., $ab + ba = dad$

$(10a + b) + (10b + a) = dad$

$11(a + b) = dad$

The sum $a + b$ can not exceed 18 (Why?).

Is *dad* a multiple of 11?

Is *dad* less than 198?

Write all the 3-digit numbers which are multiples of 11 upto 198.

Find the values of *a* and *d*.

EXERCISE 16.1

Find the values of the letters in each of the following and give reasons for the steps involved.

1.
$$
\begin{array}{r}
\text{3 A} \\
+\ \text{2 5} \\
\hline
\text{B 2}
\end{array}
$$

2.
$$
\begin{array}{r}
\text{4 A} \\
+\ \text{9 8} \\
\hline
\text{C B 3}
\end{array}
$$

3.
$$
\begin{array}{r}
\text{1 A} \\
\times\ \text{A} \\
\hline
\text{9 A}
\end{array}
$$

4.	A B	5.	A B	6.	A B
	+ 3 7		× 3		× 5
	6 A		C A B		C A B

7.	A B	8.	A 1	9.	2 A B
	× 6		+ 1 B		+ A B 1
	B B B		B 0		B 1 8

10.	1 2 A
	+ 6 A B
	A 0 9

16.5 Tests of Divisibility

In Class VI, you learnt how to check divisibility by the following divisors.

$$10, 5, 2, 3, 6, 4, 8, 9, 11.$$

You would have found the tests easy to do, but you may have wondered at the same time *why* they work. Now, in this chapter, we shall go into the "why" aspect of the above.

16.5.1 Divisibility by 10

This is certainly the easiest test of all! We first look at some multiples of 10.

$$10, 20, 30, 40, 50, 60, ... ,$$

and then at some non-multiples of 10.

$$13, 27, 32, 48, 55, 69,$$

From these lists we see that if the ones digit of a number is 0, then the number is a multiple of 10; and if the ones digit is *not* 0, then the number is *not* a multiple of 10. So, we get a test of divisibility by 10.

Of course, we must not stop with just stating the test; we must also explain *why* it "works". That is not hard to do; we only need to remember the rules of place value. Take the number. ... *cba*; this is a short form for

$$... + 100c + 10b + a$$

Here a is the one's digit, b is the ten's digit, c is the hundred's digit, and so on. The dots are there to say that there may be more digits to the left of c.

Since 10, 100, ... are divisible by 10, so are $10b$, $100c$, ... And as for the number a is concerned, it must be a divisible by 10 if the given number is divisible by 10. This is possible only when $a = 0$.

Hence, a number is divisible by 10 when its one's digit is 0.

16.5.2 Divisibility by 5

Look at the multiples of 5.

$$5, 10, 15, 20, 25, 30, 35, 40, 45, 50,$$

We see that *the one's digits are alternately 5 and 0, and no other digit ever appears in this list.*

So, we get our test of divisibility by 5.

If the ones digit of a number is 0 or 5, then it is divisible by 5.

Let us explain this rule. Any number ... *cba* can be written as:

... + 100*c* + 10*b* + *a*

Since 10, 100 are divisible by 10 so are 10*b*, 100*c*, ... which in turn, are divisible by 5 because 10 = 2 × 5. As far as number *a* is concerned it must be divisible by 5 if the number is divisible by 5. So *a* has to be either 0 or 5.

TRY THESE

(The first one has been done for you.)

1. If the division N ÷ 5 leaves a remainder of 3, what might be the ones digit of N? (The one's digit, when divided by 5, must leave a remainder of 3. So the one's digit must be either 3 or 8.)

2. If the division N ÷ 5 leaves a remainder of 1, what might be the one's digit of N?

3. If the division N ÷ 5 leaves a remainder of 4, what might be the one's digit of N?

16.5.3 Divisibility by 2

Here are the even numbers.

2, 4, 6, 8, 10, 12, 14, 16, 18, 20, 22, ... ,

and here are the odd numbers.

1, 3, 5, 7, 9, 11, 13, 15, 17, 19, 21, ... ,

We see that a natural number is even if its one's digit is

2, 4, 6, 8 or 0

A number is odd if its one's digit is

1, 3, 5, 7 or 9

Recall the test of divisibility by 2 learnt in Class VI, which is as follows.

If the one's digit of a number is 0, 2, 4, 6 or 8 then the number is divisible by 2.

The explanation for this is as follows.

Any number *cba* can be written as 100*c* + 10*b* + *a*

First two terms namely 100*c*, 10*b* are divisible by 2 because 100 and 10 are divisible by 2. So far as *a* is concerned, it must be divisible by 2 if the given number is divisible by 2. This is possible only when *a* = 0, 2, 4, 6 or 8.

TRY THESE

(The first one has been done for you.)

1. If the division N ÷ 2 leaves a remainder of 1, what might be the one's digit of N? (N is odd; so its one's digit is odd. Therefore, the one's digit must be 1, 3, 5, 7 or 9.)

2. If the division N ÷ 2 leaves no remainder (i.e., zero remainder), what might be the one's digit of N?

3. Suppose that the division N ÷ 5 leaves a remainder of 4, and the division N ÷ 2 leaves a remainder of 1. What must be the one's digit of N?

16.5.4 Divisibility by 9 and 3

Look carefully at the three tests of divisibility found till now, for checking division by 10, 5 and 2. We see something common to them: *they use only the one's digit of the given number; they do not bother about the 'rest' of the digits*. Thus, *divisibility is decided just by the one's digit*. 10, 5, 2 are divisors of 10, which is the key number in our place value.

But for checking divisibility by 9, this will not work. Let us take some number say 3573.

Its expanded form is: $3 \times 1000 + 5 \times 100 + 7 \times 10 + 3$

This is equal to $3 \times (999 + 1) + 5 \times (99 + 1) + 7 \times (9 + 1) + 3$

$$= 3 \times 999 + 5 \times 99 + 7 \times 9 + (3 + 5 + 7 + 3) \qquad \text{... (1)}$$

We see that the number 3573 will be divisible by 9 or 3 if $(3 + 5 + 7 + 3)$ is divisible by 9 or 3.

We see that $3 + 5 + 7 + 3 = 18$ is divisible by 9 and also by 3. Therefore, the number 3573 is divisible by both 9 and 3.

Now, let us consider the number 3576. As above, we get

$$3576 = 3 \times 999 + 5 \times 99 + 7 \times 9 + (3 + 5 + 7 + 6) \qquad \text{... (2)}$$

Since $(3 + 5 + 7 + 6)$ i.e., 21 is not divisible by 9 but is divisible by 3,

therefore 3576 is not divisible by 9. However 3576 is divisible by 3. Hence,

(i)   A number N is divisible by 9 if the sum of its digits is divisible by 9. Otherwise it is not divisible by 9.

(ii) A number N is divisible by 3 if the sum of its digits is divisible by 3. Otherwise it is not divisible by 3.

If the number is 'cba', then, $100c + 10b + a = 99c + 9b + (a + b + c)$

$$= \underbrace{9(11c + b)}_{\text{divisible by 3 and 9}} + (a + b + c)$$

Hence, divisibility by 9 (or 3) is possible if $a + b + c$ is divisible by 9 (or 3).

Example 4: Check the divisibility of 21436587 by 9.

Solution: The sum of the digits of 21436587 is $2 + 1 + 4 + 3 + 6 + 5 + 8 + 7 = 36$. This number is divisible by 9 (for $36 \div 9 = 4$). We conclude that 21436587 is divisible by 9. We can double-check:

$$\frac{21436587}{9} = 2381843 \qquad \text{(the division is exact)}.$$

Example 5: Check the divisibility of 152875 by 9.

Solution: The sum of the digits of 152875 is $1 + 5 + 2 + 8 + 7 + 5 = 28$. This number is **not** divisible by 9. We conclude that 152875 is not divisible by 9.

TRY THESE

Check the divisibility of the following numbers by 9.

1. 108   2. 616   3. 294   4. 432   5. 927

Example 6: If the three digit number $24x$ is divisible by 9, what is the value of x?

Solution: Since $24x$ is divisible by 9, sum of it's digits, i.e., $2 + 4 + x$ should be divisible by 9, i.e., $6 + x$ should be divisible by 9.

This is possible when $6 + x = 9$ or 18, ...
But, since x is a digit, therefore, $6 + x = 9$, i.e., $x = 3$.

THINK, DISCUSS AND WRITE

1. You have seen that a number 450 is divisible by 10. It is also divisible by 2 and 5 which are factors of 10. Similarly, a number 135 is divisible 9. It is also divisible by 3 which is a factor of 9.

    Can you say that if a number is divisible by any number m, then it will also be divisible by each of the factors of m?

2. (i) Write a 3-digit number abc as $100a + 10b + c$
    $$= 99a + 11b + (a - b + c)$$
    $$= 11(9a + b) + (a - b + c)$$

    If the number abc is divisible by 11, then what can you say about $(a - b + c)$?

    Is it necessary that $(a + c - b)$ should be divisible by 11?

    (ii) Write a 4-digit number $abcd$ as $1000a + 100b + 10c + d$
    $$= (1001a + 99b + 11c) - (a - b + c - d)$$
    $$= 11(91a + 9b + c) + [(b + d) - (a + c)]$$

    If the number $abcd$ is divisible by 11, then what can you say about $[(b + d) - (a + c)]$?

    (iii) From (i) and (ii) above, can you say that a number will be divisible by 11 if the difference between the sum of digits at its odd places and that of digits at the even places is divisible by 11?

Example 7: Check the divisibility of 2146587 by 3.

Solution: The sum of the digits of 2146587 is $2 + 1 + 4 + 6 + 5 + 8 + 7 = 33$. This number is divisible by 3 (for $33 \div 3 = 11$). We conclude that 2146587 is divisible by 3.

Example 8: Check the divisibility of 15287 by 3.

Solution: The sum of the digits of 15287 is $1 + 5 + 2 + 8 + 7 = 23$. This number is not divisible by 3. We conclude that 15287 too is not divisible by 3.

TRY THESE

Check the divisibility of the following numbers by 3.

1. 108   2. 616   3. 294   4. 432   5. 927

EXERCISE 16.2

1. If $21y5$ is a multiple of 9, where y is a digit, what is the value of y?

2. If $31z5$ is a multiple of 9, where z is a digit, what is the value of z?

   You will find that there are *two* answers for the last problem. Why is this so?

3. If $24x$ is a multiple of 3, where x is a digit, what is the value of x?

   (Since $24x$ is a multiple of 3, its sum of digits $6 + x$ is a multiple of 3; so $6 + x$ is one of these numbers: 0, 3, 6, 9, 12, 15, 18, ... But since x is a digit, it can only be that $6 + x = 6$ or 9 or 12 or 15. Therefore, $x = 0$ or 3 or 6 or 9. Thus, x can have any of four different values.)

4. If $31z5$ is a multiple of 3, where z is a digit, what might be the values of z?

WHAT HAVE WE DISCUSSED?

1. Numbers can be written in general form. Thus, a two digit number ab will be written as $ab = 10a + b$.

2. The general form of numbers are helpful in solving puzzles or number games.

3. The reasons for the divisibility of numbers by 10, 5, 2, 9 or 3 can be given when numbers are written in general form.

EXERCISE 1.1

1. (i) 2   (ii) $\dfrac{-11}{28}$

2. (i) $\dfrac{-2}{8}$ (ii) $\dfrac{5}{9}$ (iii) $\dfrac{-6}{5}$ (iv) $\dfrac{2}{9}$ (v) $\dfrac{19}{6}$

4. (i) $\dfrac{-1}{13}$ (ii) $\dfrac{-19}{13}$ (iii) 5   (iv) $\dfrac{56}{15}$ (v) $\dfrac{5}{2}$ (vi) -1

5. (i) 1 is the multiplicative identity   (ii) Commutativity

   (iii) Multiplicative inverse

6. $\dfrac{-96}{91}$ 7. Associativity   8. No, because the product is not 1.

9. Yes, because $0.3 \times 3\dfrac{1}{3} = \dfrac{3}{10} \times \dfrac{10}{3} = 1$

10. (i) 0   (ii) 1 and (-1)   (iii) 0

11. (i) No   (ii) 1, -1 (iii) $\dfrac{-1}{5}$ (iv) x (v) Rational number

    (vi) positive

EXERCISE 1.2

1. (i)

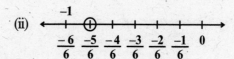

2.

3. Some of these are $1, \dfrac{1}{2}, 0, -1, \dfrac{-1}{2}$

4. $\dfrac{-7}{20}, \dfrac{-6}{20}, \dfrac{-5}{20}, \dfrac{-4}{20}, \dfrac{-3}{20}, \dfrac{-2}{20}, \dfrac{-1}{20}, 0, \dots, \dfrac{1}{20}, \dfrac{2}{20}$ (There can be many more such rational numbers)

5. (i) $\dfrac{41}{60}, \dfrac{42}{60}, \dfrac{43}{60}, \dfrac{44}{60}, \dfrac{45}{60}$ (ii) $\dfrac{-8}{6}, \dfrac{-7}{6}, 0, \dfrac{1}{6}, \dfrac{2}{6}$ (iii) $\dfrac{9}{32}, \dfrac{10}{32}, \dfrac{11}{32}, \dfrac{12}{32}, \dfrac{13}{32}$

   (There can be many more such rational numbers)

6. $-\dfrac{3}{2}, -1, \dfrac{-1}{2}, 0, \dfrac{1}{2}$ (There can be many more such rational numbers)

7. $\dfrac{97}{160}, \dfrac{98}{160}, \dfrac{99}{160}, \dfrac{100}{160}, \dfrac{101}{160}, \dfrac{102}{160}, \dfrac{103}{160}, \dfrac{104}{160}, \dfrac{105}{160}, \dfrac{106}{160}$

(There can be many more such rational numbers)

EXERCISE 2.1

1. $x = 9$	**2.** $y = 7$	**3.** $z = 4$	**4.** $x = 2$	**5.** $x = 2$	**6.** $t = 50$
7. $x = 27$	**8.** $y = 2.4$	**9.** $x = \dfrac{25}{7}$	**10.** $y = \dfrac{3}{2}$	**11.** $p = -\dfrac{4}{3}$	**12.** $x = -\dfrac{8}{5}$

EXERCISE 2.2

1. $\dfrac{3}{4}$ **2.** length = 52 m, breadth = 25 m   **3.** $1\dfrac{2}{5}$ cm   **4.** 40 and 55

5. 45, 27   **6.** 16, 17, 18   **7.** 288, 296 and 304   **8.** 7, 8, 9

9. Rahul's age: 20 years; Haroon's age: 28 years   **10.** 48 students

11. Baichung's age: 17 years; Baichung's father's age: 46 years;

Baichung's grandfather's age = 72 years   **12.** 5 years   **13** $-\dfrac{1}{2}$

14. ₹ 100 → 2000 notes; ₹ 50 → 3000 notes; ₹ 10 → 5000 notes

15. Number of ₹ 1 coins = 80; Number of ₹ 2 coins = 60; Number of ₹ 5 coins = 20

16. 19

EXERCISE 2.3

1. $x = 18$	**2.** $t = -1$	**3.** $x = -2$	**4.** $z = \dfrac{3}{2}$	**5.** $x = 5$	**6.** $x = 0$
7. $x = 40$	**8.** $x = 10$	**9.** $y = \dfrac{7}{3}$	**10.** $m = \dfrac{4}{5}$		

EXERCISE 2.4

1. 4   **2.** 7, 35   **3.** 36   **4.** 26 (or 62)

5. Shobo's age: 5 years; Shobo's mother's age: 30 years

6. Length = 275 m; breadth = 100 m   **7.** 200 m   **8.** 72

9. Grand daughter's age: 6 years; Grandfather's age: 60 years

10. Aman's age: 60 years; Aman's son's age: 20 years

EXERCISE 2.5

1. $x = \dfrac{27}{10}$ **2.** $n = 36$ **3.** $x = -5$ **4.** $x = 8$ **5.** $t = 2$

6. $m = \dfrac{7}{5}$ **7.** $t = -2$ **8.** $y = \dfrac{2}{3}$ **9.** $z = 2$ **10.** $f = 0.6$

EXERCISE 2.6

1. $x = \dfrac{3}{2}$ **2.** $x = \dfrac{35}{33}$ **3.** $z = 12$ **4.** $y = -8$ **5.** $y = -\dfrac{4}{5}$

6. Hari's age $= 20$ years; Harry's age $= 28$ years   **7.** $\dfrac{13}{21}$

EXERCISE 3.1

1. (a)   1, 2, 5, 6, 7   (b)   1, 2, 5, 6, 7   (c)   1, 2

    (d)   2   (e)   1

2. (a)   2   (b)   9   (c)   0   **3.**   360°; yes.

4. (a)   900°   (b)   1080°   (c)   1440°   (d) $(n-2)180°$

5. A polygon with equal sides and equal angles.

    (i)   Equilateral triangle   (ii)   Square   (iii)   Regular hexagon

6. (a)   60°   (b)   140°   (c)   140°   (d)   108°

7. (a) $x + y + z = 360°$ (b) $x + y + z + w = 360°$

EXERCISE 3.2

1. (a) $360° - 250° = 110°$ (b) $360° - 310° = 50°$

2. (i) $\dfrac{360°}{9} = 40°$ (ii) $\dfrac{360°}{15} = 24°$

3. $\dfrac{360}{24} = 15$ (sides)   **4.** Number of sides $= 24$

5. (i)   No; (Since 22 is not a divisor of 360)

    (ii)   No; (because each exterior angle is $180° - 22° = 158°$, which is not a divisor of 360°).

6. (a)   The equilateral triangle being a regular polygon of 3 sides has the least measure of an interior angle $= 60°$.

    (b)   By (a), we can see that the greatest exterior angle is 120°.

EXERCISE 3.3

1. (i)   BC(Opposite sides are equal)   (ii) $\angle$DAB (Opposite angles are equal)

(iii)   OA (Diagonals bisect each other)

(iv)   180° (Interior opposite angles, since $\overline{AB} \parallel \overline{DC}$)

2. (i) $x = 80°$; $y = 100°$; $z = 80°$ (ii) $x = 130°$; $y = 130°$; $z = 130°$

(iii) $x = 90°$; $y = 60°$; z = $60°$ (iv) $x = 100°$; $y = 80°$; $z = 80°$

(v) $y = 112°$; $x = 28°$; $z = 28°$

3. (i)   Can be, but need not be.

(ii)   No; (in a parallelogram, opposite sides are equal; but here, AD $\neq$ BC).

(iii)   No; (in a parallelogram, opposite angles are equal; but here, $\angle$A $\neq \angle$C).

4. A kite, for example   5. 108°; 72°;   6. Each is a right angle.

7. $x = 110°$; $y = 40°$; $z = 30°$

8. (i) $x = 6$; $y = 9$ (ii) $x = 3$; $y = 13$;   9. $x = 50°$

10. $\overline{NM} \parallel \overline{KL}$ (sum of interior opposite angles is 180°). So, KLMN is a trapezium.

11. 60°   12. $\angle$P = 50°; $\angle$S = 90°

EXERCISE 3.4

1. (b), (c), (f), (g), (h) are true; others are false.

2. (a)   Rhombus; square.   (b)   Square; rectangle

3. (i)   A square is 4 – sided; so it is a quadrilateral.

(ii)   A square has its opposite sides parallel; so it is a parallelogram.

(iii)   A square is a parallelogram with all the 4 sides equal; so it is a rhombus.

(iv)   A square is a parallelogram with each angle a right angle; so it is a rectangle.

4. (i)   Parallelogram; rhombus; square; rectangle.

(ii)   Rhombus; square   (iii)   Square; rectangle

5. Both of its diagonals lie in its interior.

6. $\overline{AD} \parallel \overline{BC}$; $\overline{AB} \parallel \overline{DC}$. So, in parallelogram ABCD, the mid-point of diagonal $\overline{AC}$ is O.

EXERCISE 5.1

1. (b), (d). In all these cases data can be divided into class intervals.

2.

Shopper	Tally marks	Number
W	$\cancel{||||}$ $\cancel{||||}$ $\cancel{||||}$ $\cancel{||||}$ $\cancel{||||}$ |||	28
M	$\cancel{||||}$ $\cancel{||||}$ $\cancel{||||}$	15
B	$\cancel{||||}$	5
G	$\cancel{||||}$ $\cancel{||||}$ ||	12

3.

Interval	Tally marks	Frequency
800 - 810	|||	3
810 - 820	||	2
820 - 830			1
830 - 840	~~||||~~ ||||	9
840 - 850	~~||||~~	5
850 - 860			1
860 - 870	|||	3
870 - 880			1
880 - 890			1
890 - 900	||||	4
	Total	**30**

4. (i) 830 - 840   (ii) 10
   (iii) 20

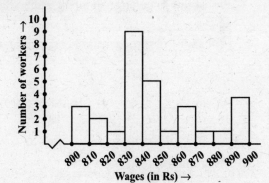

5. (i) 4 - 5 hours   (ii) 34
   (iii) 14

EXERCISE 5.2

1. (i) 200   (ii) Light music   (iii) Classical - 100, Semi classical - 200, Light - 400, Folk - 300

2. (i) Winter   (ii) Winter - 150°, Rainy - 120°, Summer - 90°   (iii)

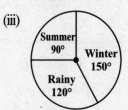

3.

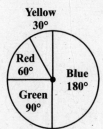

4. (i) Hindi (ii) 30 marks (iii) Yes **5.**

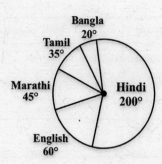

Bangla 20°
Tamil 35°
Marathi 45°
Hindi 200°
English 60°

EXERCISE 5.3

1. (a) Outcomes → A, B, C, D

(b) HT, HH, TH, TT (Here HT means Head on first coin and Tail on the second coin and so on).

2. Outcomes of an event of getting

(i) (a) 2, 3, 5   (b) 1, 4, 6

(ii) (a) 6   (b) 1, 2, 3, 4, 5

3. (a) $\dfrac{1}{5}$ (b) $\dfrac{1}{13}$ (c) $\dfrac{4}{7}$

4. (i) $\dfrac{1}{10}$ (ii) $\dfrac{1}{2}$ (iii) $\dfrac{2}{5}$ (iv) $\dfrac{9}{10}$

5. Probability of getting a green sector $= \dfrac{3}{5}$; probability of getting a non-blue sector $= \dfrac{4}{5}$

6. Probability of getting a prime number $= \dfrac{1}{2}$; probability of getting a number which is not prime $= \dfrac{1}{2}$

Probability of getting a number greater than 5 $= \dfrac{1}{6}$

Probability of getting a number not greater than 5 $= \dfrac{5}{6}$

EXERCISE 6.1

1. (i) 1   (ii) 4   (iii) 1   (iv) 9   (v) 6   (vi) 9

(vii) 4   (viii) 0   (ix) 6   (x) 5

2. These numbers end with

(i) 7   (ii) 3   (iii) 8   (iv) 2   (v) 0   (vi) 2

(vii) 0   (viii) 0

3. (i), (iii)   **4.** 10000200001, 100000020000001

5. 1020304030201, 101010101^2 **6.** 20, 6, 42, 43

7. (i) 25   (ii) 100   (iii) 144

8. (i) 1 + 3 + 5 + 7 + 9 + 11 + 13

(ii) 1 + 3 + 5 + 7 + 9 + 11 + 13 + 15 + 17 + 19 + 21

9. (i) 24   (ii) 50   (iii) 198

EXERCISE 6.2

1. (i) 1024 (ii) 1225 (iii) 7396 (iv) 8649 (v) 5041 (vi) 2116
2. (i) 6,8,10 (ii) 14,48,50 (iii) 16,63,65 (iv) 18,80,82

EXERCISE 6.3

1. (i) 1, 9 (ii) 4, 6 (iii) 1, 9 (iv) 5
2. (i), (ii), (iii) 3. 10, 13
4. (i) 27 (ii) 20 (iii) 42 (iv) 64 (v) 88 (vi) 98
    (vii) 77 (viii) 96 (ix) 23 (x) 90
5. (i) 7; 42 (ii) 5; 30 (iii) 7, 84 (iv) 3; 78 (v) 2; 54 (vi) 3; 48
6. (i) 7; 6 (ii) 13; 15 (iii) 11; 6 (vi) 5; 23 (v) 7; 20 (vi) 5; 18
7. 49 8. 45 rows; 45 plants in each row 9. 900 10. 3600

EXERCISE 6.4

1. (i) 48 (ii) 67 (iii) 59 (iv) 23 (v) 57 (vi) 37
    (vii) 76 (viii) 89 (ix) 24 (x) 32 (xi) 56 (xii) 30
2. (i) 1 (ii) 2 (iii) 2 (iv) 3 (v) 3
3. (i) 1.6 (ii) 2.7 (iii) 7.2 (iv) 6.5 (v) 5.6
4. (i) 2; 20 (ii) 53; 44 (iii) 1; 57 (iv) 41; 28 (v) 31; 63
5. (i) 4; 23 (ii) 14; 42 (iii) 4; 16 (iv) 24; 43 (v) 149; 81
6. 21 m 7. (a) 10 cm (b) 12 cm
8. 24 plants 9. 16 children

EXERCISE 7.1

1. (ii) and (iv)
2. (i) 3 (ii) 2 (iii) 3 (iv) 5 (v) 10
3. (i) 3 (ii) 2 (iii) 5 (iv) 3 (v) 11
4. 20 cuboids

EXERCISE 7.2

1. (i) 4 (ii) 8 (iii) 22 (iv) 30 (v) 25 (vi) 24
    (vii) 48 (viii) 36 (ix) 56
2. (i) False (ii) True (iii) False (iv) False (v) False (vi) False
    (vii) True
3. 11, 17, 23, 32

EXERCISE 8.1

1. (a) $1 : 2$ (b) $1 : 2000$ (c) $1 : 10$

2. (a) 75% (b) $66\dfrac{2}{3}\%$ **3.** 28% students   **4.** 25 matches   **5.** ₹ 2400

6. 10%, cricket → 30 lakh; football → 15 lakh; other games → 5 lakh

EXERCISE 8.2

1. ₹ 1,40,000   **2.** 80%   **3.** ₹ 34.80   **4.** ₹ 18,342.50

5. Gain of 2%   **6.** ₹ 2,835   **7.** Loss of ₹ 1,269.84

8. ₹ 14,560   **9.** ₹ 2,000   **10.** ₹ 5,000   **11.** ₹ 1,050

EXERCISE 8.3

1. (a) Amount = ₹ 15,377.34; Compound interest = ₹ 4,577.34

     (b) Amount = ₹ 22,869; Interest = ₹ 4869   (c) Amount = ₹ 70,304, Interest = ₹ 7,804

     (d) Amount = ₹ 8,736.20, Interest = ₹ 736.20

     (e) Amount = ₹ 10,816, Interest = ₹ 816

2. ₹ 36,659.70   **3.** Fabina pays ₹ 362.50 more   **4.** ₹ 43.20

5. (ii) ₹ 63,600   (ii) ₹ 67,416   **6.** (ii) ₹ 92,400   (ii) ₹ 92,610

7. (i) ₹ 8,820   (ii) ₹ 441

8. Amount = ₹ 11,576.25, Interest = ₹ 1,576.25 Yes.

9. ₹ 4,913   **10.** (i) About 48,980 (ii) 59,535   **11.** 5,31,616 (approx)

12. ₹ 38,640

EXERCISE 9.1

1.

	Term	Coefficient
(i)	$5xyz^2$	5
	$-3zy$	-3
(ii)	1	1
	x	1
	x^2	1
(iii)	$4x^2y^2$	4
	$-4x^2y^2z^2$	-4
	z^2	1

	Term	Coefficient
(iv)	3	3
	$-pq$	-1
	qr	1
	$-rp$	-1
(v)	$\dfrac{x}{2}$	$\dfrac{1}{2}$
	$\dfrac{y}{2}$	$\dfrac{1}{2}$
	$-xy$	-1
(vi)	$0.3a$	0.3
	$-0.6ab$	-0.6
	$0.5b$	0.5

2. Monomials: $1000, pqr$

  Binomials: $x + y, 2y - 3y^2, 4z - 15z^2, p^2q + pq^2, 2p + 2q$

  Trinomials : $7 + y + 5x, 2y - 3y^2 + 4y^3, 5x - 4y + 3xy$

  Polynomials that do not fit in these categories: $x + x^2 + x^3 + x^4, ab + bc + cd + da$

3. (i) 0 (ii) $ab + bc + ac$ (iii) $-p^2q^2 + 4pq + 9$

  (iv) $2(l^2 + m^2 + n^2 + lm + mn + nl)$

4. (a) $8a - 2ab + 2b - 15$ (b) $2xy - 7yz + 5zx + 10xyz$

  (c) $p^2q - 7pq^2 + 8pq - 18q + 5p + 28$

■■■■ EXERCISE 9.2

1. (i) $28p$ (ii) $-28p^2$ (iii) $-28p^2q$ (iv) $-12p^4$ (v) 0

2. pq; $50\,mn$; $100\,x^2y^2$; $12x^3$; $12mn^2p$

3.

First monomial → Second monomial ↓	$2x$	$-5y$	$3x^2$	$-4xy$	$7x^2y$	$-9x^2y^2$
$2x$	$4x^2$	$-10xy$	$6x^3$	$-8x^2y$	$14x^3y$	$-18x^3y^2$
$-5y$	$-10xy$	$25y^2$	$-15x^2y$	$20xy^2$	$-35x^2y^2$	$45x^2y^3$
$3x^2$	$6x^3$	$-15x^2y$	$9x^4$	$-12x^3y$	$21x^4y$	$-27x^4y^2$
$-4xy$	$-8x^2y$	$20xy^2$	$-12x^3y$	$16x^2y^2$	$-28x^3y^2$	$36x^3y^3$
$7x^2y$	$14x^3y$	$-35x^2y^2$	$21x^4y$	$-28x^3y^2$	$49x^4y^2$	$-63x^4y^3$
$-9x^2y^2$	$-18x^3y^2$	$45x^2y^3$	$-27x^4y^2$	$36x^3y^3$	$-63x^4y^3$	$81x^4y^4$

4. (i) $105a^7$ (ii) $64pqr$ (iii) $4x^4y^4$ (iv) $6abc$

5. (i) $x^2y^2z^2$ (ii) $-a^6$ (iii) $1024y^6$ (iv) $36a^2b^2c^2$ (v) $-m^3n^2p$

■■■■ EXERCISE 9.3

1. (i) $4pq + 4pr$ (ii) $a^2b - ab^2$ (iii) $7a^3b^2 + 7a^2b^3$

  (iv) $4a^3 - 36a$ (v) 0

2. (i) $ab + ac + ad$ (ii) $5x^2y + 5xy^2 - 25xy$

  (iii) $6p^3 - 7p^2 + 5p$ (iv) $4p^4q^2 - 4p^2q^4$

  (v) $a^2bc + ab^2c + abc^2$

3. (i) $8a^{50}$ (ii) $-\dfrac{3}{5}x^3y^3$ (iii) $-4p^4q^4$ (iv) x^{10}

4. (a) $12x^2 - 15x + 3$;   (i) 66 (ii) $\dfrac{-3}{2}$

  (b) $a^3 + a^2 + a + 5$;   (i) 5 (ii) 8 (iii) 4

5. (a) $p^2 + q^2 + r^2 - pq - qr - pr$ (b) $-2x^2 - 2y^2 - 4xy + 2yz + 2zx$

  (c) $5l^2 + 25ln$ (d) $-3a^2 - 2b^2 + 4c^2 - ab + 6bc - 7ac$

EXERCISE 9.4

1. (i) $8x^2 + 14x - 15$ (ii) $3y^2 - 28y + 32$ (iii) $6.25l^2 - 0.25m^2$
   (iv) $ax + 5a + 3bx + 15b$ (v) $6p^2q^2 + 5pq^3 - 6q^4$ (vi) $3a^4 + 10a^2b^2 - 8b^4$
2. (i) $15 - x - 2x^2$ (ii) $7x^2 + 48xy - 7y^2$ (iii) $a^3 + a^2b^2 + ab + b^3$
   (iv) $2p^3 + p^2q - 2pq^2 - q^3$
3. (i) $x^3 + 5x^2 - 5x$ (ii) $a^2b^3 + 3a^2 + 5b^3 + 20$ (iii) $t^3 - st + s^2t^2 - s^3$
   (iv) $4ac$ (v) $3x^2 + 4xy - y^2$ (vi) $x^3 + y^3$
   (vii) $2.25x^2 - 16y^2$ (viii) $a^2 + b^2 - c^2 + 2ab$

EXERCISE 9.5

1. (i) $x^2 + 6x + 9$ (ii) $4y^2 + 20y + 25$ (iii) $4a^2 - 28a + 49$

   (iv) $9a^2 - 3a + \dfrac{1}{4}$ (v) $1.21m^2 - 0.16$ (vi) $b^4 - a^4$

   (vii) $36x^2 - 49$ (viii) $a^2 - 2ac + c^2$ (ix) $\dfrac{x^2}{4} + \dfrac{3xy}{4} + \dfrac{9y^2}{16}$

   (x) $49a^2 - 126ab + 81b^2$
2. (i) $x^2 + 10x + 21$ (ii) $16x^2 + 24x + 5$ (iii) $16x^2 - 24x + 5$
   (iv) $16x^2 + 16x - 5$ (v) $4x^2 + 16xy + 15y^2$ (vi) $4a^4 + 28a^2 + 45$
   (vii) $x^2 y^2 z^2 - 6xyz + 8$
3. (i) $b^2 - 14b + 49$ (ii) $x^2 y^2 + 6xyz + 9z^2$ (iii) $36x^4 - 60x^2y + 25y^2$

   (iv) $\dfrac{4}{9}m^2 + 2mn + \dfrac{9}{4}n^2$ (v) $0.16p^2 + 0.04pq + 0.25q^2$ (vi) $4x^2y^2 + 20xy^2 + 25y^2$

4. (i) $a^4 - 2a^2b^2 + b^4$ (ii) $40x$ (iii) $98m^2 + 128n^2$
   (iv) $41m^2 + 80mn + 41n^2$ (v) $4p^2 - 4q^2$ (vi) $a^2b^2 + b^2c^2$ (vii) $m^4 + n^4m^2$
6. (i) 5041 (ii) 9801 (iii) 10404 (iv) 996004
   (v) 27.04 (vi) 89991 (vii) 6396 (viii) 79.21
   (ix) 99.75
7. (i) 200 (ii) 0.08 (iii) 1800 (iv) 84
8. (i) 10712 (ii) 26.52 (iii) 10094 (iv) 95.06

EXERCISE 10.1

1. (a) → (iii) → (iv) (b) → (i) → (v) (c) → (iv) → (ii)
   (d) → (v) → (iii) (e) → (ii) → (i)
2. (a) (i) → Front, (ii) → Side, (iii) → Top (b) (i) → Side, (ii) → Front, (iii) → Top
   (c) (i) → Front, (ii) → Side, (iii) → Top (d) (i) → Front, (ii) → Side, (iii) → Top
3. (a) (i) → Top, (ii) → Front, (iii) → Side (b) (i) → Side, (ii) → Front, (iii) → Top
   (c) (i) → Top, (ii) → Side, (iii) → Front (d) (i) → Side, (ii) → Front, (iii) → Top
   (e) (i) → Front, (ii) → Top, (iii) → Side

EXERCISE 10.3

1. (i) No (ii) Yes (iii) Yes   2. Possible, only if the number of faces are greater than or equal to 4
3. only (ii) and (iv)
4. (i) A prism becomes a cylinder as the number of sides of its base becomes larger and larger.
   (ii) A pyramid becomes a cone as the number of sides of its base becomes larger and larger.
5. No. It can be a cuboid also   7. Faces → 8, Vertices → 6, Edges → 30
8. No

EXERCISE 11.1

1. (a)   2. ₹ 17,875   3. Area = 129.5 m²; Perimeter = 48 m
4. 45000 tiles   5. (b)

EXERCISE 11.2

1. 0.88 m²   2. 7 cm   3. 660 m²   4. 252 m²
5. 45 cm²   6. 24 cm², 6 cm   7. ₹ 810   8. 140 m
9. 119 m²   10. Area using Jyoti's way $= 2 \times \dfrac{1}{2} \times \dfrac{15}{2} \times (30 + 15)$ m² $= 337.5$ m²,

   Area using Kavita's way $= \dfrac{1}{2} \times 15 \times 15 + 15 \times 15 = 337.5$ m²
11. 80 cm², 96 cm², 80 cm², 96 cm²

EXERCISE 11.3

1. (a)   2. 144 m   3. 10 cm   4. 11 m²
5. 5 cans
6. Similarity → Both have same heights. Difference → one is a cylinder, the other is a cube. The cube has larger lateral surface area
7. 440 m²   8. 322 cm   9. 1980 m²   10. 704 cm²

EXERCISE 11.4

1. (a) Volume   (b) Surface area   (c) Volume
2. Volume of cylinder B is greater; Surface area of cylinder B is greater.
3. 5 cm   4. 450   5. 1 m   6. 49500 L
7. (i) 4 times (ii) 8 times   8. 30 hours

EXERCISE 12.1

1. (i) $\dfrac{1}{9}$ (ii) $\dfrac{1}{16}$ (iii) 32

2. (i) $\dfrac{1}{(-4)^3}$ (ii) $\dfrac{1}{2^6}$ (iii) $(5)^4$ (iv) $\dfrac{1}{(3)^2}$ (v) $\dfrac{1}{(-14)^3}$

3. (i) 5 (ii) $\dfrac{1}{2}$ (iii) 29 (iv) 1 (v) $\dfrac{81}{16}$

4. (i) 250 (ii) $\dfrac{1}{60}$ 5. $m = 2$ 6. (i) -1 (ii) $\dfrac{512}{125}$

7. (i) $\dfrac{625t^4}{2}$ (ii) 5^5

EXERCISE 12.2

1. (i) 8.5×10^{-12} (ii) 9.42×10^{-12} (iii) 6.02×10^{15}
   (iv) 8.37×10^{-9} (v) 3.186×10^{10}

2. (i) 0.00000302 (ii) 45000 (iii) 0.00000003
   (iv) 1000100000 (v) 5800000000000 (vi) 3614920

3. (i) 1×10^{-6} (ii) 1.6×10^{-19} (iii) 5×10^{-7}
   (iv) 1.275×10^{-5} (v) 7×10^{-2}

4. 1.0008×10^2

EXERCISE 13.1

1. No

2.
Parts of red pigment	1	4	7	12	20
Parts of base	8	32	56	96	160

3. 24 parts   4. 700 bottles   5. 10^{-4} cm; 2 cm   6. 21 m
7. (i) 2.25×10^7 crystals   (ii) 5.4×10^6 crystals   8. 4 cm
9. (i) 6 m   (ii) 8 m 75 cm   10. 168 km

EXERCISE 13.2

1. (i), (iv), (v)   2. $4 \to 25{,}000$; $5 \to 20{,}000$; $8 \to 12{,}500$; $10 \to 10{,}000$; $20 \to 5{,}000$
   Amount given to a winner is inversely proportional to the number of winners.

3. $8 \to 45°$, $10 \to 36°$, $12 \to 30°$ (i) Yes   (ii) $24°$ (iii) 9
4. 6   5. 4   6. 3 days   7. 15 boxes
8. 49 machines   9. $1\dfrac{1}{2}$ hours   10. (i) 6 days (ii) 6 persons   11. 40 minutes

EXERCISE 14.1

1. (i) 12 (ii) $2y$ (iii) $14pq$ (iv) 1 (v) $6ab$ (vi) $4x$
   (vii) 10 (viii) x^2y^2

2. (i) $7(x-6)$ (ii) $6(p-2q)$ (iii) $7a(a+2)$ (iv) $4z(-4+5z^2)$

   (v) $10\,lm(2l+3a)$ (vi) $5xy(x-3y)$ (vii) $5(2a^2-3b^2+4c^2)$

   (viii) $4a(-a+b-c)$ (ix) $xyz(x+y+z)$ (x) $xy(ax+by+cz)$

3. (i) $(x+8)(x+y)$ (ii) $(3x+1)(5y-2)$ (iii) $(a+b)(x-y)$

   (iv) $(5p+3)(3q+5)$ (v) $(z-7)(1-xy)$

▰ EXERCISE 14.2

1. (i) $(a+4)^2$ (ii) $(p-5)^2$ (iii) $(5m+3)^2$ (iv) $(7y+6z)^2$

   (v) $4(x-1)^2$ (vi) $(11b-4c)^2$ (vii) $(l-m)^2$ (viii) $(a^2+b^2)^2$

2. (i) $(2p-3q)(2p+3q)$ (ii) $7(3a-4b)(3a+4b)$ (iii) $(7x-6)(7x+6)$

   (iv) $16x^3(x-3)(x+3)$ (v) $4lm$ (vi) $(3xy-4)(3xy+4)$

   (vii) $(x-y-z)(x-y+z)$ (viii) $(5a-2b+7c)(5a+2b-7c)$

3. (i) $x(ax+b)$ (ii) $7(p^2+3q^2)$ (iii) $2x(x^2+y^2+z^2)$

   (iv) $(m^2+n^2)(a+b)$ (v) $(l+1)(m+1)$ (vi) $(y+9)(y+z)$

   (vii) $(5y+2z)(y-4)$ (viii) $(2a+1)(5b+2)$ (ix) $(3x-2)(2y-3)$

4. (i) $(a-b)(a+b)(a^2+b^2)$ (ii) $(p-3)(p+3)(p^2+9)$

   (iii) $(x-y-z)(x+y+z)[x^2+(y+z)^2]$ (iv) $z(2x-z)(2x^2-2xz+z^2)$

   (v) $(a-b)^2(a+b)^2$

5. (i) $(p+2)(p+4)$ (ii) $(q-3)(q-7)$ (iii) $(p+8)(p-2)$

▰ EXERCISE 14.3

1. (i) $\dfrac{x^3}{2}$ (ii) $-4y$ (iii) $6pqr$ (iv) $\dfrac{2}{3}x^2y$ (v) $-2a^2b^4$

2. (i) $\dfrac{1}{3}(5x-6)$ (ii) $3y^4-4y^2+5$ (iii) $2(x+y+z)$

   (iv) $\dfrac{1}{2}(x^2+2x+3)$ (v) q^3-p^3

3. (i) $2x-5$ (ii) 5 (iii) $6y$ (iv) xy (v) $10abc$

4. (i) $5(3x+5)$ (ii) $2y(x+5)$ (iii) $\dfrac{1}{2}r(p+q)$ (iv) $4(y^2+5y+3)$

   (v) $(x+2)(x+3)$

5. (i) $y+2$ (ii) $m-16$ (iii) $5(p-4)$ (iv) $2z(z-2)$ (v) $\dfrac{5}{2}q(p-q)$

   (vi) $3(3x-4y)$ (vii) $3y(5y-7)$

▰ EXERCISE 14.4

1. $4(x-5)=4x-20$ **2.** $x(3x+2)=3x^2+2x$ **3.** $2x+3y=2x+3y$

4. $x+2x+3x=6x$ **5.** $5y+2y+y-7y=y$ **6.** $3x+2x=5x$

7. $(2x)^2 + 4(2x) + 7 = 4x^2 + 8x + 7$ **8.** $(2x)^2 + 5x = 4x^2 + 5x$

9. $(3x + 2)^2 = 9x^2 + 12x + 4$

10. (a) $(-3)^2 + 5(-3) + 4 = 9 - 15 + 4 = -2$ (b) $(-3)^2 - 5(-3) + 4 = 9 + 15 + 4 = 28$

   (c) $(-3)^2 + 5(-3) = 9 - 15 = -6$

11. $(y - 3)^2 = y^2 - 6y + 9$ **12.** $(z + 5)^2 = z^2 + 10z + 25$

13. $(2a + 3b)(a - b) = 2a^2 + ab - 3b^2$ **14.** $(a + 4)(a + 2) = a^2 + 6a + 8$

15. $(a - 4)(a - 2) = a^2 - 6a + 8$ **16.** $\dfrac{3x^2}{3x^2} = 1$

17. $\dfrac{3x^2 + 1}{3x^2} = \dfrac{3x^2}{3x^2} + \dfrac{1}{3x^2} = 1 + \dfrac{1}{3x^2}$ **18.** $\dfrac{3x}{3x + 2} = \dfrac{3x}{3x + 2}$

19. $\dfrac{3}{4x + 3} = \dfrac{3}{4x + 3}$ **20.** $\dfrac{4x + 5}{4x} = \dfrac{4x}{4x} + \dfrac{5}{4x} = 1 + \dfrac{5}{4x}$

21. $\dfrac{7x + 5}{5} = \dfrac{7x}{5} + \dfrac{5}{5} = \dfrac{7x}{5} + 1$

EXERCISE 15.1

1. (a)   36.5° C   (b) 12 noon   (c) 1 p.m, 2 p.m.

   (d)   36.5° C; The point between 1 p.m. and 2 p.m. on the x-axis is equidistant from the two points showing 1 p.m. and 2 p.m., so it will represent 1.30 p.m. Similarly, the point on the y-axis, between 36° C and 37° C will represent 36.5° C.

   (e)   9 a.m. to 10 a.m., 10 a.m. to 11 a.m., 2 p.m. to 3 p.m.

2. (a)   (i) ₹ 4 crore   (ii) ₹ 8 crore

   (b)   (i) ₹ 7 crore   (ii) ₹ 8.5 crore (approx.)

   (c)   ₹ 4 crore   (d) 2005

3. (a)   (i) 7 cm   (ii) 9 cm

   (b)   (i) 7 cm   (ii) 10 cm

   (c)   2 cm   (d) 3 cm   (e) Second week   (f) First week

   (g)   At the end of the 2nd week

4. (a)   Tue, Fri, Sun   (b) 35° C   (c) 15° C   (d) Thurs

6. (a)   4 units = 1 hour   (b) $3\dfrac{1}{2}$ hours   (c) 22 km

   (d)   Yes; This is indicated by the horizontal part of the graph (10 a.m. - 10.30 a.m.)

   (e)   Between 8 a.m. and 9 a.m.

7. (iii)   is not possible

EXERCISE 15.2

1. Points in (a) and (b) lie on a line; Points in (c) do not lie on a line

2. The line will cut x-axis at (5, 0) and y-axis at (0, 5)

3. O(0, 0), A(2, 0), B(2, 3), C(0, 3), P(4, 3), Q(6, 1), R(6, 5), S(4, 7), K(10, 5), L(7, 7), M(10, 8)

4. (i) True (ii) False (iii) True

EXERCISE 15.3

1. (b) (i) 20 km (ii) 7.30 a.m. (c) (i) Yes (ii) ₹ 200 (iii) ₹ 3500

2. (a) Yes (b) No

EXERCISE 16.1

1. A = 7, B = 6 **2.** A = 5, B = 4, C = 1 **3.** A = 6

4. A = 2, B = 5 **5.** A = 5, B = 0, C = 1 **6.** A = 5, B = 0, C = 2

7. A = 7, B = 4 **8.** A = 7, B = 9 **9.** A = 4, B = 7

10. A = 8, B = 1

EXERCISE 16.2

1. $y = 1$ **2.** $z = 0$ or 9 **3.** $z = 0, 3, 6$ or 9

4. 0, 3, 6 or 9

JUST FOR FUN

1. **More about Pythagorean triplets**

   We have seen one way of writing pythagorean triplets as $2m, m^2 - 1, m^2 + 1$.

   A pythagorean triplet a, b, c means $a^2 + b^2 = c^2$. If we use two natural numbers m and $n (m > n)$, and take $a = m^2 - n^2$, $b = 2mn$, $c = m^2 + n^2$, then we can see that $c^2 = a^2 + b^2$.

   Thus for different values of m and n with $m > n$ we can generate natural numbers a, b, c such that they form Pythagorean triplets.

   For example: Take, $m = 2, n = 1$.

   Then, $a = m^2 - n^2 = 3$, $b = 2mn = 4$, $c = m^2 + n^2 = 5$, is a Pythagorean triplet. (Check it!)

   For, $m = 3, n = 2$, we get,

   $a = 5, b = 12, c = 13$ which is again a Pythagorean triplet.

   Take some more values for m and n and generate more such triplets.

2. When water freezes its volume increases by 4%. What volume of water is required to make 221 cm³ of ice?

3. If price of tea increased by 20%, by what per cent must the consumption be reduced to keep the expense the same?

4. Ceremony Awards began in 1958. There were 28 categories to win an award. In 1993, there were 81 categories.

    (i) The awards given in 1958 is what per cent of the awards given in 1993?

    (ii) The awards given in 1993 is what per cent of the awards given in 1958?

5. Out of a swarm of bees, one fifth settled on a blossom of *Kadamba*, one third on a flower of *Silindhiri*, and three times the difference between these two numbers flew to the bloom of *Kutaja*. Only ten bees were then left from the swarm. What was the number of bees in the swarm? (Note, *Kadamba*, *Silindhiri* and *Kutaja* are flowering trees. The problem is from the ancient Indian text on algebra.)

6. In computing the area of a square, Shekhar used the formula for area of a square, while his friend Maroof used the formula for the perimeter of a square. Interestingly their answers were numerically same. Tell me the number of units of the side of the square they worked on.

7. The area of a square is numerically less than six times its side. List some squares in which this happens.

8. Is it possible to have a right circular cylinder to have volume numerically equal to its curved surface area? If yes state when.

9. Leela invited some friends for tea on her birthday. Her mother placed some plates and some *puris* on a table to be served. If Leela places 4 *puris* in each plate 1 plate would be left empty. But if she places 3 *puris* in each plate 1 *puri* would be left. Find the number of plates and number of *puris* on the table.

10. Is there a number which is equal to its cube but not equal to its square? If yes find it.

11. Arrange the numbers from 1 to 20 in a row such that the sum of any two adjacent numbers is a perfect square.

Answers

2. $212\dfrac{1}{2}$ cm^3

3. $16\dfrac{2}{3}\%$

4. (i) 34.5%   (ii) 289%

5. 150

6. 4 units

7. Sides = 1, 2, 3, 4, 5 units

8. Yes, when radius = 2 units

9. Number of *puris* = 16, number of plates = 5

10. – 1

11. One of the ways is, 1, 3, 6, 19, 17, 8 (1 + 3 = 4, 3 + 6 = 9 etc.). Try some other ways.